HEINEMANN MODULAR MATHEMATICS
for
LONDON AS AND A-LEVEL
Pure Mathematics 3

Geoff Mannall   Michael Kenwood

Heinemann Educational Publishers
Halley Court, Jordan Hill, Oxford, OX2 8EJ
a division of Reed Educational & Professional Publishing Ltd

MELBOURNE AUCKLAND FLORENCE PRAGUE MADRID
ATHENS SINGAPORE TOKYO SÃO PAULO CHICAGO
PORTSMOUTH (NH) MEXICO IBADAN GABORONE
JOHANNESBURG KAMPALA NAIROBI

First published 1996

96 97 98   9 8 7 6 5 4 3 2

ISBN 0 435 518 097 1

Original design by Geoffrey Wadsley: additional design work by Jim Turner

Typeset and illustrated by Keyword Typesetting Services Limited,
Wallington, Surrey

Printed in Great Britain by The Bath Press, Bath

Acknowledgements:

The publisher's and authors' thanks are due to Dr. Tony Clough and the
University of London Examinations and Assessment Council (ULEAC) for
permission to reproduce questions from past examination papers. These are
marked with an [L].

The answers have been provided by the authors and are not the responsibility
of the examining board.

About this book

This book is designed to provide you with the best preparation possible for your London Modular Mathematics P3 examination. The series authors are examiners and exam moderators themselves and have a good understanding of the exam board's requirements.

Finding your way around

To help to find your way around when you are studying and revising use the:

- **edge marks** (shown on the front page) – these help you to get to the right chapter quickly;
- **contents list** – this lists the headings that identify key syllabus ideas covered in the book so you can turn straight to them;
- **index** – if you need to find a topic the **bold** number shows where to find the main entry on a topic.

Remembering key ideas

We have provided clear explanations of the key ideas and techniques you need throughout the book. Key ideas you need to remember are listed in a **summary of key points** at the end of each chapter and marked like this in the chapters:

■ $$N(-1) = i$$

Exercises and exam questions

In this book questions are carefully graded so they increase in difficulty and gradually bring you up to exam standard.

- **past exam questions** are marked with an L;
- **review exercises** on pages **55, 149** and **230** help you practise answering questions from several areas of mathematics at once, as in the real exam;
- **examination style practice paper** – this is designed to help you prepare for the exam itself;
- **answers** are included at the end of the book – use them to check your work.

Contents

$$a\frac{\mathrm{d}^2 y}{\mathrm{d}x^2} + b\frac{\mathrm{d}y}{\mathrm{d}x} + cy = \mathrm{f}(x)$$

Algebra I

1

1.1 Further inequalities solved algebraically

Book P1 shows you how to solve inequalities such as:

$$4(x - 3) < 3(3x + 2)$$

and:

$$6x^2 + x - 2 \geqslant 0$$

The solution depends on finding critical values of x. These are values of x for the inequality $f(x) > 0$, say, where the sign of $f(x)$ changes between values of x on either side of the critical value.

Example 1

$$4(x - 3) < 3(3x + 2)$$
$$\Rightarrow \quad 4x - 12 < 9x + 6$$
$$\Rightarrow \quad -18 < 5x$$
$$\Rightarrow \quad 5x > -18$$

The critical value here is $x = -\frac{18}{5}$ and the solution required is $x > -\frac{18}{5}$.

Example 2

$$6x^2 + x - 2 \geqslant 0$$

Here

$$6x^2 + x - 2 \equiv (3x + 2)(2x - 1)$$

and critical values occur at $x = -\frac{2}{3}$ and $x = \frac{1}{2}$. You take the intervals into which the number line is divided by the critical values and consider the signs of $f(x) \equiv 6x^2 + x - 2$:

	$x < -\frac{2}{3}$	$-\frac{2}{3} < x < \frac{1}{2}$	$x > \frac{1}{2}$
Sign of $f(x)$	$+$	$-$	$+$

As you require $f(x) \geqslant 0$, the solution is $x \leqslant -\frac{2}{3}$ or $x \geqslant \frac{1}{2}$.

The following examples illustrate how other inequalities are solved.

Example 3

Find the set of values of x for which

$$\frac{4x - 1}{x + 2} < 1$$

Since

$$\frac{4x - 1}{x + 2} < 1 \Rightarrow \frac{4x - 1}{x + 2} - 1 < 0$$

you should consider

$$\begin{aligned} f(x) &\equiv \frac{4x - 1}{x + 2} - 1 \\ &= \frac{4x - 1 - x - 2}{x + 2} \\ &= \frac{3x - 3}{x + 2} \end{aligned}$$

A sketch of the graph of $y = \dfrac{3x - 3}{x + 2}$ looks like this:

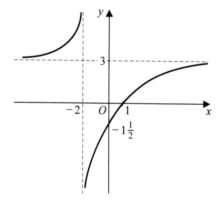

From this you can see that the function changes from positive to negative where the graph crosses the x-axis and also at the asymptote. So, unlike the inequalities in Book P1 where the critical values occurred only where $f(x) = 0$, for some inequalities, the critical values occur where $f(x) = 0$ *and also* at the asymptotes of $y = f(x)$ which are parallel to the y-axis. So the critical values of $f(x)$, where $f(x) \equiv \dfrac{3x - 3}{x + 2}$, are $x = 1$ and $x = -2$.

	$x < -2$	$-2 < x < 1$	$x > 1$
Sign of $f(x)$	$+$	$-$	$+$

The solution of $\dfrac{4x-1}{x+2} < 1$ is

$$-2 < x < 1$$

Note: A common mistake made by some students is to multiply the inequality by $x+2$, but *crucially* they forget that $x+2$ may be either negative or positive: both possibilities should be considered, particularly since, if negative, the inequality sign is reversed. The approach shown in Example 3 avoids this possible trouble and that is why it is used and recommended.

Example 4
Find the set of values of x for which

$$x^3 \geqslant 7x - 6$$

Since $x^3 \geqslant 7x - 6 \Rightarrow x^3 - 7x + 6 \geqslant 0$

you consider $\qquad f(x) \equiv x^3 - 7x + 6$

By inspection: $\qquad f(1) = 1 - 7 + 6 = 0$

Hence $(x-1)$ is a factor of $f(x)$.

$$f(x) \equiv (x-1)(x^2 + x - 6)$$
$$\equiv (x-1)(x-2)(x+3)$$

The critical values occur at $x = -3$, $x = 1$, $x = 2$.

	$x < -3$	$-3 < x < 1$	$1 < x < 2$	$x > 2$
Sign of $f(x)$	$-$	$+$	$-$	$+$

The solution set of $x^3 \geqslant 7x - 6$ is

$$-3 \leqslant x \leqslant 1 \text{ or } x \geqslant 2$$

Exercise 1A

In questions 1–15, find the set of values of x for which:

1 $2x - 1 < 4(x - 3)$ **2** $5(x - 2) \geqslant 2(2x + 7)$

3 $(x - 1)(x - 5) > 0$ **4** $(x + 3)(2x + 7) \leqslant 0$

5 $x^2 < 3x + 4$ **6** $\dfrac{3}{x - 1} > 1$

7 $x^2 < \dfrac{1}{x}$ **8** $\dfrac{x}{x - 1} < 2$

9 $\dfrac{x - 1}{x + 1} > 2$ **10** $\dfrac{1}{3x^2 - x - 2} < 0$

11 $x^3 - x^2 \geqslant 6x$

12 $\dfrac{x^2 + 10}{x} > 7$

13 $\dfrac{4x - 1}{x + 1} < 2x$

14 $\dfrac{x + 3}{x - 1} < \dfrac{x - 3}{x + 1}$

15 $\dfrac{4x + 8}{x - 1} > 3$

16 Show that $x + 1$ is a factor of $x^3 - 7x - 6$. Find the values of x for which $x^3 - 7x - 6 \geqslant 0$.

17 Find the complete solution set of

$$\frac{2}{x - 2} > \frac{3}{x + 1}$$

18 Show that for $x \in \mathbb{R}$, $-1 \leqslant \dfrac{2x}{x^2 + 1} \leqslant 1$.

19 Find the values of x for which

$$\frac{x^2 + 7x + 10}{x + 1} > 2x + 7$$

20 Find the set of values of x for which

$$-1 < \frac{2 - x}{2 + x} \leqslant 1$$

1.2 Solution sets of inequalities from graphs

Books P1 and P2 introduce the idea of curve sketching. You may have a calculator with graph sketching facilities; if so, you will find it useful here. If not, just sketch the curves as shown in Book P1 and in Book P2 (page 318).

Example 5

Find the set of values of x for which

$$6 + 5x - 2x^2 - x^3 > 0$$

You can verify that the curve with equation $y = 6 + 5x - 2x^2 - x^3$ cuts the x-axis at the points $(-3, 0)$, $(-1, 0)$ and $(2, 0)$ and the y-axis at the point $(0, 6)$. A sketch of the curve is:

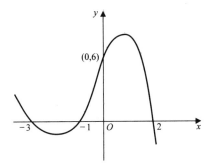

and you can see at once that the curve is above the x-axis for $x < -3$ and for $-1 < x < 2$. The solution set of the inequality is therefore

$$x < -3 \text{ or } -1 < x < 2$$

Note: With a graphical calculator, you type in the equation of the curve, *zoom* in on the intersection points of the curve with the x-axis and read off their coordinates. Record the solution set as shown above *but also produce a rough sketch graph to illustrate your method.*

Example 6
Find the set of values of x for which

$$\frac{2x}{x - 1} > x, \quad x \in \mathbb{R}, \quad x \neq 1$$

First sketch the graphs of $y = \dfrac{2x}{x - 1}$ and $y = x$ or, using your graphical calculator, type in the two curves so that they are displayed on the same screen. You should obtain a sketch like this:

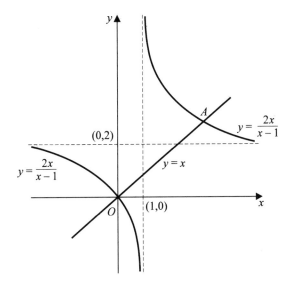

The asymptotes of the curve $y = \dfrac{2x}{x-1}$ are the lines $x = 1$ and $y = 2$.
The curve meets the line $y = x$ at the points O and A, as shown. Zooming in on A, or checking by direct calculation, you can show that its coordinates are $(3, 3)$.

The solution set of $\dfrac{2x}{x-1} > x$ is found by identifying those regions where the curve is 'higher' than the line. You can now see these at once. The solution set is:

$$x < 0 \quad \text{or} \quad 1 < x < 3$$

Exercise 1B

Many of the questions in Exercise 1A are suitable for solution by a graphical method. You can always check an algebraic solution by sketching a graph too.

Find, by a graphical method, the solution sets of the following inequalities:

1 $\dfrac{2x}{x+3} < 1$

2 $x(x+1) > x+4$

3 $\dfrac{5}{x} > x - 4$

4 $\dfrac{4x}{x+2} > 1$

5 $\dfrac{1}{x^2 - 6x + 7} > \dfrac{1}{2}$

6 $4x^3 < 3 + x - 12x^2$

7 $\dfrac{2x}{x+1} > x$

8 $\dfrac{x}{2x-1} < 4x$

9 $\dfrac{1+x}{1-x} < \dfrac{2-x}{2+x}$

10 $\dfrac{x^2 + 7x + 10}{x+1} > 2x + 7$

1.3 Inequalities involving the modulus sign

You may already have met modulus functions in Book P1 (page 45) and Book P2 (page 326). You should use a graphical approach when solving inequalities that include modulus functions. Avoid techniques such as squaring, because they are unnecessary. The following examples are typical of those set at Advanced level.

Example 7

Find the set of values of x for which

$$|3x + 2| < 4x$$

You will recall that the graph of $y = |3x + 2|$ is 'V-shaped' and meets the x-axis at the point $(-\frac{2}{3}, 0)$, as shown. The graph of the line $y = 4x$ passes through the origin O and meets the graph of $y = |3x + 2|$ where $4x = 3x + 2$ only; that is, at the point $A(2, 8)$.

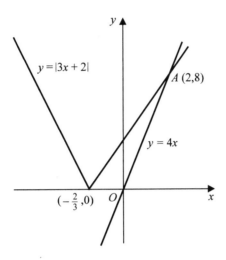

You require the set of values for which $4x$ is greater than $|3x + 2|$. That is, $x > 2$ is the solution set.

Example 8

Sketch the graphs of (a) $y = \dfrac{x-1}{x+2}$ (b) $y = \left| \dfrac{x-1}{x+2} \right|$ on separate diagrams.

Using your graph of $y = \left| \dfrac{x-1}{x+2} \right|$, find the set of values of x for which

$$\left| \frac{x-1}{x+2} \right| < 2.$$

This is a sketch of the graph of $y = \dfrac{x-1}{x+2}$:

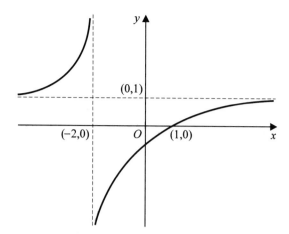

The part of the curve $y = \dfrac{x-1}{x+2}$ for which $y < 0$ is reflected in the

x-axis to obtain the curve $y = \left| \dfrac{x-1}{x+2} \right|$:

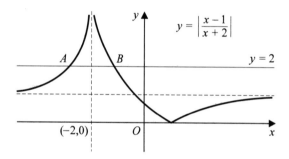

In order to solve this inequality, the line $y = 2$ and the graph of

$y = \left| \dfrac{x-1}{x+2} \right|$ are sketched. These two meet at the points A and B, as

shown.

For A, $\dfrac{x-1}{x+2} = 2 \Rightarrow x = -5$ and A is $(-5, 2)$.

For B, $\dfrac{-x+1}{x+2} = 2 \Rightarrow x = -1$ and B is $(-1, 2)$.

The solution is the set of values of x for which the graph of

$y = \left| \dfrac{x-1}{x+2} \right|$ is 'below' the line $y = 2$.

That is: $x < -5$ or $x > -1$ is the solution set.

Exercise 1C

Find the solution set of:

1 $|x - 2| > 4$

2 $|2x + 3| < 7$

3 $|3x - 4| > 7x$

4 $3|x + 1| \geqslant 1 - x$

5 $|4 - x^2| \leqslant 3$

6 $|x + 1| + |x - 2| \leqslant 5$

7 $\left| \dfrac{2x}{x - 2} \right| < 1$

8 $|x^2 - 2x| < x$

9 $|8 - 2x - x^2| < 8$

10 $2x + |x| < 6$

11 Show that for all real x,

$$\left| \frac{x + 1}{x^2 + 2x + 2} \right| \leqslant \frac{1}{2}$$

$\left(\text{Hint: Consider the graph of the curve } y = \dfrac{x + 1}{x^2 + 2x + 2} \right)$

12 The function f is defined for all real x by

$$f(x) = \begin{cases} \dfrac{1}{x} & \text{for} \quad x > 0 \\ |x| & \text{for} \quad x \leqslant 0 \end{cases}$$

(a) Sketch the graph of f.

(b) Find the set of values of x for which

$$f(x) \leqslant 4$$

SUMMARY OF KEY POINTS

1 Critical values of x for an inequality such as $f(x) > 0$ are those values of x where the sign of $f(x)$ changes for values of x on either side of the critical value.

2 Avoid multiplying an inequality by an expression which could be positive or negative.

3 When using a graphical calculator to solve an inequality, reproduce a rough sketch in your solution to illustrate your method.

4 Use a graphical approach to solve inequalities containing the modulus sign.

Algebra II

2

2.1 Summation of finite series using the method of differences

There is no general method for summing a series. Book P1 (pages 99, 104) shows you how to sum arithmetic and geometric series to n terms.

The series $$\sum_{r=1}^{n} 1 = 1 + 1 + 1 + \cdots + 1 = n$$

and $$\sum_{r=1}^{n} r = 1 + 2 + 3 + \cdots + n$$

which is an arithmetic series with first term 1 and common difference 1, were dealt with in Book P1.

Notice that $\sum_{r=1}^{n} r = 1 + \quad 2 \quad + \quad 3 \quad + \cdots + n$ (frontwards)

and also: $\sum_{r=1}^{n} r = n + (n-1) + (n-2) + \cdots + 1$ (backwards)

Adding: $2 \sum_{r=1}^{n} r = (n+1) + (n+1) + (n+1) + \cdots + (n+1)$

$$= n(n+1)$$

■
$$\sum_{r=1}^{n} r = \tfrac{1}{2}n(n+1)$$

Here is another way in which you could sum the series

$$1 + 2 + 3 + \cdots$$

to n terms. Consider the identity

$$2r \equiv r(r+1) - (r-1)r$$

If you take successive values $1, 2, 3, \ldots, n$ for r you get:

$$
\begin{aligned}
2(1) &= (1)(2) - (0)(1) \\
2(2) &= (2)(3) - (1)(2) \\
2(3) &= (3)(4) - (2)(3) \\
&\vdots \qquad \vdots \qquad \vdots \\
2(n-1) &= (n-1)(n) - (n-2)(n-1) \\
2n &= n(n+1) - (n-1)(n)
\end{aligned}
$$

Adding up each side gives:

$$
2[1 + 2 + 3 + \cdots + (n-1) + n] = n(n+1)
$$

All other terms cancel out on the right-hand side. This gives:

$$
2 \sum_{r=1}^{n} r = n(n+1)
$$

That is:
$$
\sum_{r=1}^{n} r = \tfrac{1}{2} n(n+1) \quad \text{as before.}
$$

This method is called **summing a series by the method of differences**. It is a very elegant and effective way of summing some finite series. Generally, if it is possible to find a function, $f(r)$, such that the rth term u_r of a series can be expressed as

$$
u_r \equiv f(r+1) - f(r)
$$

then it is easy to find $\sum_{r=1}^{n} u_r$. You have for $r = 1, 2, 3, \cdots, n$:

$$
\begin{aligned}
u_1 &= f(2) - f(1) \\
u_2 &= f(3) - f(2) \\
u_3 &= f(4) - f(3) \\
&\vdots \qquad \vdots \qquad \vdots \\
u_n &= f(n+1) - f(n)
\end{aligned}
$$

Adding:

■
$$
\sum_{r=1}^{n} \boldsymbol{u_r} = \mathbf{f}(\boldsymbol{n+1}) - \mathbf{f}(\mathbf{1})
$$

because all the other terms on the right-hand side cancel out. This is the method of summation of a series using differences. In an examination you will usually be given a hint about what function to consider. Here are some examples.

Example 1

Find $\displaystyle\sum_{r=1}^{n} r^2$.

Consider the identity

$$24r^2 + 2 \equiv (2r + 1)^3 - (2r - 1)^3$$

and take $r = 1, 2, 3, \cdots n$.

$$24(1^2) + 2 = 3^3 - 1^3$$

$$24(2^2) + 2 = 5^3 - 3^3$$

$$24(3^2) + 2 = 7^3 - 5^3$$

$$\vdots \quad \vdots \quad \vdots$$

$$24[(n-1)^2] + 2 = (2n-1)^3 - (2n-3)^3$$

$$24[(n)^2] + 2 = (2n+1)^3 - (2n-1)^3$$

Adding you get:

$$24[1^2 + 2^2 + 3^2 + \cdots + (n-1)^2 + n^2] + 2n = (2n+1)^3 - 1^3$$
$$= 8n^3 + 12n^2 + 6n$$

That is:
$$24 \sum_{r=1}^{n} r^2 + 2n = 8n^3 + 12n^2 + 6n$$

$$24 \sum_{r=1}^{n} r^2 = 8n^3 + 12n^2 + 4n = 4n(2n^2 + 3n + 1)$$

$$\sum_{r=1}^{n} r^2 = \frac{n}{6}[2n^2 + 3n + 1]$$

$$= \frac{n}{6}(2n+1)(n+1)$$

$$\blacksquare \qquad \qquad \sum_{r=1}^{n} r^2 = \tfrac{1}{6}n(n+1)(2n+1)$$

Example 2

Find $\sum_{r=1}^{n} r^3$.

Consider the identity

$$4r^3 \equiv r^2(r+1)^2 - (r-1)^2 r^2$$

and take $r = 1, 2, 3, \cdots, n$.

$$4(1^3) = 1^2(2^2) - 0^2(1^2)$$
$$4(2^3) = 2^2(3^2) - 1^2(2^2)$$
$$4(3^3) = 3^2(4^2) - 2^2(3^2)$$

$$\vdots \qquad \vdots \qquad \vdots$$

$$4(n^3) = n^2(n+1)^2 - (n-1)^2(n^2)$$

Adding you get:

$$4(1^3 + 2^3 + 3^3 + \cdots + n^3) = n^2(n+1)^2$$

That is:

■
$$\sum_{r=1}^{n} r^3 = \tfrac{1}{4} n^2 (n+1)^2$$

Notice that since $\sum_{r=1}^{n} r = \tfrac{1}{2} n(n+1)$, then

$$\sum_{r=1}^{n} r^3 = \left[\sum_{r=1}^{n} r \right]^2$$

Example 3

Find $\sum_{r=1}^{n} r(r+1)$.

Consider the identity

$$3r(r+1) \equiv r(r+1)(r+2) - (r-1)(r)(r+1)$$

and take $r = 1, 2, 3 \cdots, n$.

$$3(1)(2) = (1)(2)(3) - 0(1)(2)$$
$$3(2)(3) = (2)(3)(4) - (1)(2)(3)$$
$$3(3)(4) = (3)(4)(5) - (2)(3)(4)$$

$$\vdots \qquad \vdots \qquad \vdots$$

$$3(n)(n+1) = (n)(n+1)(n+2) - (n-1)(n)(n+1)$$

Adding you get:

$$3[(1)(2) + (2)(3) + (3)(4) + \cdots + n(n+1)] = n(n+1)(n+2)$$

That is:

$$\sum_{r=1}^{n} r(r+1) = \tfrac{1}{3}n(n+1)(n+2)$$

Exercise 2A

In each case, use the identity given to find the sum to n terms of the given series.

	Identity	Series
1	$\dfrac{1}{r(r+1)} \equiv \dfrac{1}{r} - \dfrac{1}{r+1}$	$\displaystyle\sum_{r=1}^{n} \dfrac{1}{r(r+1)}$
2	$2r + 1 \equiv (r+1)^2 - r^2$	$\displaystyle\sum_{r=1}^{n} (2r+1)$
3	$\dfrac{2}{4r^2 - 1} \equiv \dfrac{1}{2r-1} - \dfrac{1}{2r+1}$	$\displaystyle\sum_{r=1}^{n} \dfrac{1}{4r^2-1}$
4	$r^2(r+1) - (r-1)^2(r) \equiv 3r^2 - r$	$\displaystyle\sum_{r=1}^{n} r(3r-1)$
5	$\dfrac{r}{r+1} - \dfrac{r-1}{r} \equiv \dfrac{1}{r(r+1)}$	$\displaystyle\sum_{r=1}^{n} \dfrac{1}{r(r+1)}$
6	$4r(r+1)(r+2) \equiv r(r+1)(r+2)(r+3)$ $-(r-1)(r)(r+1)(r+2)$	$\displaystyle\sum_{r=1}^{n} r(r+1)(r+2)$
7	$\dfrac{2}{r(r+1)(r+2)} \equiv \dfrac{1}{r(r+1)} - \dfrac{1}{(r+1)(r+2)}$	$\displaystyle\sum_{r=1}^{n} \dfrac{1}{r(r+1)(r+2)}$
8	$\dfrac{2r+1}{r^2(r+1)^2} \equiv \dfrac{1}{r^2} - \dfrac{1}{(r+1)^2}$	$\displaystyle\sum_{r=1}^{n} \dfrac{2r+1}{r^2(r+1)^2}$

9 Use the identity $(r+1)^3 - r^3 \equiv 3r^2 + 3r + 1$ to find

$$\sum_{r=1}^{n} r(r+1).$$

10 Show that $\dfrac{1}{r!} - \dfrac{1}{(r+1)!} \equiv \dfrac{r}{(r+1)!}$. Hence find $\displaystyle\sum_{r=1}^{n} \dfrac{r}{(r+1)!}$.

2.2 Summation of finite series using standard results

In addition to formulae for arithmetic and geometric series, your ULEAC formula booklet gives the following:

■
$$\sum_{r=1}^{n} r = \tfrac{1}{2}n(n+1)$$

■
$$\sum_{r=1}^{n} r^2 = \tfrac{1}{6}n(n+1)(2n+1)$$

■
$$\sum_{r=1}^{n} r^3 = \tfrac{1}{4}n^2(n+1)^2$$

The following examples show how you can use these formulae to sum finite series.

Example 4

Find (a) $\displaystyle\sum_{r=7}^{20} r^2$ (b) $\displaystyle\sum_{r=12}^{25} r^3$.

(a)
$$\sum_{r=7}^{20} r^2 = \sum_{r=1}^{20} r^2 - \sum_{r=1}^{6} r^2$$
$$= \frac{20}{6}(21)(41) - \frac{6}{6}(7)(13)$$
$$= 2870 - 91$$
$$= 2779$$

(b)
$$\sum_{r=12}^{25} r^3 = \sum_{r=1}^{25} r^3 - \sum_{r=1}^{11} r^3$$
$$= \frac{25^2}{4}(26^2) - \frac{11^2}{4}(12^2)$$
$$= 105\,625 - 4356$$
$$= 101\,269$$

Example 5

Show that $\displaystyle\sum_{r=1}^{n} r(r+1) \equiv \tfrac{1}{3}n(n+1)(n+2)$.

$$\sum_{r=1}^{n} r(r+1) = \sum_{r=1}^{n} (r^2 + r)$$

$$= \sum_{r=1}^{n} r^2 + \sum_{r=1}^{n} r$$

$$= \tfrac{1}{6}n(n+1)(2n+1) + \tfrac{1}{2}n(n+1)$$

$$= \tfrac{1}{6}n(n+1)[(2n+1)+3]$$

$$= \tfrac{1}{6}n(n+1)(2n+4)$$

■ **So:** $\displaystyle\sum_{r=1}^{n} r(r+1) = \tfrac{1}{3}n(n+1)(n+2)$

as required.

Example 6

Find $\displaystyle\sum_{r=1}^{n}(6r^2 + 2^r)$.

Now $$\sum_{r=1}^{n}(6r^2 + 2^r) = \sum_{r=1}^{n} 6r^2 + \sum_{r=1}^{n} 2^r$$

$$\sum_{r=1}^{n} 6r^2 = 6\sum_{r=1}^{n} r^2 = n(n+1)(2n+1)$$

$\displaystyle\sum_{r=1}^{n} 2^r$ is a geometric series with first term 2 and common ratio 2, having n terms. The sum of a geometric series:

$$a + ar + \cdots + ar^{n-1}$$

is given by:

$$S = \frac{a(r^n - 1)}{r - 1}$$

where a is the first term and r is the common ratio. (There is more about this in Book P1 page 104.)

Hence: $$\sum_{r=1}^{n} 2^r = \frac{2(2^n - 1)}{2 - 1} = 2^{n+1} - 2$$

So: $$\sum_{r=1}^{n}(6r^2 + 2^r) = n(n+1)(2n+1) + 2^{n+1} - 2$$

Exercise 2B

Evaluate:

1 $\displaystyle\sum_{r=1}^{13} r^2$

2 $\displaystyle\sum_{r=4}^{11} r^3$

3 $\displaystyle\sum_{r=11}^{24} r(r+1)$

4 $\displaystyle\sum_{r=1}^{19} r(r+4)$

5 $\displaystyle\sum_{r=1}^{20} \frac{1}{r(r+1)}$

6 $\displaystyle\sum_{r=3}^{16} (r+2)^3$

7 $\displaystyle\sum_{r=1}^{14} \left(\frac{3}{4}\right)^r$

8 $\displaystyle\sum_{r=1}^{20} \frac{1}{(r+3)(r+6)}$

9 $\displaystyle\sum_{r=4}^{16} (2r-1)^3$

10 $\displaystyle\sum_{r=3}^{23} r(r+1)(r+2)$

11 Show that $\displaystyle\sum_{r=1}^{n} (2r-1)^2 \equiv \frac{1}{3}n(4n^2-1)$.

12 Show that $\displaystyle\sum_{r=1}^{n} r(2+r) \equiv \frac{1}{6}n(n+1)(2n+7)$.

13 Find $\displaystyle\sum_{r=1}^{20} \frac{1}{4r^2-1}$.

14 Find $\displaystyle\sum_{r=n}^{2n} r^2$.

15 Given that $\mathrm{f}(r) \equiv \dfrac{1}{r(r+1)}$, show that

$$\mathrm{f}(r) - \mathrm{f}(r+1) \equiv \frac{2}{r(r+1)(r+2)}$$

Hence find $\displaystyle\sum_{r=5}^{25} \frac{1}{r(r+1)(r+2)}$.

16 Prove that $\displaystyle\sum_{r=1}^{n} \frac{1}{(r+1)(r+2)} = \frac{n}{2(n+2)}$.

17 Find the sum of all even numbers between 2 and 200 inclusive, excluding those which are multiples of 3.

18 Find $\displaystyle\sum_{r=1}^{100} 2r^2 - \sum_{r=1}^{200} r^2$.

19 Find the sum of the series

$$1^2 - 2^2 + 3^2 - 4^2 + \cdots - (2n)^2$$

20 Given that $u_r = r(2r+1) + 2^{r+2}$, find $\displaystyle\sum_{r=1}^{n} u_r$.

2.3 The binomial series $(1 + x)^n$, $n \in \mathbb{Q}$, $|x| < 1$

Book P2 (page 139) introduces the binomial series $(1 + x)^n$, where n is a positive integer, as

$$(1 + x)^n = 1 + \binom{n}{1}x + \binom{n}{2}x^2 + \cdots + \binom{n}{r}x^r + \cdots + x^n$$

This may be written as:

$$(1 + x)^n = 1 + nx + \frac{n(n-1)}{2!}x^2 + \frac{n(n-1)(n-2)}{3!}x^3 + \cdots + x^n$$

This result can be extended to include *all* values of n which are rational, such as $n = \frac{3}{4}$ or $n = -2$ or $n = -\frac{5}{4}$ and so on. You can write

$$(1 + x)^n = 1 + nx + \frac{n(n-1)}{2!}x^2 + \frac{n(n-1)(n-2)}{3!}x^3 + \cdots + \frac{n(n-1)\cdots(n-r+1)}{r!}x^r + \cdots$$

For a positive integer value of n, this series is the one shown in Book P2 because the series comes to an end after $(n + 1)$ terms. If, on the other hand, n is *not* a positive integer, then the series is infinite and is only valid for $|x| < 1$; that is, $-1 < x < 1$ is an essential condition.

■ **In the form given, for $|x| < 1$,**

$$(1 + x)^n = 1 + nx + \frac{n(n-1)}{2!}x^2 + \frac{n(n-1)(n-2)}{3!}x^3 + \cdots + \frac{n(n-1)\cdots(n-r+1)}{r!}x^r + \cdots$$

is called the binomial series of $(1 + x)^n$.

This result is quoted in the ULEAC formula book. You need to be able to expand series of the form $(a + bx)^n$ and to state the set of values of x for which the series is valid. The following examples are typical.

Example 7

Given that $|x| < 1$, expand in ascending powers of x up to and including the term in x^3: (a) $(1 + x)^{-1}$ (b) $(1 - x)^{-1}$ (c) $(1 - x)^{-2}$.

In each case, use the expansion of $(1 + x)^n$, where

$$(1 + x)^n = 1 + nx + \frac{n(n-1)}{2!}x^2 + \frac{n(n-1)(n-2)}{3!}x^3 + \cdots$$

(a) You take x as x and $n = -1$ to obtain

$$(1 + x)^{-1} = 1 + (-1)(x) + \frac{(-1)(-1-1)}{2!}(x)^2 + \frac{(-1)(-1-1)(-1-2)}{3!}(x)^3 + \cdots$$

$$= 1 - x + x^2 - x^3 + \cdots$$

(b) You take x as $-x$ and $n = -1$ to obtain

$$(1-x)^{-1} = 1 + (-1)(-x) + \frac{(-1)(-1-1)}{2!}(-x)^2 + \frac{(-1)(-1-1)(-1-2)}{3!}(-x)^3 + \cdots$$

$$= 1 + x + x^2 + x^3 + \cdots$$

(c) You take x as $-x$ and $n = -2$ to obtain

$$(1-x)^{-2} = 1 + (-2)(-x) + \frac{(-2)(-2-1)}{2!}(-x)^2 + \frac{(-2)(-2-1)(-2-2)}{3!}(-x)^3 + \cdots$$

$$= 1 + 2x + 3x^2 + 4x^3 + \cdots$$

Example 8

Expand (a) $(1+2x)^{\frac{3}{2}}$ (b) $(1-3x)^{-\frac{2}{3}}$ in ascending powers of x up to and including the term in x^3. State the set of values of x for which your expansion is valid.

(a) In the general expansion of $(1+x)^n$, take x as $2x$ and take $n = \frac{3}{2}$ to obtain

$$(1+2x)^{\frac{3}{2}} = 1 + \tfrac{3}{2}(2x) + \frac{\frac{3}{2}(\frac{3}{2}-1)}{2!}(2x)^2 + \frac{\frac{3}{2}(\frac{3}{2}-1)(\frac{3}{2}-2)}{3!}(2x)^3 + \cdots$$

$$= 1 + 3x + \tfrac{3}{2}x^2 - \tfrac{1}{2}x^3 + \cdots$$

This series is valid for $|2x| < 1$, that is $|x| < \frac{1}{2}$ or $-\frac{1}{2} < x < \frac{1}{2}$.

(b) In the general expansion of $(1+x)^n$, take x as $-3x$ and take $n = -\frac{2}{3}$ to obtain

$$(1-3x)^{-\frac{2}{3}} = 1 + (-\tfrac{2}{3})(-3x) + \frac{(-\frac{2}{3})(-\frac{2}{3}-1)}{2!}(-3x)^2 + \frac{(-\frac{2}{3})(-\frac{2}{3}-1)(-\frac{2}{3}-2)}{3!}(-3x)^3 + \cdots$$

$$= 1 + 2x + 5x^2 + \tfrac{40}{3}x^3 + \cdots$$

This series is valid for $|3x| < 1$, that is $|x| < \frac{1}{3}$ or $-\frac{1}{3} < x < \frac{1}{3}$.

You should note carefully how each series is built up, using brackets at the first stage to avoid introducing sign errors.

Example 9

Expand $(1-3x)^{\frac{1}{5}}$ in ascending powers of x up to and including the term in x^3. Using your series, take $x = \frac{1}{32}$ to find an approximation for $29^{\frac{1}{5}}$, giving your answer to five decimal places.

$$(1-3x)^{\frac{1}{5}} = 1 + \tfrac{1}{5}(-3x) + \frac{\frac{1}{5}(\frac{1}{5}-1)}{2!}(-3x)^2 + \frac{\frac{1}{5}(\frac{1}{5}-1)(\frac{1}{5}-2)}{3!}(-3x)^3 + \cdots$$

$$= 1 - \tfrac{3}{5}x - \tfrac{18}{25}x^2 - \tfrac{162}{125}x^3 - \cdots$$

$$x = \tfrac{1}{32} \Rightarrow (1-\tfrac{3}{32})^{\frac{1}{5}} = (\tfrac{29}{32})^{\frac{1}{5}} = \tfrac{1}{2}(29)^{\frac{1}{5}}$$

Putting $x = \frac{1}{32}$ in the series then gives:

$$\tfrac{1}{2}(29)^{\frac{1}{3}} \approx 1 - 0.018\,75 - 0.000\,703\,125 - 0.000\,039\,550\,781 - \cdots$$

$$\Rightarrow (29)^{\frac{1}{3}} = 1.961\,01 \text{ (to 5 d.p.)}$$

Example 10

Expand $(4 - x)^{-\frac{1}{2}}$ in ascending powers of x up to and including the term in x^3.

You should recognise at once that $(4 - x)^{-\frac{1}{2}}$ is *not* in the form $(1 + x)^n$. This means that you need to rewrite $(4 - x)^{-\frac{1}{2}}$ like this:

$$(4 - x)^{-\frac{1}{2}} = \left[4\left(1 - \frac{x}{4}\right)\right]^{-\frac{1}{2}} = 4^{-\frac{1}{2}}\left(1 - \frac{x}{4}\right)^{-\frac{1}{2}} = \tfrac{1}{2}\left(1 - \frac{x}{4}\right)^{-\frac{1}{2}}$$

and then $\left(1 - \dfrac{x}{4}\right)^{-\frac{1}{2}}$ can be expanded in the usual way, using the standard binomial series with x replaced by $-\dfrac{x}{4}$ and $n = -\tfrac{1}{2}$. Notice also that the series is valid for $\left|\dfrac{x}{4}\right| < 1$, that is $|x| < 4$ or $-4 < x < 4$.

$$(4 - x)^{-\frac{1}{2}} = \tfrac{1}{2}\left(1 - \frac{x}{4}\right)^{-\frac{1}{2}}$$

$$= \tfrac{1}{2}\left[1 + \left(-\tfrac{1}{2}\right)\left(-\frac{x}{4}\right) + \frac{\left(-\tfrac{1}{2}\right)\left(-\tfrac{1}{2} - 1\right)}{2!}\left(-\frac{x}{4}\right)^2 + \frac{\left(-\tfrac{1}{2}\right)\left(-\tfrac{1}{2} - 1\right)\left(-\tfrac{1}{2} - 2\right)}{3!}\left(-\frac{x}{4}\right)^3 + \cdots\right.$$

$$= \tfrac{1}{2}\left[1 + \tfrac{1}{8}x + \tfrac{3}{128}x^2 + \tfrac{5}{1024}x^3 + \cdots\right]$$

$$= \tfrac{1}{2} + \tfrac{1}{16}x + \tfrac{3}{256}x^2 + \tfrac{5}{2048}x^3 + \cdots$$

Example 11

$$f(x) \equiv \frac{x}{(3 - 2x)(2 - x)}$$

(a) Express $f(x)$ in partial fractions.

(b) Expand $f(x)$ in ascending powers of x up to and including the term in x^3.

(c) State the set of values of x for which the series is valid.

(a) Let

$$\frac{x}{(3 - 2x)(2 - x)} \equiv \frac{A}{3 - 2x} + \frac{B}{2 - x}$$

then:

$$x \equiv A(2 - x) + B(3 - 2x)$$

When $x = 2$:　　　　$2 = B(3 - 4) \Rightarrow B = -2$

When $x = \frac{3}{2}$:　　　　$\frac{3}{2} = A(2 - \frac{3}{2}) \Rightarrow A = 3$

So:　　　　　　$f(x) \equiv \dfrac{3}{3 - 2x} - \dfrac{2}{2 - x}$

(b) Rewrite $f(x)$ as $3(3 - 2x)^{-1} - 2(2 - x)^{-1}$

$$= 3(3^{-1})\left(1 - \frac{2x}{3}\right)^{-1} - 2(2^{-1})\left(1 - \frac{x}{2}\right)^{-1}$$

$$= \left(1 - \frac{2x}{3}\right)^{-1} - \left(1 - \frac{x}{2}\right)^{-1}$$

$$(1 - \tfrac{2}{3}x)^{-1} = 1 + (-1)(-\tfrac{2}{3}x) + \frac{(-1)(-2)}{2!}(-\tfrac{2}{3}x)^2 + \frac{(-1)(-2)(-3)}{3!}(-\tfrac{2}{3}x)^3 + \cdots$$

$$= 1 + \tfrac{2}{3}x + \tfrac{4}{9}x^2 + \tfrac{8}{27}x^3 + \cdots$$

$$\left(1 - \frac{x}{2}\right)^{-1} = 1 + (-1)(-\tfrac{1}{2}x) + \frac{(-1)(-2)}{2!}(\tfrac{1}{2}x)^2 + \frac{(-1)(-2)(-3)}{3!}(-\tfrac{1}{2}x)^3 + \cdots$$

$$= 1 + \tfrac{1}{2}x + \tfrac{1}{4}x^2 + \tfrac{1}{8}x^3 + \cdots$$

So:　　　$f(x) = (\tfrac{2}{3} - \tfrac{1}{2})x + (\tfrac{4}{9} - \tfrac{1}{4})x^2 + (\tfrac{8}{27} - \tfrac{1}{8})x^3 + \cdots$

$$= \tfrac{1}{6}x + \tfrac{7}{36}x^2 + \tfrac{37}{216}x^3 + \cdots$$

(c) The expansion of $(1 - \frac{2}{3}x)^{-1}$ is valid for $|\frac{2}{3}x| < 1$, that is:

$$-\tfrac{3}{2} < x < \tfrac{3}{2}$$

The expansion of $\left(1 - \frac{1}{2}x\right)^{-1}$ is valid for $|\frac{1}{2}x| < 1$, that is:

$$-2 < x < 2$$

The expansion of $f(x)$ is valid when *both* sets of conditions are satisfied, that is, for the *intersection* of these two sets, when:

$$-\tfrac{3}{2} < x < \tfrac{3}{2}$$

Exercise 2C

In questions 1–15, find, in ascending powers of x, the expansions up to and including the term in x^3, simplifying the coefficients. State the set of values of x for which the expansion is valid.

1 $(1 + x)^{-2}$ 　　　　**2** $(1 - x)^{-3}$ 　　　　**3** $(1 - x)^{-5}$

4 $(1 + x)^{-\frac{1}{2}}$ 　　　　**5** $(1 + x)^{\frac{3}{2}}$ 　　　　**6** $(1 - x)^{\frac{3}{4}}$

7 $(1 - 3x)^{\frac{1}{3}}$ **8** $(1 + 3x)^{-\frac{1}{3}}$ **9** $\left(1 - \frac{1}{2}x\right)^{-2}$

10 $(1 + 6x)^{-1}$ **11** $(3 + x)^{-1}$ **12** $(2 - x)^{-2}$

13 $(4 + 3x)^{\frac{1}{2}}$ **14** $(8 - 5x)^{\frac{1}{3}}$ **15** $(100 + x)^{-\frac{1}{2}}$

By using partial fractions find, in ascending powers of x, up to and including the term in x^3, expansions for the functions of x given in questions 16–20. State the set of values of x for which the expansion is valid.

16 $\dfrac{2 - 3x}{1 - 3x + 2x^2}$ **17** $\dfrac{3}{1 + x - 2x^2}$ **18** $\dfrac{2}{x^2 + 2x - 8}$

19 $\dfrac{1}{x^2 + 3x + 2}$ **20** $\dfrac{8 - x}{x^2 - x - 6}$

21 Given that $|x| < \frac{1}{2}$, expand $(1 + x)^2(1 - 2x)^{-\frac{1}{2}}$ in ascending powers of x up to and including the term in x^3, simplifying each coefficient.

22 Given that $|x| > 2$ find the first four terms in the series expansion of $\left(1 - \dfrac{2}{x}\right)^{\frac{1}{2}}$ in descending powers of x.

By taking $x = 200$ use your series to find a value of $\sqrt{99}$, giving your answer to 7 decimal places. Use your series to find $\sqrt{101}$ to the same degree of accuracy.

23 The series expansion of $(1 + px)^q$ in ascending powers of x has coefficients of -10 and 75 in the x and x^2 terms respectively.
   (a) Find the value of p and of q.
   (b) Find the coefficients of the x^3 and x^4 terms in the expansion.
   (c) State the set of values of x for which the series is valid.

24 Given that $|x| < 1$, expand $\left(\dfrac{1 + x}{1 - x}\right)^{\frac{1}{3}}$ in ascending powers of x up to and including the term in x^2.

25 The coefficients of x and x^2 in the expansion of $(1 + px + qx^2)^{-2}$ in ascending powers of x are 4 and 14 respectively. Find the value of p and of q.

26 The coefficients of the x and x^2 terms in the expansion of $(1 + px)^q$ in ascending powers of x are -6 and 6 respectively.
   (a) Find the value of p and of q.
   (b) Find the x^3 term and the x^4 term in the expansion.
   (c) State the set of values of x for which the expansion is valid.

2.4 Maclaurin's series

In section 2.3 the function $(1 + x)^n$ was expressed as a series in ascending powers of x for $|x| < 1$. Many other functions can be expressed as an infinite series, or **power series** as it is often called, provided that certain conditions are observed. It is also necessary to make an assumption about the *validity* of differentiating an infinite series term by term.

Consider the function f given by $f(x) \equiv (1 + x)^n$, and suppose that $f(x)$ can also be expressed as

$$f(x) \equiv A_0 + A_1x + A_2x^2 + A_3x^3 + \cdots + A_rx^r + \cdots$$

where $A_0, A_1, A_2, A_3, \cdots, A_r, \cdots$ are constants.

At $x = 0$: $\qquad\qquad (1 + x)^n = (1 + 0)^n = 1$

Also, at $x = 0$: $\qquad A_0 + A_1x + A_2x^2 + \cdots = A_0$

So: $\qquad\qquad\qquad\qquad A_0 = 1$

Differentiating $f(x)$ with respect to x you obtain

$$f'(x) \equiv A_1 + 2A_2x + 3A_3x^2 + \cdots + rA_rx^{r-1} + \cdots$$

But $\qquad\qquad\qquad f'(x) = n(1 + x)^{n-1}$

So at $x = 0$, you have:

$$f'(x) = A_1 = n(1 + 0)^{n-1} \Rightarrow A_1 = n$$

Differentiating both expressions for $f'(x)$:

$$f''(x) \equiv 2A_2 + 3(2)A_3x + \cdots + r(r - 1)A_rx^{r-2} + \cdots$$

Also: $\qquad\qquad f''(x) = n(n - 1)(1 + x)^{n-2}$

At $x = 0$, $2A_2 = n(n - 1)(1 + 0)^{n-2} \Rightarrow A_2 = \dfrac{n(n - 1)}{2}$

Continuing the differentiating and equating gives:

$$A_3 = \frac{n(n - 1)(n - 2)}{3!} \text{ and } A_r = \frac{n(n - 1)(n - 2) \cdots (n - r + 1)}{r!}$$

Hence:

$$(1 + x)^n = 1 + nx + \frac{n(n - 1)}{2!}x^2 + \frac{n(n - 1)(n - 2)}{3!}x^3 + \cdots + \frac{n(n - 1)(n - 2) \cdots (n - r + 1)}{r!}x^r + \cdots$$

which you know from section 2.3 as the binomial series. In arriving at this result, you should appreciate that it has been *assumed* that it is valid mathematically to differentiate an infinite series term by term. You cannot prove this assumption at present.

■ **Generally, for the continuous function f, given by**

$$f : x \mapsto f(x), \ x \in \mathbb{R}$$

if f(0), f'(0), f''(0), $\cdots$ f$^{(r)}$(0), $\cdots$ all have finite values, then

$$f(x) = f(0) + xf'(0) + \frac{x^2}{2!}f''(0) + \cdots + \frac{x^r}{r!}f^{(r)}(0) + \cdots$$

This series is known as the **Maclaurin expansion of f(x) in ascending powers of** x.

For a given function the series may converge to f(x) for *all* values of x. However, frequently the expansion only holds for a restricted range of values of x.

Example 12

Expand e^x in ascending powers of x.

$$f(x) = e^x, \ f'(x) = e^x, \ f''(x) = e^x, \cdots, f^{(r)}(x) = e^x$$

At $x = 0$: $\ f(0) = f'(0) = f''(0) = f'''(0) = \cdots = f^{(r)}(0) = 1$

Hence, using Maclaurin's series you have:

$$e^x = 1 + x + \frac{x^2}{2!} + \frac{x^3}{3!} + \cdots + \frac{x^r}{r!} + \cdots$$

The expansion is valid for all values of x.

Example 13

Expand $\cos x$ in ascending powers of x.

Let $\ f(x) = \cos x$
$$f'(x) = -\sin x, \ f''(x) = -\cos x, \ f'''(x) = \sin x, \ f^{IV}(x) = \cos x$$

and you then have: $f(0) = 1$, $f'(0) = 0$, $f''(0) = -1$, $f'''(0) = 0$, $f^{IV}(0) = 1$ and the cycle of four values $1, 0, -1, 0$ repeats itself. So you have from Maclaurin's expansion:

$$\cos x = 1 - \frac{x^2}{2!} + \frac{x^4}{4!} - \cdots + (-1)^r \frac{x^{2r}}{(2r)!} + \cdots$$

This expansion is valid for all values of x.

Example 14

Expand $\ln(1 + x)$ in ascending powers of x.

$$f(x) = \ln(1 + x)$$

$$f'(x) = \frac{1}{1 + x} = (1 + x)^{-1}; \quad f''(x) = -(1 + x)^{-2};$$

$$f'''(x) = (-1)(-2)(1 + x)^{-3}; \quad f^{IV}(x) = (-1)(-2)(-3)(1 + x)^{-4}$$

and $\quad f^{(r)}(x) = (-1)(-2)(-3)\cdots(-r + 1)(1 + x)^{-r}$

So $f(0) = 0$, $f'(0) = 1$, $f''(0) = -1$, $f'''(0) = 2!$, $f^{IV}(0) = -3! \cdots$
$f^{(r)}(0) = (-1)^{r+1}(r - 1)!$

So the Maclaurin expansion is

$$\ln(1 + x) = x - \frac{x^2}{2!} + \frac{2!x^3}{3!} - \frac{3!x^4}{4!} + \cdots + \frac{(-1)^{r+1}(r - 1)!x^r}{r!} + \cdots$$

$$= x - \frac{x^2}{2} + \frac{x^3}{3} - \frac{x^4}{4} + \cdots + \frac{(-1)^{r+1}x^r}{r} + \cdots$$

This expansion is valid for $-1 < x \leqslant 1$.

The series for $\sin x$ is set as an exercise below. The series is valid for all values of x.

You should learn the conditions of validity for these series.

Exercise 2D

Using Maclaurin's expansion, and differentiation, show that:

1 $e^{-x} = 1 - x + \dfrac{x^2}{2!} - \dfrac{x^3}{3!} + \cdots + (-1)^r \dfrac{x^r}{r!} + \cdots$

2 $(1 - x)^{-1} = 1 + x + x^2 + x^3 + \cdots + x^r + \cdots$

3 $e^{2x} = 1 + 2x + 2x^2 + \frac{4}{3}x^3 + \cdots + \dfrac{2^r x^r}{r!} + \cdots$

4 $\sin x = x - \dfrac{x^3}{3!} + \dfrac{x^5}{5!} - \cdots + (-1)^r \dfrac{x^{2r+1}}{(2r + 1)!} + \cdots$

5 $\ln(1 - x) = -x - \dfrac{x^2}{2} - \dfrac{x^3}{3} - \cdots - \dfrac{x^r}{r} - \cdots$

Find the first three non-zero terms in the Maclaurin expansion of the function given in ascending powers of x:

6 $\tan x$ **7** $\sin^2 x$ **8** $\ln\left(\dfrac{1 + x}{1 - x}\right)$, $|x| < 1$

9 $(1 - 2x^2)^{\frac{1}{2}}$ **10** $e^x \cos x$

2.5 Using the polynomial series form of functions to find approximations for the functions

When x is small, it is evident that $x^2, x^3 \cdots$ get successively smaller. For example:

$$x = \tfrac{1}{10}, \quad x^2 = \tfrac{1}{100}, \quad x^6 = \tfrac{1}{1\,000\,000}, \text{ etc.}$$

By using this fact, you can take an approximation of the polynomial form of a function to represent the function, if x is sufficiently small. For example, you know that

$$\sin x = x - \frac{x^3}{3!} + \frac{x^5}{5!} - \cdots$$

$$\cos x = 1 - \frac{x^2}{2!} + \frac{x^4}{4!} - \cdots$$

So if you take terms in x^3 and higher powers of x to be negligible, then

■ $$\sin x \approx x \quad \text{and} \quad \cos x \approx 1 - \frac{x^2}{2}$$

Also in Exercise 2D, question 6, you should have found that:

$$\tan x = x + \tfrac{1}{3}x^3 + \tfrac{2}{15}x^5 \cdots$$

So you can also say, for small x, that

■ $$\tan x \approx x$$

These three approximations have widespread applications in science, technology and engineering, together with approximations from the binomial series such as

■ $$(1 + x)^{\frac{1}{2}} \approx 1 + \tfrac{1}{2}x - \tfrac{1}{8}x^2$$

Example 15

Find a quadratic polynomial approximation for $\dfrac{\sin 2x}{1 + x}$, given that x is small.

$$\frac{\sin 2x}{1 + x} = \sin 2x(1 + x)^{-1}$$

You can say that: $\qquad \sin 2x \approx 2x$

$$(1 + x)^{-1} = 1 + (-1)(x) + \frac{(-1)(-2)}{2!}(x)^2 + \cdots$$

$$= 1 - x + x^2 - \cdots$$

So:
$$\sin 2x (1+x)^{-1} \approx 2x(1 - x + x^2)$$
$$\approx 2x - 2x^2$$

(x^3 and higher powers of x being negligible).

Example 16

Given that x is small, show that $\dfrac{3\sin x}{2 + \cos x} \approx x$.

$$3\sin x = 3\left(x - \frac{x^3}{3!} + \cdots\right)$$

$$(2 + \cos x)^{-1} \approx \left(2 + 1 - \frac{x^2}{2}\right)^{-1}$$

$$= 3^{-1}\left(1 - \frac{x^2}{6}\right)^{-1}$$

$$= 3^{-1}\left(1 + \frac{x^2}{6} + \cdots\right) \text{ (binomial series)}$$

So:
$$\frac{3\sin x}{2 + \cos x} \approx 3\left(x - \frac{x^3}{6}\right)(3^{-1})\left(1 + \frac{x^2}{6}\right)$$

$$= x + \frac{x^3}{6} - \frac{x^3}{6} - \frac{x^5}{36}$$

$$= x\left(1 - \frac{x^4}{36}\right)$$

$$\approx x, \text{ as required.}$$

Example 17

Show that $\displaystyle\lim_{x \to 0}\left(\frac{1 - \cos 4x + x\sin 3x}{x^2}\right) = 11$.

Using the approximations for small x:

$$\cos 4x \approx 1 - \frac{(4x)^2}{2} \quad \text{and} \quad \sin 3x \approx 3x$$

you have:

$$\frac{1 - \cos 4x + x\sin 3x}{x^2} \approx \frac{1 - (1 - 8x^2) + 3x^2}{x^2}$$

$$= 11$$

Notice that other terms would have x^2, x^4, etc. in them, so that:

$$\lim_{x \to 0}\left(\frac{1 - \cos 4x + x\sin 3x}{x^2}\right) = 11, \text{ as required.}$$

Exercise 2E

1 Given that x is small, find the constants A and B such that

$$(x + \sin x) \cos x \approx Ax + Bx^3$$

2 Given that x is small, find the constants C and D such that

$$\tan x \approx Cx + Dx^3$$

3 Find $\displaystyle\lim_{x \to 0} \left(\frac{\sin(\frac{\pi}{6} + x) - \sin \frac{\pi}{6}}{\sin 2x} \right)$.

4 Given that x is small, show that

$$\frac{\sin x - x \cos x}{x^3} \approx \tfrac{1}{3}$$

5 Given that x is so small that terms in x^3 and higher powers of x may be disregarded, show that

$$\ln \left[\frac{(1 + 2x)^2}{1 - 3x} \right] = 7x + \tfrac{1}{2} x^2$$

6 Show that for small x:

$$\frac{(1 + x)^{\frac{1}{2}}}{(1 - x)^2} \approx 1 + \tfrac{5}{2} x + \tfrac{31}{8} x^2$$

7 Given that x takes a value near $\frac{\pi}{2}$, explain why $\cos x \approx \frac{\pi}{2} - x$.
Use this approximation to find (to 2 decimal places) the smallest positive root of the equation

$$\cos x = \frac{x}{10}$$

8 Given that x is small, show that
$$e^{\sin x} = 1 + x + \tfrac{1}{2} x^2 + Ax^3$$
and determine the value of A. You may assume that terms in x^4 and higher powers of x can be disregarded.

9 Evaluate: (a) $\displaystyle\lim_{x \to 0} \left(\frac{\sin x - x}{\sin x - x \cos x} \right)$ (b) $\displaystyle\lim_{x \to 0} \left(\frac{\ln(1 + x) - x}{\sin^2 x} \right)$.

10 Given that x is small and that terms in x^4 and higher powers of x may be disregarded, show that

$$\ln(\sec x + \tan x) = x + \tfrac{1}{6} x^3$$

SUMMARY OF KEY POINTS

1 $\displaystyle\sum_{r=1}^{n} 1 = n$

2 $\displaystyle\sum_{r=1}^{n} r = \tfrac{1}{2}n(n+1)$

3 If $u_r \equiv \mathrm{f}(r+1) - \mathrm{f}(r)$, then

$$\sum_{r=1}^{n} u_r = \mathrm{f}(n+1) - \mathrm{f}(1)$$

4 $\displaystyle\sum_{r=1}^{n} r^2 = \tfrac{1}{6}n(n+1)(2n+1)$

5 $\displaystyle\sum_{r=1}^{n} r^3 = \tfrac{1}{4}n^2(n+1)^2 = \left[\sum_{r=1}^{n} r\right]^2$

6 $\displaystyle\sum_{r=1}^{n} r(r+1) = \tfrac{1}{3}n(n+1)(n+2)$

7 The binomial series

$$(1+x)^n = 1 + nx + \frac{n(n-1)}{2!}x^2 + \frac{n(n-1)(n-2)}{3!}x^3 + \cdots$$
$$+ \frac{n(n-1)\cdots(n-r+1)}{r!}x^r + \cdots$$

  (a) has $(n+1)$ terms only if n is a positive integer

  (b) has an infinite number of terms if n is rational, but not a positive integer. The series expansion is only valid in this case if $|x| < 1$.

8 Maclaurin's expansion:

$$\mathrm{f}(x) = \mathrm{f}(0) + \frac{x}{1!}\mathrm{f}'(0) + \frac{x^2}{2!}\mathrm{f}''(0) + \cdots + \frac{x^r}{r!}\mathrm{f}^{(r)}(0) + \cdots$$

9 $\sin x = x - \dfrac{x^3}{3!} + \dfrac{x^5}{5!} - \cdots + (-1)^r \dfrac{x^{2r+1}}{(2r+1)!} + \cdots$

10 $\cos x = 1 - \dfrac{x^2}{2!} + \dfrac{x^4}{4!} - \cdots + (-1)^r \dfrac{x^{2r}}{(2r)!} + \cdots$

11 $\ln(1+x) = x - \dfrac{x^2}{2} + \dfrac{x^3}{3} - \cdots + (-1)^{r+1}\dfrac{x^r}{r} + \cdots$
$$(-1 < x \leqslant 1)$$

12 $\mathrm{e}^x = 1 + x + \dfrac{x^2}{2!} + \dfrac{x^3}{3!} + \cdots + \dfrac{x^r}{r!} + \cdots$

For sufficiently small x, where x^3 and higher powers of x are disregarded:

13 $\sin x \approx x \approx \tan x$

14 $\cos x \approx 1 - \frac{1}{2}x^2$

15 $(1 + x)^{\frac{1}{2}} \approx 1 + \frac{1}{2}x - \frac{1}{8}x^2$

16 $\ln(1 + x) \approx x - \frac{1}{2}x^2$

17 $e^x \approx 1 + x + \frac{1}{2}x^2$

Trigonometry

3

Books P1 (page 149) and P2 (page 161) show you how to solve trigonometric equations when the unknown to be found lies in a specific interval (for example, $0 < x \leqslant 2\pi$). This chapter shows you how to derive *general* solutions to trigonometric equations and introduces the inverse trigonometric functions with their graphs and derivatives.

3.1 Alternative forms of $a\cos\theta + b\sin\theta$

The form of the curve with equation $y = \cos x$ is well known to you and is shown below for real values of x.

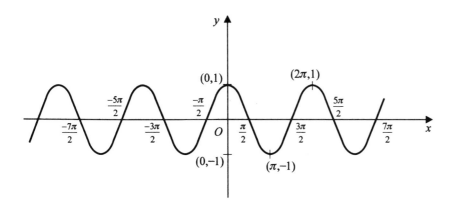

Note that the domain of the function $\cos x$ is $x \in \mathbb{R}$, that the range is $[-1, 1]$ and that it is a many–one mapping.

Book P1 described simple transformations of graphs. Any curve with equation $y = R\cos(x + \alpha)$, where R is a positive constant and α is constant looks like this:

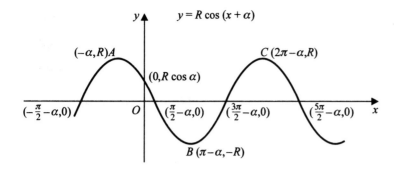

This curve is similar to that of $y = \cos x$ but it is enlarged by a factor R parallel to the y-axis and translated by α in the direction of the negative x-axis. The curve meets the y-axis at $(0, R\cos\alpha)$ and the x-axis at the points $\cdots\left(-\frac{\pi}{2} - \alpha, 0\right), \left(\frac{\pi}{2} - \alpha, 0\right), \left(\frac{3\pi}{2} - \alpha, 0\right), \cdots$. The stationary points $\cdots A(-\alpha, R), C(2\pi - \alpha, R), \cdots$ are maximum points, and $\cdots B(\pi - \alpha, -R), \cdots$ are minimum points.

Now:

$$y = R\cos(x + \alpha)$$
$$\equiv R\cos x \cos\alpha - R\sin x \sin\alpha$$

and this expression for y is of the form $a\cos x + b\sin x$, where a and b are constants.

Notice that $a = R\cos\alpha$ and $b = -R\sin\alpha$.

In a similar way $a\cos\theta + b\sin\theta$ can be expressed in the form $R\sin(\theta + \beta)$, where R is a positive constant and β is a constant.

That is:
$$a\cos\theta + b\sin\theta \equiv R\sin(\theta + \beta)$$

because
$$a\cos\theta + b\sin\theta \equiv R\sin\theta\cos\beta + R\cos\theta\sin\beta$$

and you can see that $a = R\sin\beta$ and $b = R\cos\beta$. When expressing $a\cos\theta + b\sin\theta$ in these forms, the values of the constants α and β are usually chosen to be the smallest value, either positive or negative, that is possible.

Example 1

Express each of the following in the form $R\cos(x \pm \alpha)$, where $R > 0$ and $|\alpha|$ is as numerically small as possible:

(a) $8\cos x - 6\sin x$ (b) $-8\cos x + 6\sin x$

(a) You have $R\cos(x + \alpha) \equiv 8\cos x - 6\sin x$

That is: $R\cos x \cos\alpha - R\sin x \sin\alpha \equiv 8\cos x - 6\sin x$

Hence $R\cos\alpha = 8$ and $R\sin\alpha = 6$

By squaring and adding:
$$R^2(\cos^2\alpha + \sin^2\alpha) = 8^2 + 6^2 = 100 \Rightarrow R = 10$$

$$\tan\alpha = \frac{R\sin\alpha}{R\cos\alpha} = \frac{6}{8} \Rightarrow \alpha = 36.9°$$

So: $8\cos x - 6\sin x \equiv 10\cos(x + 36.9°)$

(b) You have: $R\cos(x + \alpha) \equiv -8\cos x + 6\sin x$

So: $R\cos x\cos\alpha - R\sin x\sin\alpha \equiv -8\cos x + 6\sin x$

and remember $R > 0$.

$$R\cos\alpha = -8 \text{ and } R\sin\alpha = -6$$

$$R^2(\cos^2\alpha + \sin^2\alpha) = (-8)^2 + (-6)^2 = 100$$

$\Rightarrow$ $$R = 10$$

$$\cos\alpha = -\tfrac{8}{10} \quad\text{and}\quad \sin\alpha = -\tfrac{6}{10}$$

that is, α lies in the *third* quadrant, i.e.
$$-180° < \alpha < -90°, \quad\text{so}\quad \alpha = -143.1°$$

So: $-8\cos x + 6\sin x \equiv 10\cos(x - 143.1°)$

Example 2
Express each of the following in the form $R\sin(x \pm \alpha)$ where $R > 0$ and $|\alpha|$ is as small as possible:

(a) $8\cos x - 6\sin x$ (b) $-8\cos x + 6\sin x$

(a) You have $R\sin(x + \alpha) \equiv 8\cos x - 6\sin x$

So: $R\sin x\cos\alpha + R\cos x\sin\alpha \equiv 8\cos x - 6\sin x$

Hence: $R\cos\alpha = -6$ and $R\sin\alpha = 8$

$R^2(\cos^2\alpha + \sin^2\alpha) = (-6)^2 + 8^2 = 100 \Rightarrow R^2 = 100$

R is positive $\Rightarrow R = 10$

Hence: $\cos\alpha = -\tfrac{6}{10}$ and $\sin\alpha = \tfrac{8}{10}$

That is, α lies in the second quadrant $(90° < \alpha < 180°)$, and $\alpha = 126.9°$.

$$8\cos x - 6\sin x \equiv 10\sin(x + 126.9°)$$

(b) You have $R\sin(x - \alpha) \equiv 6\sin x - 8\cos x$

That is: $R\sin x\cos\alpha - R\cos x\sin\alpha \equiv 6\sin x - 8\cos x$

Hence: $$R\cos\alpha = 6 \text{ and } R\sin\alpha = 8$$

As before, $R^2(\cos^2\alpha + \sin^2\alpha) = 6^2 + 8^2 \Rightarrow R = 10$

$$\cos\alpha = \tfrac{6}{10} \text{ and } \sin\alpha = \tfrac{8}{10}$$

As both $\cos\alpha$ and $\sin\alpha$ are positive, α is in the first quadrant $(0° < \alpha < 90°) \Rightarrow \alpha = 53.1°$.

$$6\sin x - 8\cos x = 10\sin(x - 53.1°)$$

The advantages of taking $a\cos\theta + b\sin\theta$ in the form $R\cos(\theta + \alpha)$ or in the form $R\sin(\theta + \beta)$ are many. In particular, you can write down maximum and minimum values of the expression immediately, and solve equations of the form $a\cos\theta + b\sin\theta = c$ economically without further processing, by using a calculator. The shape of the curve $y = a\cos x + b\sin x$ can be determined at once. Further advantages will be apparent when you study complex numbers in Book P4.

Example 3

Express $3\cos x + 4\sin x$ in the form $R\cos(x - \alpha)$, where $R > 0$ and α is acute. Hence find the maximum value of $3\cos x + 4\sin x$ and the smallest positive value of x for which this occurs.

You have: $$R\cos(x - \alpha) \equiv 3\cos x + 4\sin x$$

That is: $$R\cos x\cos\alpha + R\sin x\sin\alpha \equiv 3\cos x + 4\sin x$$

$\Rightarrow$ $$R\cos\alpha = 3, \quad R\sin\alpha = 4$$

Squaring and adding gives

$$R^2(\cos^2\alpha + \sin^2\alpha) = 3^2 + 4^2 = 25$$

$$R^2 = 25 \Rightarrow R = 5$$

$$\tan\alpha = \frac{R\sin\alpha}{R\cos\alpha} = \tfrac{4}{3} \Rightarrow \alpha = 53.1° \text{ (or 0.93 radians)}$$

That is: $$3\cos x + 4\sin x \equiv 5\cos(x - 53.1°)$$

Since $-1 \leqslant \cos x \leqslant 1$, you have:

$$-5 \leqslant 5\cos(x - 53.1°) \leqslant 5$$

The maximum value of $3\cos x + 4\sin x$ is 5 and the smallest value of x for which this occurs is $53.1°$ (because when $x = 53.1°$ then $x - 53.1° = 0$).

Example 4

Express $12 \sin x - 5 \cos x$ in the form $R \sin(x - \alpha)$, where $R > 0$ and α lies in $(0, \frac{\pi}{2})$. Hence solve the equation

$$12 \sin x - 5 \cos x = 7, \qquad 0 \leqslant x < 2\pi$$

You have: $\qquad R \sin(x - \alpha) \equiv 12 \sin x - 5 \cos x$

$\Rightarrow \qquad R \sin x \cos \alpha - R \cos x \sin \alpha \equiv 12 \sin x - 5 \cos x$

$\Rightarrow \qquad R \cos \alpha = 12$ and $R \sin \alpha = 5$

Squaring and adding:

$$R^2(\cos^2 \alpha + \sin^2 \alpha) = 144 + 25 = 169$$

$$R^2 = 169 \Rightarrow R = 13$$

$$\tan \alpha = \frac{R \sin \alpha}{R \cos \alpha} = \tfrac{5}{12} \Rightarrow \alpha = 0.3948 \text{ radians}$$

Hence: $\qquad 12 \sin x - 5 \cos x \equiv 13 \sin(x - 0.3948)$

The equation $12 \sin x - 5 \cos x = 7$ can now be rewritten as

$$13 \sin(x - 0.3948) = 7$$

That is: $\qquad \sin(x - 0.3948) = \tfrac{7}{13}$

Hence: $\qquad x - 0.3948 = 0.5686$ or $\pi - 0.5686$

$\Rightarrow \qquad x = 0.963$ or 2.968 radians (to 3 decimal places)

Sometimes an equation will need processing before you can express it in a form like $R \cos(x + \alpha)$.

Example 5

Solve, for $0 \leqslant \theta \leqslant 360°$, the equation

$$4 \cos \theta + 3 \sin \theta = 3.5 \sec \theta$$

Multiply by $\cos \theta$ to give

$$4 \cos^2 \theta + 3 \cos \theta \sin \theta = 3.5$$

Remember that $\cos 2\theta \equiv 2 \cos^2 \theta - 1$, so $4 \cos^2 \theta \equiv 2 + 2 \cos 2\theta$ and $\sin 2\theta \equiv 2 \sin \theta \cos \theta$, so $3 \sin \theta \cos \theta \equiv \tfrac{3}{2} \sin 2\theta$.

So the equation can be written as

$$2 + 2 \cos 2\theta + \tfrac{3}{2} \sin 2\theta = 3.5$$

That is: $\qquad 4 \cos 2\theta + 3 \sin 2\theta = 3$

Now you can express $4\cos 2\theta + 3\sin 2\theta$ in the form $R\cos(2\theta - \alpha)$.

$$R\cos 2\theta \cos \alpha + R\sin 2\theta \sin \alpha \equiv 4\cos 2\theta + 3\sin 2\theta$$

So:
$$R\cos \alpha = 4, \quad R\sin \alpha = 3$$

Hence $R = 5$ and $\tan \alpha = \frac{3}{4} \Rightarrow \alpha = 36.87°$. The equation can now be written as

$$5\cos(2\theta - 36.87°) = 3$$

$$\Rightarrow \qquad \cos(2\theta - 36.87°) = \frac{3}{5}$$

$$2\theta - 36.87° = 53.13° \text{ or } 306.87° \text{ or } 360° + 53.13° \text{ or } 360° + 306.87°$$

$$2\theta = 90° \text{ or } 343.74° \text{ or } 450° \text{ or } 703.74°$$

$$\theta = 45° \text{ or } 171.9° \text{ or } 225° \text{ or } 351.9° \text{ (1 d.p.)}$$

Exercise 3A

In questions 1–5, $R > 0$ and α is the smallest positive angle possible. Express each in the form required, stating the value of R and the value of α, to the nearest tenth of a degree.

1 $8\cos x - 15\sin x, \; R\cos(x + \alpha)$
2 $5\sin x + 12\cos x, \; R\sin(x + \alpha)$
3 $3\sin x - \cos x, \; R\sin(x - \alpha)$
4 $6\cos x + 8\sin x, \; R\cos(x - \alpha)$
5 $\cos x - \sin x, \; R\cos(x + \alpha)$

In questions 6–10, use the results of your work in questions 1–5 to find for each function the greatest and least values, stating the smallest positive value of x for which these occur.

6 $8\cos x - 15\sin x$ **7** $5\sin x + 12\cos x$
8 $3\sin x - \cos x$ **9** $6\cos x + 8\sin x$
10 $\cos x - \sin x$

In questions 11–15 find the values of x in degrees to 1 d.p. in the interval $[0, 360°]$ for which:

11 $4\sin x - 3\cos x = 2.5$ **12** $5\cos x + 12\sin x = 6$
13 $\cos x + \sin x = \frac{1}{2}$ **14** $5\cos 2x + 2\sin 2x = 3$
15 $15\cos 3x - 8\sin 3x = 17$

In questions 16–20, find the values of x in radians to 2 d.p. in the interval $[0, 2\pi]$.

16 $\cos x - \sin x = 1$

17 $4\cos x + 3\sin x = 3$

18 $8\cos x + 15\sin x = -11$

19 $6\sin 2x - \cos 2x = 3$

20 $20\sin\dfrac{x}{2} - 21\cos\dfrac{x}{2} = 14.5$

21 Solve the equation $7\cos x - 24\sin x = 12.5$, giving all solutions in degrees to 1 decimal place between 0 and 360°.
Find also the least value of $7\cos x - 24\sin x$ and state the smallest positive value of x for which this occurs.

22 Given that $3\sin x - \cos x \equiv R\sin(x - \alpha)$, $R > 0$ and $0 < \alpha < 90°$, find R and α.
Hence solve the equation

$$3\sin x - \cos x = 2$$

giving all solutions in the interval $[0, 720°]$.

23 Find, to the nearest tenth of a degree, all solutions in the interval $[-360°, 360°]$ of the equation

$$3\cos x + 4\sin x = \frac{5\sqrt{3}}{2}$$

24 Express $2\cos 4x + 3\sin 4x$ in the form $R\cos(4x - \alpha)$, where $R > 0$ and α lies in the interval $[0, \frac{\pi}{2}]$.
Hence find:
(a) the minimum value of

$$\frac{1}{2\cos 4x + 3\sin 4x}$$

and the smallest positive value of x when this occurs.

(b) the values of x, in radians to 2 decimals places, for which $2\cos 4x + 3\sin 4x = 2$ in the interval $[0, 2\pi]$.

25 Express $4\sin x + 3\cos x$ in the form $R\sin(x + \alpha)$ where $R > 0$ and α lies in the interval $[0, \frac{\pi}{2}]$.
(a) Find the greatest and the least values of

$$\frac{1}{4\sin x + 3\cos x + 12}$$

(b) Determine, in radians to 2 decimal places, the values of x in the interval $[0, 2\pi]$ for which

$$(4\sin x + 3\cos x)^2 = \tfrac{1}{2}$$

3.2 General solutions of trigonometric equations

From the curves with equation $y = \cos x$ and $y = \sin x$ you know that the functions $\cos x$ and $\sin x$ are periodic over 2π radians (or $360°$). That is, each curve repeats itself over 2π radians ($360°$) as you can see:

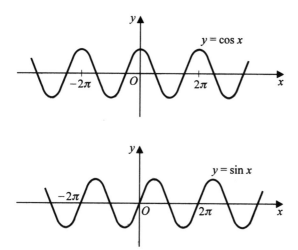

From the graph of $y = \tan x$, you can see that the function $\tan x$ is periodic over π radians (or $180°$).

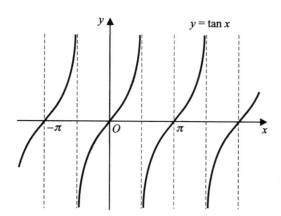

You will be asked to solve equations in both degrees and radians, and should be completely familiar with both. To begin with, consider an example with angles given in degrees.

From the curve $y = \sin x$, you can see that the function $\sin x$ has the same value at

$$x, 180° - x, 2 \times 180° + x, 3 \times 180° - x, 4 \times 180° + x, \cdots$$

This sequence of values can be generalised and expressed in the formula:

$$180°n + (-1)^n x \quad \text{for } n = 0, 1, 2, 3, \cdots$$

From the graph of $y = \cos x$, you can see that the function $\cos x$ has the same value at

$$x, 360° - x, 360° + x, 2 \times 360° - x, 2 \times 360° + x, \cdots$$

This sequence of values can be generalised and expressed in the formula:

$$360°n \pm x \quad \text{for } n = 0, 1, 2, 3, \cdots$$

From the graph of $y = \tan x$, you can see that the function $\tan x$ has the same value at

$$x, 180° + x, 2 \times 180° + x, 3 \times 180° + x, \cdots$$

This sequence of values can be generalised and expressed in the formula:

$$180°n + x \quad \text{for } n = 0, 1, 2, 3, \cdots$$

Note: the formulae are also true for all *negative integral* values of n.

You can use these general formulae to find the general solutions of trigonometric equations, as follows.

You know that the equation $\sin x = \frac{1}{2}$ has many solutions; some of these are $\cdots 30°, 150°, 390°, 510°, \cdots$. However, your calculator gives just $30°$ when programmed to evaluate inverse $\sin \frac{1}{2}$. In fact, $30°$ (in degrees) or $\frac{\pi}{6}$ (in radians) is called the **principal value** of inverse $\sin \frac{1}{2}$, written **arcsin** $\frac{1}{2}$.

The general solution of the equation $\sin x = \frac{1}{2}$ is

$$180°n + (-1)^n 30°, \text{ in degrees}$$

or

$$\pi n + (-1)^n \tfrac{\pi}{6}, \text{ in radians}$$

where n is any integer.

Suppose now that the equation $\sin x = b$, where $-1 \leqslant b \leqslant 1$, requires a general solution. Since $-1 \leqslant b \leqslant 1$, there is just one value of x in the interval $-\frac{\pi}{2} \leqslant x \leqslant \frac{\pi}{2}$ for which $\sin x = b$. Take this value to be α; then α is called the principal value of inverse sine b, written often as $\arcsin b$.

■ **The general solution of the equation $\sin x = b$, where $\arcsin b = \alpha$, is:**

$$\mathbf{180°n + (-1)^n \alpha, \text{ if } \alpha \text{ is measured in degrees}}$$

or $\quad \boldsymbol{\pi n + (-1)^n \alpha, \text{ if } \alpha \text{ is measured in radians}}$

where n is any integer.

Suppose now that the equation $\cos x = c$, where $-1 \leqslant c \leqslant 1$, requires a general solution. Since $-1 \leqslant c \leqslant 1$, there is just one value of x in the interval $0 \leqslant x \leqslant \pi$ for which $\cos x = c$. Take this value to be β; then β is called the principal value of inverse $\cos c$, often written as $\arccos c$.

- **The general solution of the equation $\cos x = c$, where $\arccos c = \beta$, is**
  $$360°n \pm \beta, \text{ if } \beta \text{ is measured in degrees}$$
  or $\quad 2\pi n \pm \beta, \text{ if } \beta \text{ is measured in radians}$
  where n is any integer.

Finally, suppose that the equation $\tan x = t$, where $t \in \mathbb{R}$, requires a general solution. Since t is real, there is just one value of x in the interval $-\frac{\pi}{2} < x < \frac{\pi}{2}$ for which $\tan x = t$. Take this value to be γ, then γ is called the principal value of inverse $\tan t$, often written as $\arctan t$.

- **The general solution of the equation $\tan x = t$, where $\arctan t = \gamma$ is**
  $$180°n + \gamma, \text{ if } \gamma \text{ is measured in degrees}$$
  or $\quad \pi n + \gamma, \text{ if } \gamma \text{ is measured in radians}$
  where n is any integer.

In solving trigonometric equations, you should aim to reduce any given equation to one, or more, of the forms

$$\sin x = b, \quad \cos x = c \quad \text{or} \quad \tan x = t$$

Once this has been achieved, you can use the general solutions given.

Note: These general solutions are not given in the ULEAC formula booklet. **You should memorise them.**

Example 6

Find (a) in degrees (b) in radians in terms of π, the general solution of the equation $\sin x = \dfrac{1}{\sqrt{2}}$.

(a) From a right-angled isosceles triangle, you know that $\sin 45° = \frac{1}{\sqrt{2}}$. So, write the equation as $\sin x = \sin 45°$.

Using the formula, you have

$$x = 180°n + (-1)^n 45°$$

as the general solution in degrees.

(b) In radians, you have $\sin x = \sin \frac{\pi}{4}$, since $\frac{\pi}{4} \equiv 45°$. The general solution in radians is

$$x = n\pi + (-1)^n \frac{\pi}{4}$$

Example 7
Find (a) in degrees (b) in radians in terms of π, the general solution
of the equation $\cos 2x = -\frac{1}{2}$.

(a) Rewrite the equation as $\cos 2x = \cos 120°$.

Then: $$2x = 360°n \pm 120°$$

that is, $x = 180°n \pm 60°$ is the general solution in degrees.

(b) Rewrite the equation as $\cos 2x = \cos \frac{2\pi}{3}$

Then: $$2x = 2n\pi \pm \frac{2\pi}{3}$$

that is, $x = n\pi \pm \frac{\pi}{3}$ is the general solution in radians in terms of π.

Example 8
Find (a) in degrees (b) in radians in terms of π, the general solution
of the equation $\tan^2 x = \frac{1}{3}$.

Taking the square roots gives the two equations

$$\tan x = \frac{1}{\sqrt{3}} \quad \text{and} \quad \tan x = -\frac{1}{\sqrt{3}}$$

(a) That is, $\tan x = \tan 30°$ and $\tan x = \tan(-30°)$.

$$x = 180°n + 30° \quad \text{and} \quad x = 180°n - 30°$$

The general solution is

$$x = 180°n \pm 30°$$

(b) In radians, $\tan x = \tan \frac{\pi}{6}$ or $\tan x = \tan(-\frac{\pi}{6})$.

$$x = n\pi + \frac{\pi}{6} \quad \text{and} \quad x = n\pi - \frac{\pi}{6}$$

The general solution in radians in terms of π is

$$x = n\pi \pm \frac{\pi}{6}$$

Example 9
Find, in radians in terms of π, the general solution of the equation

$$4 \sin x = \sec x$$

You can multiply by $\cos x$ so that the equation becomes

$$4 \sin x \cos x = 1$$

Since $\sin 2x \equiv 2 \sin x \cos x$, you have

$$2 \sin 2x = 1 \Rightarrow \sin 2x = \frac{1}{2}$$

So that $$\sin 2x = \sin \frac{\pi}{6}$$

The general solution is then given by

$$2x = n\pi + (-1)^n \frac{\pi}{6}$$

that is:
$$x = \tfrac{1}{2}n\pi + (-1)^n \tfrac{\pi}{12}$$

Example 10

Find, in degrees, the general solution of the equation

$$4\cos 2\theta + 3\sin 2\theta = 3$$

This equation was solved for θ in the interval $[0, 360°]$ in example 5 on page 37. It can be expressed in the form

$$\cos(2\theta - 36.87°) = \tfrac{3}{5} = \cos 53.13°$$

So the general solution is obtained by writing

$$2\theta - 36.87° = 360°n \pm 53.13°$$

where n is any integer.

Taking the $+$ sign: $2\theta - 36.87° = 360°n + 53.13°$

which gives $\qquad\qquad \theta = 180°n + 45°$

Taking the $-$ sign: $2\theta - 36.87° = 360°n - 53.13°$

which gives: $\qquad\qquad \theta = 180°n - \dfrac{16.26°}{2}$

$$= 180°n - 8.13°$$

The general solution of the equation is

$$180°n + 45° \quad \text{and} \quad 180°n - 8.13°$$

Example 11

Find, in radians in terms of π, the general solution of the equation $\cos 3\theta = \sin 2\theta$.

There are two approaches worth consideration and both use identities to start with.

Approach (i): Using the identity $\sin A \equiv \cos(\tfrac{\pi}{2} - A)$, the equation can be expressed as

$$\cos 3\theta = \cos(\tfrac{\pi}{2} - 2\theta)$$

Then using the general solution formula you have

$$3\theta = 2n\pi \pm \left(\tfrac{\pi}{2} - 2\theta\right)$$

Taking the $+$ sign: $5\theta = 2n\pi + \tfrac{\pi}{2} \Rightarrow \theta = \tfrac{2}{5}n\pi + \tfrac{\pi}{10}$

Taking the $-$ sign: $\theta = 2n\pi - \tfrac{\pi}{2}$

The general solution is

$$\tfrac{2}{5}n\pi + \tfrac{\pi}{10} \quad \text{and} \quad 2n\pi - \tfrac{\pi}{2}$$

where n is any integer.

Approach (ii): You can also make use of the identities

$$\cos 3A \equiv 4\cos^3 A - 3\cos A$$
$$\sin 2A \equiv 2\sin A \cos A$$

to change the equation to

$$4\cos^3 \theta - 3\cos \theta = 2\sin \theta \cos \theta$$

That is: $\qquad\qquad \cos \theta(4\cos^2 \theta - 3 - 2\sin \theta) = 0$

Using the identity $\cos^2 A + \sin^2 A \equiv 1$, you get

$$\cos \theta(4 - 4\sin^2 \theta - 3 - 2\sin \theta) = 0$$

Hence, either: $\qquad\qquad\qquad \cos \theta = 0$

or: $\qquad\qquad\qquad 4\sin^2 \theta + 2\sin \theta - 1 = 0$

$$\Rightarrow \qquad\qquad \sin \theta = \frac{-2 \pm \sqrt{(4+16)}}{8} = \frac{-1 \pm \sqrt{5}}{4}$$

So: $\quad \cos \theta = 0 \quad or \quad \sin \theta = \dfrac{-1 + \sqrt{5}}{4} \quad or \quad \sin \theta = \dfrac{-1 - \sqrt{5}}{4}$

That is: $\quad \cos \theta = \cos \tfrac{\pi}{2}$

or: $\qquad \sin \theta = \sin 18°$ (from calculator) $\therefore \ \sin \theta = \sin \tfrac{\pi}{10}$

or: $\qquad \sin \theta = \sin(-54°)$ (from calculator) $\therefore \ \sin \theta = \sin(-\tfrac{3\pi}{10})$

$$\begin{cases} \theta = 2n\pi \pm \tfrac{\pi}{2} & \text{from } \cos \theta = \cos \tfrac{\pi}{2} \\[4pt] \theta = n\pi + (-1)^n \tfrac{\pi}{10} & \text{from } \sin \theta = \sin \tfrac{\pi}{10} \\[4pt] \theta = n\pi + (-1)^{n+1}\left(\tfrac{3\pi}{10}\right) & \text{from } \sin \theta = \sin(-\tfrac{3\pi}{10}) \end{cases}$$

is the general solution.

You can test by taking $n = 0, \pm 1, \pm 2, \pm 3, \cdots$ that this general form gives the same values as those obtained from the general solution found in Approach (i).

Exercise 3B

Find (a) in degrees (b) in radians general solutions of the equations in questions 1–15.

1 $\tan x = 1$ **2** $\cos x = \frac{1}{2}$

3 $\sin x = \frac{1}{2}\sqrt{3}$ **4** $\tan x = -\sqrt{3}$

5 $\cos x = -\frac{\sqrt{3}}{2}$ **6** $\sin x = -\frac{1}{2}$

7 $\cos 2x = 0$ **8** $\tan 3x = -1$

9 $\sin \frac{1}{2}x = 0.766$ **10** $\cos 2x = \cos x$

11 $\tan 3x = \tan x$ **12** $\cos 2x = \sin x$

13 $12 \sin x - 5 \cos x = 6.5$ **14** $2\cos^2 x - \cos x - 1 = 0$

15 $\tan^4 x - 4 \tan^2 x + 3 = 0$

16 Use the identities for $\sin(A + B)$ and $\sin(A - B)$ to show that

   (a) $2 \sin A \cos B \equiv \sin(A + B) + \sin(A - B)$

   (b) $2 \cos A \sin B \equiv \sin(A + B) - \sin(A - B)$

   By writing $A + B = C$ and $A - B = D$, hence show that

   * (c) $\sin C + \sin D \equiv 2 \sin \dfrac{C + D}{2} \cos \dfrac{C - D}{2}$

   * (d) $\sin C - \sin D \equiv 2 \cos \dfrac{C + D}{2} \sin \dfrac{C - D}{2}$

17 Use the results found in question 16(c) and (d) to find the general solutions of the equations

   (a) $\sin 4x + \sin 2x = 0$

   (b) $\sin 4x - \sin 2x = \sin x$

   giving your solutions in radians in terms of π.

18 Show that the general solution of the equation

$$\sin 3x + \sin x = 0$$

   can be expressed as $\frac{1}{2}n\pi$, where n is any integer.

19 Using a method similar to that required in question 16 and the identities for $\cos(A + B)$ and $\cos(A - B)$, show that

   * (a) $\cos C + \cos D \equiv 2 \cos \dfrac{C + D}{2} \cos \dfrac{C - D}{2}$

   * (b) $\cos D - \cos C \equiv 2 \sin \dfrac{C + D}{2} \sin \dfrac{C - D}{2}$

The four identities marked * in questions 16 and 19 are sometimes called **the product formulae**. They are given in your ULEAC formulae booklet.

20 Find the general solution of the equations

(a) $\cos 4x + \cos 2x = 0$

(b) $\cos 4x + \cos 2x = \cos x$

(c) $\cos x + \cos 3x + \cos 5x = 0$

giving your solutions in radians in terms of π.

21 Show that $\tan x \equiv -\tan(-x)$.

Hence find the general solution of the equation

$$\tan 3x + \tan x = 0$$

giving your solution in radians in terms of π.

22 Prove that the solutions of the equation

$$\cos x - \sqrt{3}\sin x = \sqrt{2} \text{ in } (0, 2\pi)$$

are $\frac{17\pi}{12}$ and $\frac{23\pi}{12}$.

Hence find the general solution of the equation.

23 Find the general solution of the equation

$$2\sec^2\theta + 1 = 5\tan\theta$$

giving your answer in degrees to the nearest $0.1°$.

24 Prove that $\sec^2\theta + \operatorname{cosec}^2\theta \equiv \sec^2\theta\operatorname{cosec}^2\theta$. Hence find the general solution of the equation

$$\sec^2\theta + \operatorname{cosec}^2\theta = 8$$

giving your answer in radians in terms of π.

25 Find, in degrees, the general solution of the equation

$$\cos(2x + 70°) = \cos(x - 30°)$$

3.3 Inverse trigonometric functions

Book P1 (page 41) showed that only one–one functions can have an inverse function. The functions $\sin x$, $\cos x$ and $\tan x$ for $x \in \mathbb{R}$ are many–one functions, as you saw in section 3.2.

If, however, the domain of each of these functions is suitably restricted, then it is possible to make the function one–one and to define an inverse function. This is how it is done for the function $\sin x$.

You know that $\sin x$ for the domain $-\frac{\pi}{2} \leqslant x \leqslant \frac{\pi}{2}$ takes all real values in the range $-1 \leqslant \sin x \leqslant 1$ and that it is a one–one function. The graph of the curve $y = \sin x$, $-\frac{\pi}{2} \leqslant x \leqslant \frac{\pi}{2}$, looks like this, where x is in radians:

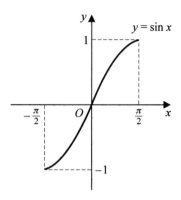

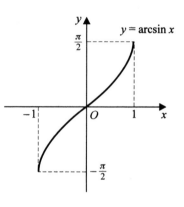

The inverse function of $\sin x$, $-\frac{\pi}{2} \leqslant x \leqslant \frac{\pi}{2}$, is called **arcsin x**. Its domain is $-1 \leqslant x \leqslant 1$ and its range is $-\frac{\pi}{2} \leqslant \arcsin x \leqslant \frac{\pi}{2}$. The graph of $y = \arcsin x$, $-1 \leqslant x \leqslant 1$ looks like this:

The curves $y = \sin x$ and $y = \arcsin x$ are reflections of each other in the line $y = x$.

The inverse functions of $\cos x$ and $\tan x$ are given by

arccos x with domain $-1 \leqslant x \leqslant 1$ and range $0 \leqslant \arccos x \leqslant \pi$

arctan x with domain $x \in \mathbb{R}$ and range $-\frac{\pi}{2} < x < \frac{\pi}{2}$

The graphs of the functions and the inverse functions look like this:

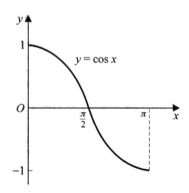

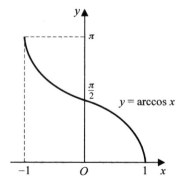

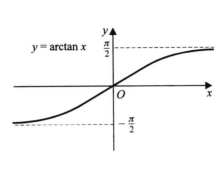

Note: In solutions you may sometimes need to use degrees but more usually for work of this level radians are used; furthermore, radians must be used if derivatives or integrals are being considered.

Example 12

Write down, in radians, the values of (a) $\arcsin(-\frac{1}{2})$ (b) $\arccos(-\frac{1}{2})$ (c) $\arctan\frac{1}{2}$.

(a) $\arcsin(-\frac{1}{2}) = -\frac{\pi}{6}$ (or -0.524 from your calculator)

(b) $\arccos(-\frac{1}{2}) = \frac{2\pi}{3}$ (or 2.094 from your calculator)

(c) $\arctan\frac{1}{2} = 0.464$ radians (3 decimal places)

3.4 The derivatives of inverse trigonometric functions

Given that $y = \arcsin x,\ \left\{\begin{array}{l} -1 \leqslant x \leqslant 1 \\ -\frac{\pi}{2} \leqslant y \leqslant \frac{\pi}{2} \end{array}\right\}$ then $\sin y = x,$ where $-\frac{\pi}{2} \leqslant y \leqslant \frac{\pi}{2}$. Using the chain rule, differentiate with respect to x:

$$\cos y \frac{\mathrm{d}y}{\mathrm{d}x} = 1$$

and

$$\frac{\mathrm{d}y}{\mathrm{d}x} = \frac{1}{\cos y}$$

But

$$\cos^2 y + \sin^2 y \equiv 1$$

So:

$$\cos y = \sqrt{(1 - \sin^2 y)} = \sqrt{(1 - x^2)}$$

taking the positive square root because $\cos y \geqslant 0$ in the interval $-\frac{\pi}{2} \leqslant y \leqslant \frac{\pi}{2}$.

- So: $$\frac{d}{dx}(\arcsin x) = \frac{1}{\sqrt{(1-x^2)}}$$

For $y = \arccos x$, $\left\{ \begin{matrix} -1 \leqslant x \leqslant 1 \\ 0 \leqslant y \leqslant \pi \end{matrix} \right\}$

you have $\cos y = x$, where $0 \leqslant y \leqslant \pi$.

Differentiating with respect to x:

$$-\sin y \frac{dy}{dx} = 1$$

that is: $$\frac{dy}{dx} = -\frac{1}{\sin y}$$

But $\sin^2 y + \cos^2 y \equiv 1$, so $\sin y = \sqrt{(1 - \cos^2 y)}$ and:

$$\sin y = \sqrt{(1 - x^2)}$$

because $\sin y \geqslant 0$ for $0 \leqslant y \leqslant \pi$.

- So: $$\frac{d}{dx}(\arccos x) = -\frac{1}{\sqrt{(1-x^2)}}$$

You should notice also that the gradient of the curve $y = \arcsin x$, shown on page 48, is positive; the gradient of the curve $y = \arccos x$, shown on page 48, is negative. These signs agree with the signs of $\frac{dy}{dx}$ just derived for $y = \arcsin x$ and $y = \arccos x$.

Given that $y = \arctan x$, $\left\{ \begin{matrix} x \in \mathbb{R} \\ -\frac{\pi}{2} < y < \frac{\pi}{2} \end{matrix} \right\}$

then: $\tan y = x$, where $-\frac{\pi}{2} < y < \frac{\pi}{2}$.

Differentiating with respect to x, you get

$$\sec^2 y \frac{dy}{dx} = 1$$

that is: $$\frac{dy}{dx} = \frac{1}{\sec^2 y}$$

But $$\sec^2 y \equiv 1 + \tan^2 y = 1 + x^2$$

and this gives

- $$\frac{d}{dx}(\arctan x) = \frac{1}{1 + x^2}$$

Example 13

Find $\dfrac{dy}{dx}$ when (a) $y = \arccos x^2$ (b) $y = \arctan(e^{3x})$.

(a) Let $t = x^2$, then $y = \arccos t$,

$$\frac{dt}{dx} = 2x \text{ and } \frac{dy}{dt} = \frac{-1}{\sqrt{(1-t^2)}} = \frac{-1}{\sqrt{(1-x^4)}}$$

By the chain rule:

$$\frac{dy}{dx} = \frac{dy}{dt} \cdot \frac{dt}{dx} = \frac{-2x}{\sqrt{(1-x^4)}}$$

(b) Let $u = e^{3x}$, then $y = \arctan u$,

$$\frac{du}{dx} = 3e^{3x}, \quad \frac{dy}{du} = \frac{1}{1+u^2} = \frac{1}{1+e^{6x}}$$

By the chain rule:

$$\frac{dy}{dx} = \frac{dy}{du} \cdot \frac{du}{dx} = \frac{3e^{3x}}{1+e^{6x}}$$

Example 14

Find an equation of the normal to the curve with equation $y = \arcsin 2x$ at the point where $x = \frac{1}{4}$.

$y = \arcsin 2x$, so:

$$\frac{dy}{dx} = \frac{1}{\sqrt{(1-(2x)^2)}} \frac{d}{dx}(2x)$$
$$= \frac{2}{\sqrt{(1-4x^2)}}$$

At $x = \frac{1}{4}$, $y = \arcsin\frac{1}{2} = \frac{\pi}{6}$

and:

$$\frac{dy}{dx} = \frac{2}{\sqrt{(1-\frac{1}{4})}} = \frac{4}{\sqrt{3}}$$

The gradient of the normal at $(\frac{1}{4}, \frac{\pi}{6})$ is $-\frac{\sqrt{3}}{4}$. The equation of the normal is

$$y - \frac{\pi}{6} = -\frac{\sqrt{3}}{4}\left(x - \frac{1}{4}\right)$$

Exercise 3C

1 Find, in radians in terms of π, the value of:

(a) $\arcsin 1$ (b) $\arcsin(-\frac{\sqrt{3}}{2})$ (c) $\arccos \frac{\sqrt{3}}{2}$

(d) $\arccos 0$ (e) $\arctan(-\sqrt{3})$ (f) $\arctan(2 + \sqrt{3})$

2 Giving your answer in radians to 2 decimal places, find the value of:

(a) $\arcsin(0.75)$ (b) $\arctan 7$ (c) $\arccos(-0.735)$

(d) $\arcsin(-0.993)$ (e) $\arccos(-0.111)$ (f) $\arctan(-0.352)$

3 Given that $y = \operatorname{cosec} x$, $-\frac{\pi}{2} \leqslant x \leqslant \frac{\pi}{2}$, $x \neq 0$, sketch the graphs of the curves $y = \operatorname{cosec} x$ and $y = \operatorname{arccosec} x$, where $\operatorname{arccosec} x$ is the inverse function of $\operatorname{cosec} x$, $-\frac{\pi}{2} \leqslant x \leqslant \frac{\pi}{2}$, $x \neq 0$.

4 Given that $y = \cot x$, $-\frac{\pi}{2} < x < \frac{\pi}{2}$, $x \neq 0$, sketch the graphs of the curves $y = \cot x$ and $y = \operatorname{arccot} x$, where $\operatorname{arccot} x$ is the inverse function of $\cot x$, $-\frac{\pi}{2} < x < \frac{\pi}{2}$, $x \neq 0$.

5 Given that $y = \sec x$, $0 \leqslant x \leqslant \pi$, $x \neq \frac{\pi}{2}$, sketch the graphs of the curves $y = \sec x$ and $y = \operatorname{arcsec} x$, where $\operatorname{arcsec} x$ is the inverse function of $\sec x$, $0 \leqslant x \leqslant \pi$, $x \neq \frac{\pi}{2}$.

6 Find the smallest positive value of x for which

(a) $\tan 2x = \sqrt{3}$

(b) $\sin(2x - 3) = \frac{1}{2}$

(c) $\sin x = \cos(\arctan 1)$

7 Differentiate with respect to x:

(a) $\arcsin 3x$ (b) $(\arcsin x)^2$ (c) $\arcsin\left(\frac{1}{x}\right)$

8 Differentiate with respect to x:

(a) $\arccos\left(\frac{x}{2}\right)$ (b) $\arccos(3x^2)$ (c) $\arccos\left(\frac{1}{x+2}\right)$

9 Differentiate with respect to x:

(a) $\arctan(2x)$ (b) $e^{\arctan x}$ (c) $\arctan(\ln x)$

10 Differentiate with respect to x:

(a) $x \arcsin x$ (b) $e^x \arccos x$ (c) $\dfrac{e^x}{\arctan x}$

(d) $\arctan\left(\dfrac{1 - \sqrt{x}}{1 + \sqrt{x}}\right)$ (e) $\operatorname{arcsec} x^2$

11 Given that $y = \arcsin x$, show that:

$$(1 - x^2)\frac{d^2 y}{dx^2} - x\frac{dy}{dx} = 0$$

12 Given that $y = x - \arctan x$, show that:

$$\frac{d^2y}{dx^2} - 2x\left(1 - \frac{dy}{dx}\right)^2 = 0$$

13 Find (a) $\dfrac{d}{dx}(\operatorname{arcsec} x)$ (b) $\dfrac{d}{dx}(\operatorname{arccot} x)$.

14 Find an equation at the point where $x = \frac{2}{\sqrt{3}}$ of the tangent to the curve $y = \operatorname{arccosec} x$.

15 Given that k is a positive constant, differentiate

(a) $\arccos \dfrac{x}{k}$ (b) $\arcsin \dfrac{k}{x}$ (c) $\arctan \dfrac{k}{x}$

SUMMARY OF KEY POINTS

1 $a\cos\theta + b\sin\theta \equiv R\cos(\theta + \alpha)$ where $a = R\cos\alpha$ and $b = -R\sin\alpha$. Also:

$$R = \sqrt{(a^2 + b^2)} \text{ and } \tan\alpha = -\frac{b}{a}$$

2 $a\cos\theta + b\sin\theta \equiv R\sin(\theta + \beta)$ where $a = R\sin\beta$ and $b = R\cos\beta$. Also:

$$R = \sqrt{(a^2 + b^2)} \text{ and } \tan\beta = \frac{a}{b}$$

3 The general solution of the equation
$$\sin x = b, \text{ where } \arcsin b = \alpha$$

is: $180°n + (-1)^n\alpha$, if α is in degrees
and: $n\pi + (-1)^n\alpha$, if α is in radians

4 The general solution of the equation
$$\cos x = c, \text{ where } \arccos c = \beta$$

is: $360°n \pm \beta$, if β is in degrees,
and: $2\pi n \pm \beta$, if β is in radians

5 The general solution of the equation
$$\tan x = t, \text{ where } \arctan t = \gamma$$

is: $180°n + \gamma$, if γ is in degrees
and: $\pi n + \gamma$, if γ is in radians

6 The inverse function of $\sin x$, $-\frac{\pi}{2} \leqslant x \leqslant \frac{\pi}{2}$, is $\arcsin x$, its domain is $-1 \leqslant x \leqslant 1$ and its range is $-\frac{\pi}{2} \leqslant \arcsin x \leqslant \frac{\pi}{2}$.

7 The inverse function of $\cos x$, $0 \leqslant x \leqslant \pi$, is $\arccos x$, its domain is $-1 \leqslant x \leqslant 1$ and its range is $0 \leqslant \arccos x \leqslant \pi$.

8 The inverse function of $\tan x$, $-\frac{\pi}{2} < x < \frac{\pi}{2}$, is $\arctan x$, its domain is $x \in \mathbb{R}$ and its range is $-\frac{\pi}{2} < \arctan x < \frac{\pi}{2}$.

9 $\dfrac{d}{dx}(\arcsin x) = \dfrac{1}{\sqrt{(1 - x^2)}}$

$\dfrac{d}{dx}(\arccos x) = \dfrac{-1}{\sqrt{(1 - x^2)}}$

$\dfrac{d}{dx}(\arctan x) = \dfrac{1}{1 + x^2}$

Review exercise 1

1 (a) Sketch the graphs of $y = |x - 8|$ and $y = 8x$ using the same pair of axes.

(b) Determine the set of values of x for which $|x - 8| > 8x$.

[L]

2 By using the series expansions of e^x and $\cos x$, or otherwise, find the expansion of $e^x \cos 3x$ in ascending powers of x up to and including the term in x^3.

[L]

3 Differentiate with respect to x:

(a) $\arccos 2x$ (b) $\arctan\left(\dfrac{1 - x}{1 + x}\right)$.

Simplify your answers.

[L]

4 Find, in degrees, the value of the acute angle α, for which

$$\cos\theta - (\sqrt{3})\sin\theta \equiv 2\cos(\theta + \alpha)$$

for all values of θ.

Solve the equation

$$\cos x - (\sqrt{3})\sin x = \sqrt{2},\ 0° \leqslant x \leqslant 360°$$

5 Find the complete set of values of x for which

$$\frac{3x}{x - 1} > x$$

[L]

6 Provided that x is so small that terms in x^3 and higher powers of x may be neglected, show that

$$4\sqrt{(1 + x)} = 3 + 2\sin x + \cos x$$

[L]

7 Write down in ascending powers of x, as far as the term in x^3, the binomial expansion of $(1 - 2x)^{\frac{1}{4}}$.

[L]

8 Find, in radians in terms of π, the general solution of the equation $\cos\theta = \sin 2\theta$. [L]

9 Show that $\displaystyle\sum_{r=1}^{n} r(r+2) = \frac{n}{6}(n+1)(2n+7)$.

Using this result, or otherwise, find, in terms of n, the sum of the series

$$3\ln 2 + 4\ln 2^2 + 5\ln 2^3 + \ldots + (n+2)\ln 2^n$$

Express your answer in its simplest form. [L]

10 Find, in radians in terms of π, the general solution of the equation

$$\sin 6x - \sin 4x = \sin 5x - \sin 3x$$

[L]

11 Express $\dfrac{2}{4x^2 - 1}$ in partial fractions.

Hence, or otherwise, show that

$$\sum_{r=1}^{n} \frac{2}{4r^2 - 1} = \frac{2n}{2n+1}$$

[L]

12 The figure shows a right-angled triangle ABC in which $\angle BAC = \frac{\pi}{4} + x$.

(a) Show that $\dfrac{BC}{BA} = \dfrac{1+\tan x}{1-\tan x}$.

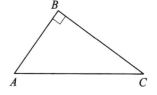

Given that x is small,
(b) use the approximation $\tan x \approx x$ to show that

$$\frac{BC}{BA} \approx 1 + 2x$$

[L]

13 Write down and simplify the expansion of $(1 - 8x)^{\frac{1}{2}}$, in ascending powers of x, up to and including the term in x^3. State the set of values of x for which the expansion is valid. [L]

14 By using the power series expansion for $\cos x$ and the power series expansion for $\ln(1 + x)$, find the series expansion for $\ln(\cos x)$ in ascending powers of x up to and including the term in x^4.

Hence, or otherwise, obtain the first two non-zero terms in the
series expansion for $\ln(\sec x)$ in ascending powers of x.   [L]

15 (a) Show that $\displaystyle\sum_{r=1}^{n} r(r+1) = \frac{n}{3}(n+1)(n+2)$.

(b) Express $\dfrac{1}{(x+1)(x+2)}$ in partial fractions and hence, or
otherwise, show that

$$\sum_{r=1}^{n} \frac{2}{(r+1)(r+2)} = \frac{n}{n+2}$$

[L]

16 Find, in terms of π, the general solution of the equation

$$\cos\left(3x - \frac{\pi}{3}\right) = \cos\left(x + \frac{\pi}{6}\right)$$

[L]

17 Find the complete set of values of x for which

$$\frac{1+x}{1-x} > \frac{2-x}{2+x}$$

[L]

18 (a) Show that the first four terms of the expansion of $e^{\tan x}$ in a
series of ascending powers of x are

$$1 + x + \tfrac{1}{2}x^2 + \tfrac{1}{2}x^3$$

(b) Deduce the first four terms of the expansion of $e^{-\tan x}$ in a
series of ascending powers of x.   [L]

19 Given that x is so small that terms in x^3 and higher powers of x
may be neglected, show that

$$11\sin x - 6\cos x + 5 = A + Bx + Cx^2$$

and state the values of the constants A, B and C.   [L]

20 Find the general solution of
(a) $\cos 2x - \cos 4x = \sin 2x$
(b) $2\cos^2 x - 4\sin x \cos x - \sin^2 x = 1$
giving your answer to (a) in radians and to (b) in degrees.

[L]

21 Using the same axes, sketch the curves

$$y = \frac{1}{x} \quad \text{and} \quad y = \frac{x}{x+2}$$

State the equations of any asymptotes, the coordinates of any points of intersection with the axes and the coordinates of any points of intersection of the two curves.

Hence, or otherwise, find the set of values of x for which

$$\frac{1}{x} > \frac{x}{x+2} \qquad \qquad \text{[L]}$$

22 (a) Express $\dfrac{\sqrt{(1+x)}}{1-x}$ as a series of ascending powers of x up to and including the term in x^2. Use this series to find, correct to 2 decimal places, the percentage change in the value of $\dfrac{a^{\frac{1}{2}}}{b}$ produced by an increase of 1% in the value of a and a decrease of 1% in the value of b.

 (b) Prove that

$$1^2 + 2^2 + 3^2 + \ldots + n^2 = \tfrac{1}{6}n(n+1)(2n+1)$$

[L]

23 Given that $f(r) = \dfrac{1}{r^2}$, show that

$$f(r) - f(r+1) = \frac{2r+1}{r^2(r+1)^2}$$

and hence find $\displaystyle\sum_{r=1}^{n} \frac{2r+1}{r^2(r+1)^2}.$ [L]

24 (a) Find, to the nearest tenth of a degree, the values of θ in the interval $0° \leqslant \theta \leqslant 360°$ for which

$$\sin\theta + 2\cos\theta = 1$$

 (b) Find the set of real values of x for which

$$\frac{2x^2 + 6}{x+6} > 1$$

[L]

25 Find the expansion, in ascending powers of x, of $\ln\left(\dfrac{1+x}{1-x}\right)$,

giving the first three non-zero terms and the general term. State the range x for which the expansion is valid.

Find values of the positive constants a and b such that the expansion of

$$2x(1+ax)(1+bx)^{-\frac{2}{3}}$$

in ascending powers of x is identical with that for $\ln\left(\dfrac{1+x}{1-x}\right)$ up to and including the term in x^3.   [L]

26 Sketch with the same axes the graphs of

$$y = |3x+1| \quad \text{and} \quad y = |2-x|$$

Find the set of values of x for which

$$|3x+1| - |2-x| < 3$$

[L]

27 Find, in radians, the general solution of the equation

$$\cos 3\theta = \cos 2\theta$$

[L]

28 By expressing $5\cos\theta + 12\sin\theta$ in the form $R\sin(\theta+\alpha)$ find the greatest and least values of

$$(5\cos\theta + 12\sin\theta)^2$$

as θ varies.   [L]

29 Given that $|2x| < 1$, find the first two non-zero terms in the expansion of

$$\ln[(1+x)^2(1-2x)]$$

in a series of ascending powers of x.   [L]

30 Express

$$\frac{3r+1}{r(r-1)(r+1)}$$

in partial fractions. Hence, or otherwise, show that

$$\sum_{r=2}^{n} \frac{3r+1}{r(r-1)(r+1)} = \frac{5}{2} - \frac{2}{n} - \frac{1}{n+1}$$

[L]

31 (a) On the same diagram, sketch the graphs of

$$y = \frac{1}{x-a} \quad \text{and} \quad y = 4|x-a|$$

where a is a positive constant. Show clearly the coordinates of any points of intersection with the coordinate axes.

(b) Hence, or otherwise, find the set of values of x for which

$$\frac{1}{x-a} < 4|x-a|$$

[L]

32 Expand $(1 + x - 3x^2)^4$ in ascending powers of x as far as the term in x^3, showing that the coefficients of x and x^2 are 4 and -6 respectively.

If $a > b$ and the first three terms in the expansion, in ascending powers of x, of

$$\frac{1 + ax}{\sqrt{(1 + bx)}}$$

are the same as those in the previous expansion, find a and b. State the set of values of x for which this second expansion is valid. [L]

33 (a) Find, in radians, the general solution of the equation

$$\sin x + \sin 2x = \sin 3x$$

(b) By expressing $\sec 2x$ and $\tan 2x$ in terms of $\tan x$, or otherwise, solve the equation

$$2 \tan x + \sec 2x = 2 \tan 2x$$

giving all solutions between $-180°$ and $+180°$. [L]

34 Given that $y = \arcsin \dfrac{x}{a}$, where a is a constant, show that

$$\frac{d^2 y}{dx^2} - x\left(\frac{dy}{dx}\right)^3 = 0$$

[L]

35 (a) By expressing $\cos 2\theta$ and $\sin 2\theta$ in terms of $\tan \theta$, or otherwise, find the values of θ between $0°$ and $360°$ which satisfy the equation

$$1 + \cos 2\theta + \sin 2\theta = \tan(\theta + 45°)$$

(b) Express $3 \cos x + 2 \sin x$ in the form $R \cos(x - \alpha)$, where R is positive and α is an acute angle. Find, to $0.1°$, the values of x between $0°$ and $360°$ which satisfy the equation

$$3 \cos x + 2 \sin x = 2.75$$

[L]

36 Expand $\ln \dfrac{(1 + 2x)^2}{(1 - 3x)}$ as a series of ascending powers of x as far as the term in x^3. [L]

37 Find the set of values of x for which

$$\frac{x^2 + 7x + 10}{x + 1} > 2x + 7$$

[L]

38 Find the first three non-zero terms of the expansion, in ascending powers of x, of

$$\ln(1 + xe^x)$$

[L]

39 The binomial expansion of $(8 + x)^{\frac{1}{3}}$ in ascending powers of x, as far as the term in x^2, is

$$(8 + x)^{\frac{1}{3}} = 2 + px + qx^2 + \ldots, |x| < 8$$

(a) Determine the values of the constants p and q.

(b) Use the expression $2 + px + qx^2$, and your values of p and q, to obtain an estimate for $\sqrt[3]{15}$, giving your answer to 3 significant figures.

(c) Find the percentage error involved in using this estimate.

[L]

40 (a) Obtain the first 4 non-zero terms of the binomial expansion in ascending powers of x of

$$(1 - x^2)^{-\frac{1}{2}}, \text{ given that } |x| < 1$$

(b) Show that, when $x = \frac{1}{3}$, $(1 - x^2)^{-\frac{1}{2}} = \frac{3}{4}\sqrt{2}$.

(c) Substitute $x = \frac{1}{3}$ into your expansion and hence obtain an approximation to $\sqrt{2}$, giving your answer to 5 decimal places. [L]

41 (a) Solve the equation $\sin 2x = \cos^2 x$, for $0° \leqslant x \leqslant 360°$, giving your answer in degrees to one decimal place where appropriate.

(b) Solve the equation $\cos 2x = 2 \sin^2 x$ giving the general solution, in radians, as a multiple of π. [L]

42 Given that $f(x) \equiv \ln(2x + \sqrt{(1 + 4x^2)})$,

(a) show that $f'(x) \equiv \dfrac{2}{\sqrt{(1 + 4x^2)}}$.

(b) Obtain the Maclaurin expansion for $f(x)$ in ascending powers of x, up to and including the term in x^3.

This series expansion is the same as the Maclaurin series expansion for $\sin(kx)$, up to and including the term in x^3.

(c) Write down the value of k.

43 Given that the first 2 non-zero terms in the expansion in ascending powers of x of

$$e^{ax} \cos 2x - \ln(1 + bx) - 1$$

are $7x^2$ and $-\frac{21}{2} x^3$, find the values of a and b. [L]

44 Show that $\displaystyle\sum_{r=1}^{2n} (2r - 1)^2 = \frac{2}{3} n(16n^2 - 1)$. [L]

45 Find all the values of θ for which $\sin 8\theta = \sin 2\theta$ giving your answer in radians in terms of π. [L]

46 Given that $f(x) \equiv \dfrac{11 - 5x^2}{(x + 1)(2 - x)}$, find constants A and B such that

$$f(x) \equiv 5 + \frac{A}{x + 1} + \frac{B}{2 - x}$$

Given that x is so small that x^3 and higher powers of x may be neglected, find the series expansion of $f(x)$ in ascending powers of x up to and including the term in x^2. [L]

47 Express $7 \cos x - \sin x$ in the form $R \cos(x + \alpha)$, where $R > 0$ and $0 < \alpha < \frac{\pi}{2}$.

Hence determine the values of x in the interval $0 \leqslant x \leqslant 2\pi$ for which

$$7 \cos x - \sin x = \sqrt{2}$$

giving your answers in radians to 2 decimal places. [L]

48 Find the general solution of the equation

$$3\cos x + 4\sin x = 2$$

giving your answer to the nearest degree.   [L]

49 Find the first three derivatives of $(1 + x)^2 \ln(1 + x)$. Hence, or otherwise, find the expansion of $(1 + x)^2 \ln(1 + x)$ in ascending powers of x up to and including the term in x^3.   [L]

50 By considering $f(r) - f(r + 1)$, where $f(r) = \dfrac{r + 2}{r(r + 1)}$, or otherwise, show that

$$\sum_{r=1}^{n} \frac{r + 4}{r(r + 1)(r + 2)} = \frac{3}{2} - \frac{n + 3}{(n + 1)(n + 2)}$$

[L]

51 $f : x \mapsto \arcsin x, \ -1 \leqslant x \leqslant 1$
   (a) Evaluate $f(-\frac{1}{2})$.
   (b) Find an equation of the tangent to the curve $y = f(x)$ at the point where $x = \frac{1}{\sqrt{2}}$.

52 Given that $y = \arctan \dfrac{x}{a}$, where a is a constant, show that

$$x\frac{dy}{dx} = \frac{\tan y}{1 + \tan^2 y}$$ [L]

53 Find an expansion for $\sec x$ in ascending powers of x as far as the term containing x^4.   [L]

54 Given that $y = e^x \sec x$, show that
   (a) $\dfrac{dy}{dx} = y(1 + \tan x)$
   (b) $\dfrac{d^2y}{dx^2} = \dfrac{dy}{dx}(1 + \tan x) + y\sec^2 x$

   Hence or otherwise, find the first four non-zero terms in the expansion of y in ascending powers of x.   [L]

55 Expand $\ln(1 + \sin x)$ in ascending powers of x up to and including the term in x^4.
   Hence find an approximation for

$$\int_0^{\frac{\pi}{6}} \ln(1 + \sin x) \, dx$$

giving your answer to 3 decimal places.   [L]

56 Given that x is sufficiently small, use the approximations $\sin x \simeq x$ and $\cos x \simeq 1 - \frac{1}{2}x^2$ to show that

$$\frac{\cos x}{1 + \sin x} \approx 1 - x + \tfrac{1}{2}x^2$$

A student estimates the value of $\dfrac{\cos x}{1 + \sin x}$ when $x = 0.1$ by evaluating the approximation $1 - x + \frac{1}{2}x^2$ when $x = 0.1$. Find, to 3 decimal places, the percentage error made by the student.

[L]

57 Given that $f(x) \equiv x(x - 2)(x - 3)$, find the complete set of values of x for which

(a) $f(x) > 0$

(b) $|f(x)| > f(x)$

(c) $f(x) > 3 - x$.

[L]

58 (a) Prove that $\displaystyle\sum_{r=1}^{n} \frac{1}{r(r+1)} = \frac{n}{n+1}$.

(b) Expand $(1 + x)^{\frac{1}{2}}$ in ascending powers of x up to and including the term in x^3. Given that the expansion of

$$\frac{(1 + x)^{\frac{1}{2}}}{1 - ax}$$

in ascending powers of x as far as the term in x^2 is $1 + bx^2$, find the values of a and b.

[L]

59 (a) Show that $7\cos x - 4\sin x$ may be expressed in the form $R\cos(x + \alpha)$, where R is $\sqrt{65}$ and $\tan \alpha = \frac{4}{7}$.

(b) Find, in radians to 2 decimal places, the smallest positive value of x for which $7\cos x - 4\sin x$ takes its maximum value.

(c) Find, in radians to 2 decimal places, the two smallest positive values of x for which

$$7\cos x - 4\sin x = 4.88$$

[L]

60 (a) By using the series expansions of e^x and $\sin x$, or otherwise, show that the first three non-zero terms in the expansion of $e^{\sin x}$ in ascending powers of x are

$$1 + x + \tfrac{1}{2}x^2$$

and that the coefficient of x^3 in this expansion is zero.

(b) Write down the first three non-zero terms in the expansion of $e^{-\sin x}$ in ascending powers of x.

The coefficient of x^5 in the expansion of $e^{\sin x}$ is $-\tfrac{1}{15}$.

(c) Find the coefficient of x^5 in the expansion of $e^{\sin x}$.

[L]

Hyperbolic functions

4

4.1 Definitions in terms of exponential functions

The exponential functions e^x and e^{-x} can be combined to form functions that have strong similarities to the trigonometric (or circular) functions. These functions are called **hyperbolic functions**. The **hyperbolic sine of x**, written **sinh x**, and pronounced 'shine x', is defined by:

■ $$\sinh x \equiv \tfrac{1}{2}(e^x - e^{-x}), \ x \in \mathbb{R}$$

The **hyperbolic cosine of x**, written **cosh x**, and pronounced 'cosh x', is defined by:

■ $$\cosh x \equiv \tfrac{1}{2}(e^x + e^{-x}), \ x \in \mathbb{R}$$

These two definitions are basic and from them four other hyperbolic functions are defined as follows. The **hyperbolic tangent of x**, written **tanh x**, and pronounced 'tansh x', is defined by:

■ $$\tanh x \equiv \frac{\sinh x}{\cosh x} = \frac{e^x - e^{-x}}{e^x + e^{-x}} = \frac{e^{2x} - 1}{e^{2x} + 1}, \ x \in \mathbb{R}$$

The **hyperbolic secant of x**, written **sech x** and pronounced 'sech x', is defined by:

■ $$\operatorname{sech} x \equiv \frac{1}{\cosh x} \equiv \frac{2}{e^x + e^{-x}}, \ x \in \mathbb{R}$$

The **hyperbolic cosecant of x**, written **cosech x** and pronounced 'cosech x', is defined by:

■ $$\operatorname{cosech} x \equiv \frac{1}{\sinh x} \equiv \frac{2}{e^x - e^{-x}}, \ x \in \mathbb{R}, \ x \neq 0$$

The **hyperbolic cotangent of x**, written **coth x** and pronounced 'coth x', is defined by:

■ $$\coth x \equiv \frac{1}{\tanh x} \equiv \frac{\cosh x}{\sinh x} \equiv \frac{e^x + e^{-x}}{e^x - e^{-x}} \equiv \frac{e^{2x} + 1}{e^{2x} - 1}, \ x \in \mathbb{R}, \ x \neq 0$$

4.2 Graphs of the hyperbolic functions

You can see that:

$$\sinh(-x) \equiv \frac{e^{(-x)} - e^{-(-x)}}{2} = \frac{-(e^x - e^{-x})}{2} = -\sinh x$$

So sinh x is an odd function. Similarly you have:

$$\cosh(-x) \equiv \frac{e^{(-x)} + e^{-(-x)}}{2} = \frac{e^x + e^{-x}}{2} = \cosh x$$

So cosh x is an even function.

Also: $$\cosh x \equiv \frac{e^x + e^{-x}}{2} > \frac{e^x - e^{-x}}{2} \equiv \sinh x$$

for all values of x.

The curves with equations $y = e^x$ and $y = e^{-x}$ look like this:

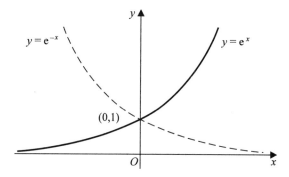

Notice that $e^x > 0$ and $e^{-x} > 0$ for all values of x. The curves with equations $y = \sinh x$ and $y = \cosh x$ look like this:

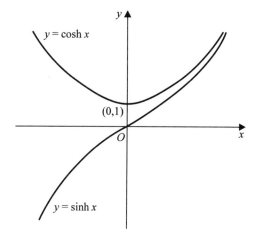

Since $\tanh x \equiv \dfrac{e^{2x} - 1}{e^{2x} + 1}$, you can see that at $x = 0$, $\tanh x = 0$.

Also: $\tanh(-x) \equiv \dfrac{e^{-2x} - 1}{e^{-2x} + 1} = \dfrac{1 - e^{2x}}{1 + e^{2x}} \equiv -\tanh x$

So $\tanh x$ is an odd function.

Now $\tanh x \equiv \dfrac{e^{2x} - 1}{e^{2x} + 1} = \dfrac{1 - e^{-2x}}{1 + e^{-2x}}$

As $x \to \infty$, $e^{-2x} \to 0$ and $\tanh x \to 1$

As $x \to -\infty$, $e^{2x} \to 0$ and $\tanh x \to -1$
The curve with equation $y = \tanh x$ lies completely in the interval $-1 < \tanh x < 1$ and looks like this:

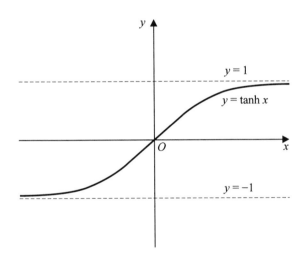

The lines $y = \pm 1$ are asymptotes to the curve.

Example 1
Sketch the graph of the curve $y = \operatorname{sech} x$, $x \in \mathbb{R}$.

Since $\operatorname{sech} x = \dfrac{1}{\cosh x} = \dfrac{1}{\cosh(-x)} = \operatorname{sech}(-x)$, $\operatorname{sech} x$ is an even function and so it is symmetrical about the y-axis.

Since $\cosh x \geqslant 1$ then $\operatorname{sech} x$ lies in the interval $0 < \operatorname{sech} x \leqslant 1$. The curve $y = \operatorname{sech} x$ looks like this:

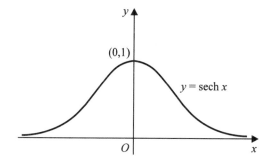

Example 2

Find the value of x for which $\tanh x = \frac{1}{2}$.

You know that $\tanh x \equiv \dfrac{e^{2x} - 1}{e^{2x} + 1}$, so:

$$\frac{e^{2x} - 1}{e^{2x} + 1} = \frac{1}{2}$$

$$\Rightarrow \quad 2e^{2x} - 2 = e^{2x} + 1$$

$$\Rightarrow \quad e^{2x} = 3$$

Taking logarithms to the base e gives

$$2x = \ln 3$$

So:
$$x = \tfrac{1}{2}\ln 3$$

4.3 Identities

Many identities exist for hyperbolic functions and these have similarities to the ones you have already met in trigonometry. Here are some examples. In nearly every case you can prove hyperbolic identities by using the definitions given in section 4.1.

Example 3

Prove that $\cosh^2 x - \sinh^2 x \equiv 1$.

By factorising:

$$\text{left-hand side} = (\cosh x - \sinh x)(\cosh x + \sinh x)$$

From the definitions of $\cosh x$ and $\sinh x$:

$$\cosh x - \sinh x = \frac{e^x + e^{-x}}{2} - \frac{e^x - e^{-x}}{2} = e^{-x}$$

$$\cosh x + \sinh x = \frac{e^x + e^{-x}}{2} + \frac{e^x - e^{-x}}{2} = e^x$$

Hence: $\cosh^2 x - \sinh^2 x = (e^{-x})(e^x) = e^0 = 1$

■ $$\cosh^2 x - \sinh^2 x \equiv 1$$

Two further identities can be easily deduced from the identity $\cosh^2 x - \sinh^2 x \equiv 1$. If you divide by $\cosh^2 x$, you obtain

$$1 - \frac{\sinh^2 x}{\cosh^2 x} \equiv \frac{1}{\cosh^2 x}$$

that is:

■ $$1 - \tanh^2 x \equiv \text{sech}^2 x$$

If $x \neq 0$, dividing by $\sinh^2 x$ gives you

$$\frac{\cosh^2 x}{\sinh^2 x} - 1 \equiv \frac{1}{\sinh^2 x}, \quad x \neq 0$$

that is:

■ $$\coth^2 x - 1 \equiv \text{cosech}^2 x, \ x \neq 0$$

Example 4
Prove that

$$\cosh(x + y) \equiv \cosh x \cosh y + \sinh x \sinh y$$

Right-hand side $= \left(\dfrac{e^x + e^{-x}}{2}\right)\left(\dfrac{e^y + e^{-y}}{2}\right) + \left(\dfrac{e^x - e^{-x}}{2}\right)\left(\dfrac{e^y - e^{-y}}{2}\right)$

$= \frac{1}{4}[e^{x+y} + e^{x-y} + e^{-x+y} + e^{-x-y} + e^{x+y} - e^{x-y} - e^{-x+y} + e^{-x-y}]$

$= \frac{1}{4}(2e^{x+y} + 2e^{-x-y})$

$= \frac{1}{2}(e^{x+y} + e^{-(x+y)})$

$= \cosh(x + y)$ as required on the left-hand side.

Thus:

$$\cosh(x + y) \equiv \cosh x \cosh y + \sinh x \sinh y$$

By writing $x = y = A$, you get:

■ $$\cosh 2A \equiv \cosh^2 A + \sinh^2 A$$

which is another well known hyperbolic identity.

Example 5

Find an identity for $\sinh 2A$ in terms of $\cosh A$ and $\sinh A$. Hence find an identity for $\tanh 2A$ in terms of $\tanh A$.

You have
$$\begin{aligned}
\sinh 2A &\equiv \tfrac{1}{2}(e^{2A} - e^{-2A}) \\
&= \tfrac{1}{2}(e^{A} + e^{-A})(e^{A} - e^{-A}) \\
&= 2\left[\frac{e^{A} + e^{-A}}{2}\right]\left[\frac{e^{A} - e^{-A}}{2}\right] \\
&= 2\cosh A \sinh A
\end{aligned}$$

■ So: $\qquad\qquad$ **$\sinh 2A \equiv 2\cosh A \sinh A$**

In example 4, you were shown that $\cosh 2A \equiv \cosh^2 A + \sinh^2 A$. You can now write:

$$\tanh 2A \equiv \frac{\sinh 2A}{\cosh 2A} \equiv \frac{2\cosh A \sinh A}{\cosh^2 A + \sinh^2 A}$$

Dividing numerator and denominator by $\cosh^2 A$ gives:

$$\tanh 2A \equiv \frac{\dfrac{2\sinh A \cosh A}{\cosh^2 A}}{\dfrac{\cosh^2 A}{\cosh^2 A} + \dfrac{\sinh^2 A}{\cosh^2 A}}$$

Since $\dfrac{\sinh A}{\cosh A} \equiv \tanh A$

■ $\qquad\qquad\qquad$ **$\tanh 2A \equiv \dfrac{2\tanh A}{1 + \tanh^2 A}$**

Osborn's rule

You notice that there is much similarity between trigonometric identities and hyperbolic identities. Many are of the same form, often with signs changed but not always:

trigonometric	hyperbolic
$\cos^2 A + \sin^2 A \equiv 1$	$\cosh^2 A - \sinh^2 A \equiv 1$
$\sin 2A \equiv 2\sin A \cos A$	$\sinh 2A \equiv 2\sinh A \cosh A$

Osborn's rule gives you a simple way to remember when to make a sign change when moving from a trigonometric identity to its hyperbolic counterpart.

■ **The rule is to replace each trigonometric function by the corresponding hyperbolic function and change the sign of every product (or implied product) of two sines.**

The justification of this rule will be given in Book P4.

Example 6

Give the equivalent hyperbolic identity for the trigonometric identity:

(a) $\cos 2x \equiv 1 - 2\sin^2 x$,

(b) $\tan(A - B) \equiv \dfrac{\tan A - \tan B}{1 + \tan A \tan B}$

In (a), you have a product of sines: $\sin x \sin x$, so the equivalent hyperbolic identity is

$$\cosh 2x \equiv 1 + 2\sinh^2 x$$

In (b), you have an *implied* product of sines in the term:

$$\tan A \tan B \equiv \frac{\sin A \sin B}{\cos A \cos B}$$

so the equivalent hyperbolic identity is

$$\tanh(A - B) \equiv \frac{\tanh A - \tanh B}{1 - \tanh A \tanh B}$$

4.4 Inverse hyperbolic functions

You know that only one–one functions can have an inverse function. Since $\sinh x$ is a one–one function, its inverse function is **arsinh x** and the graphs of these functions look like this:

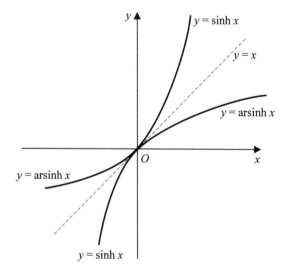

Similarly, tanh x is a one–one function, its inverse function is **artanh** x and the graphs of these functions look like this:

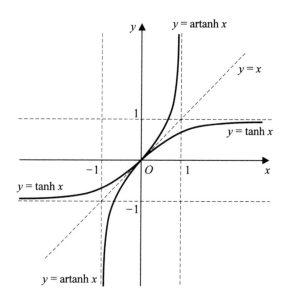

For the function cosh x, you need to take the domain $x \geqslant 0$, so that it is a one–one function. Then the inverse function **arcosh** x is defined for the domain $x \geqslant 1$ and range arcosh $x \geqslant 0$. The graphs of cosh x and arcosh x look like this:

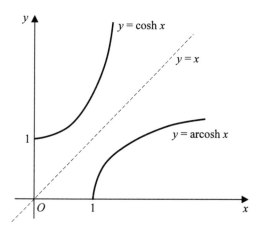

Example 7

In the same diagram, sketch the curves

$y = \text{sech } x, \ x \in \mathbb{R}, \ x \geqslant 0$
$y = \text{arsech } x, \ x \in \mathbb{R}, \ 0 < x \leqslant 1$

The curves are shown in the diagram. One is the reflection of the other in the line $y = x$.

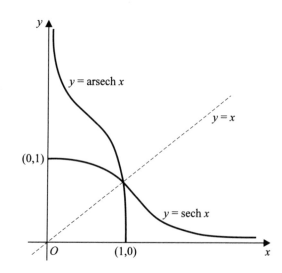

4.5 The logarithmic form of inverse hyperbolic functions

Since hyperbolic functions are defined in terms of the exponential functions e^x and e^{-x}, it is possible to express their inverse functions in terms of natural logarithms, like this:

Write $\operatorname{arsinh} x = u$, then:

$$x = \sinh u = \tfrac{1}{2}(e^u - e^{-u})$$

that is:
$$e^u - 2x - e^{-u} = 0$$
$$\Rightarrow \quad e^{2u} - 2xe^u - 1 = 0$$

This is a quadratic equation in e^u. By adding x^2 to both sides, you can write it as:

$$e^{2u} - 2xe^u + x^2 = x^2 + 1$$
$$(e^u - x)^2 = x^2 + 1$$

Hence:
$$e^u - x = \pm\sqrt{(x^2 + 1)}$$

$$\Rightarrow \quad e^u = x \pm \sqrt{(x^2 + 1)}$$

But $e^u > 0$ always, and therefore the negative sign can be rejected because $\sqrt{(x^2 + 1)} > x$.

So:
$$e^u = x + \sqrt{(x^2 + 1)}$$
$$u = \ln[x + \sqrt{(x^2 + 1)}]$$

That is:

■ $$\mathbf{arsinh}\, x \equiv \ln[x + \sqrt{(x^2 + 1)}]$$

Similarly, you can show that:

■ $$\mathbf{arcosh}\, x \equiv \ln[x + \sqrt{(x^2 - 1)}], \ x \geqslant 1$$

■ $$\mathbf{artanh}\, x \equiv \tfrac{1}{2}\ln\left(\frac{1 + x}{1 - x}\right), \ |x| < 1$$

Example 8
Express (a) $\operatorname{arsinh}\tfrac{3}{4}$ (b) $\operatorname{arcosh} 3$ (c) $\operatorname{artanh}\left(-\tfrac{3}{4}\right)$ in logarithmic form.

(a) $\operatorname{arsinh}\tfrac{3}{4} = \ln\left[\tfrac{3}{4} + \sqrt{(\tfrac{9}{16} + 1)}\right] = \ln(\tfrac{3}{4} + \tfrac{5}{4}) = \ln 2$

(b) $\operatorname{arcosh} 3 = \ln[3 + \sqrt{(3^2 - 1)}] = \ln(3 + 2\sqrt{2})$

(c) $\operatorname{artanh}\left(-\tfrac{3}{4}\right) = \tfrac{1}{2}\ln\left(\dfrac{1 - \tfrac{3}{4}}{1 + \tfrac{3}{4}}\right) = \tfrac{1}{2}\ln(\tfrac{1}{7}) = -\tfrac{1}{2}\ln 7$

Example 9

Find the values of x for which

$$\sinh^2 x + 5 = 4\cosh x$$

Since $\cosh^2 x - \sinh^2 x \equiv 1$, you have

$$\cosh^2 x - 1 + 5 - 4\cosh x = 0$$

that is:

$$\cosh^2 x - 4\cosh x + 4 = 0$$

Factorising:

$$(\cosh x - 2)^2 = 0$$

so:

$$\cosh x = 2$$

From the definition of $\cosh x$ in terms of e^x you have

$$e^x + e^{-x} = 4$$

Multiplying by e^x and rearranging:

$$e^{2x} - 4e^x + 1 = 0$$

so:

$$e^x = \frac{4 \pm \sqrt{(16-4)}}{2} = 2 \pm \sqrt{3}$$

Hence:

$$x = \ln(2 + \sqrt{3}) \text{ or } \ln(2 - \sqrt{3})$$

Notice that the equation $\cosh x = 2$ has two roots, but $\operatorname{arcosh} 2 = \ln(2 + \sqrt{3})$ only.

Exercise 4A

1 Express in terms of e:
  (a) $\sinh 2$ (b) $\cosh \frac{1}{2}$ (c) $\tanh(-3)$
  (d) $\cosh(\sqrt{2})$ (e) $\sinh \pi$ (f) $\tanh 1 - \tanh(-1)$

2 Find, to 3 decimal places, the values of x for which:
  (a) $\sinh x = 3$ (b) $\sinh x = -3$ (c) $\cosh x = \frac{3}{2}$
  (d) $\cosh x = \sqrt{5}$ (e) $\tanh x = \frac{3}{4}$ (f) $\tanh x = -\frac{2}{3}$

3 Find the value of each of the following, giving each answer to 4 significant figures:
  (a) $\cosh 4$ (b) $\sinh \frac{2}{3}$ (c) $\tanh(-2)$
  (d) $\sinh\left(-\frac{1}{2}\right)$ (e) $\cosh \pi$ (f) $\tanh(e^{\frac{1}{2}})$

4 Given that $\cosh x = \frac{5}{3}$, show that $\sinh x = \pm\frac{4}{3}$. Hence find the values of e^x and x.

5 Sketch, in separate diagrams, the curves with equations
  (a) $y = \operatorname{cosech} x$, $x \in \mathbb{R}$, $x \neq 0$

(b) $y = \coth x$, $x \in \mathbb{R}$, $x \neq 0$

Give the equations of the asymptotes to each curve.

6 Sketch, in the same diagram, the curves with equations

$y = \sinh 2x$ and $y = \sinh 3x$.

Find the x-coordinates of the points where the curves meet the line $y = 2$, giving your answer to 2 decimal places.

In questions 7–20, prove the given identity and, where appropriate, check the identity independently by using Osborn's rule when you know the comparable trigonometric identity.

7 $\sinh A \equiv - \sinh(-A)$

8 $\sinh 2A \equiv 2 \sinh A \cosh A$

9 $\cosh 2A \equiv 2 \cosh^2 A - 1$

10 $\sinh 3A \equiv 3 \sinh A + 4 \sinh^3 A$

11 $\cosh 3A \equiv 4 \cosh^3 A - 3 \cosh A$

12 $\tanh^2 A + \operatorname{sech}^2 A \equiv 1$

13 $\sinh(A - B) \equiv \sinh A \cosh B - \cosh A \sinh B$

14 $\cosh(A - B) \equiv \cosh A \cosh B - \sinh A \sinh B$

15 $\cosh A + \cosh B \equiv 2 \cosh \dfrac{A + B}{2} \cosh \dfrac{A - B}{2}$

16 $\sinh A + \sinh B \equiv 2 \sinh \dfrac{A + B}{2} \cosh \dfrac{A - B}{2}$

17 $2 \sinh A \sinh B \equiv \cosh(A + B) - \cosh(A - B)$

18 $\dfrac{\cosh x - 1}{\cosh x + 1} \equiv \tanh^2 \dfrac{x}{2}$

19 $\sinh x \equiv \dfrac{2 \tanh \frac{x}{2}}{1 - \tanh^2 \frac{x}{2}}$

20 $\dfrac{\cosh x + \sinh x + 1}{\cosh x + \sinh x - 1} \equiv \coth \dfrac{x}{2}$

21 Given that $\sinh x = \tan \theta$, $0 < \theta < \frac{\pi}{2}$, express $\cosh x$ and $\tanh x$ in terms of θ.

22 Given that $x > 0$, show that

$$\sinh(\ln x) = \frac{x^2 - 1}{2x}$$

Express $\cosh(\ln x)$ in a similar form.

23 Find the value, or values, of x for which

$$4 \sinh x - 3 \cosh x = 5$$

giving your answer, or answers, to 3 significant figures.

24 Given that $\tanh t = \frac{1}{3}$, find the value of e^{2t}. Hence find the exact value of t.

25 Using Maclaurin's expansion for e^x and e^{-x}, express $\sinh x$ and $\cosh x$ as power series in increasing powers of x, up to and including terms in x^5 and x^6 respectively.

26 Given that $\sinh y = x$, show that

$$y = \ln[x + (1 + x^2)^{\frac{1}{2}}]$$

By differentiating this result, show that

$$(1 + x^2)\left(\frac{dy}{dx}\right)^2 = 1$$

27 Solve the equation $2\cosh x + \sinh x = 2$.

28 Solve the equation $13\cosh\theta + 12\sinh\theta = \frac{25}{4}$.

29 Prove that $\cosh(x + y) \equiv \cosh x \cosh y + \sinh x \sinh y$.

Given that $a\cosh t + b\sinh t = R\cosh(t + \alpha)$, $a > b > 0$, show that

$$\alpha = \frac{1}{2}\ln\left(\frac{a + b}{a - b}\right)$$

Find R in terms of a and b.

30 Using the definitions of $\sinh x$ and $\cosh x$, in terms of e^x, show that for $|x| < 1$,

$$\text{artanh } x = \frac{1}{2}\ln\frac{1 + x}{1 - x}$$

Hence expand artanh x in ascending powers of x up to and including the term in x^5.

31 Solve for x the equation

$$3\,\text{sech}^2\,x + 4\tanh x + 1 = 0$$

giving the root as a natural logarithm.

32 Solve the equation

$$\cosh^2 t + \sinh^2 t = 3$$

giving the answers in terms of natural logarithms.

33 Solve the equation

$$4 \tanh t - \operatorname{sech} t = 1$$

giving the answer in terms of a natural logarithm.

34 Prove that $\operatorname{arsinh} x = \ln[x + (1 + x^2)^{\frac{1}{2}}]$.

Given that x is large and positive, show that:

$$\operatorname{arsinh} x \approx \ln 2 + \ln x + \frac{1}{4x^2}$$

35 Solve the equation $\cosh 2x = 3 \sinh x$, giving your answers to 3 significant figures.

36 Given that $p = \frac{1}{2} \ln 2$, find the value of $\tanh p$. Find also the values of $\sinh 2p$, $\cosh 2p$ and $\tanh 2p$.

37 Prove that $\operatorname{coth} A + \operatorname{cosech} A \equiv \operatorname{coth} \dfrac{A}{2}$.

38 Given that $x = \sin \theta \cosh t$ and $y = \cos \theta \sinh t$, find a relation between

(a) x, y and θ (b) x, y and t.

39 Prove that $\displaystyle \lim_{x \to 0} \frac{\sinh x - \sin x}{x^3} = \frac{1}{3}$

40 Prove that $\cosh^6 A - \sinh^6 A \equiv 1 + \frac{3}{4} \sinh^2 2A$.

Hence show that

$$8(\cosh^6 A - \sinh^6 A) \equiv 3 \cosh 4A + 5$$

4.6 The derivatives of hyperbolic functions

You know that $\dfrac{\mathrm{d}}{\mathrm{d}x}(\mathrm{e}^x) = \mathrm{e}^x$ and $\dfrac{\mathrm{d}}{\mathrm{d}x}(\mathrm{e}^{-x}) = -\mathrm{e}^{-x}$.

Since $\sinh x \equiv \frac{1}{2}(\mathrm{e}^x - \mathrm{e}^{-x})$,

$$\frac{\mathrm{d}}{\mathrm{d}x}(\sinh x) = \frac{1}{2}\frac{\mathrm{d}}{\mathrm{d}x}(\mathrm{e}^x - \mathrm{e}^{-x}) = \frac{1}{2}(\mathrm{e}^x + \mathrm{e}^{-x})$$

But $\cosh x \equiv \frac{1}{2}(\mathrm{e}^x + \mathrm{e}^{-x})$. So:

■
$$\frac{\mathrm{d}}{\mathrm{d}x}(\sinh x) = \cosh x$$

Similarly you have:

$$\frac{d}{dx}(\cosh x) = \tfrac{1}{2}\frac{d}{dx}(e^x + e^{-x}) = \tfrac{1}{2}(e^x - e^{-x})$$

∎
$$\frac{d}{dx}(\cosh x) = \sinh x$$

As with the trigonometric functions, these results form the basis for finding the derivatives of the other four functions $\tanh x$, $\operatorname{sech} x$, $\operatorname{cosech} x$ and $\coth x$.

Example 10

Find $\dfrac{d}{dx}(\tanh x)$.

You know that $\tanh x \equiv \dfrac{\sinh x}{\cosh x}$, so you can use the formula for differentiating a quotient. Remember that:

$$\frac{d}{dx}\left(\frac{u}{v}\right) = \frac{v\dfrac{du}{dx} - u\dfrac{dv}{dx}}{v^2}$$

where u and v are functions of x. So let

$$y = \tanh x \equiv \frac{\sinh x}{\cosh x} \equiv \frac{u}{v}$$

$$u = \sinh x \qquad v = \cosh x$$

Differentiating: $\qquad \dfrac{du}{dx} = \cosh x \qquad \dfrac{dv}{dx} = \sinh x$

$$\frac{dy}{dx} = \frac{v\dfrac{du}{dx} - u\dfrac{dv}{dx}}{v^2} = \frac{\cosh x \cosh x - \sinh x \sinh x}{\cosh^2 x}$$

$$= \frac{\cosh^2 x - \sinh^2 x}{\cosh^2 x}$$

But $\qquad \cosh^2 x - \sinh^2 x \equiv 1 \qquad$ (see example 3, page 70). So:

∎
$$\frac{d}{dx}(\tanh x) = \frac{1}{\cosh^2 x} = \operatorname{sech}^2 x$$

Using a similar method, you can show that

∎
$$\frac{d}{dx}(\coth x) = -\frac{1}{\sinh^2 x} = -\operatorname{cosech}^2 x$$

Example 11

Find $\dfrac{d}{dx}(\operatorname{sech} x)$.

You know that $\operatorname{sech} x \equiv \dfrac{1}{\cosh x} = (\cosh x)^{-1}$, and so you can find $\dfrac{dy}{dx}$ for $y = (\cosh x)^{-1}$ by using the chain rule: $\dfrac{dy}{dx} = \dfrac{dy}{dt} \cdot \dfrac{dt}{dx}$.

If you take $t = \cosh x$, then you have

$$y = t^{-1} \qquad\qquad\qquad t = \cosh x$$

$$\frac{dy}{dt} = -t^{-2} \qquad\qquad\qquad \frac{dt}{dx} = \sinh x$$

$$= -(\cosh x)^{-2}$$

$$\frac{dy}{dx} = \frac{dy}{dt} \cdot \frac{dt}{dx} = -(\cosh x)^{-2}(\sinh x)$$

$$= -\frac{\sinh x}{\cosh^2 x}$$

$$= -\frac{\sinh x}{\cosh x} \cdot \frac{1}{\cosh x}$$

$$= -\tanh x \operatorname{sech} x$$

■ So: $$\frac{d}{dx}(\operatorname{sech} x) = -\tanh x \operatorname{sech} x$$

Similarly, you can show that:

■ $$\frac{d}{dx}(\operatorname{cosech} x) = -\coth x \operatorname{cosech} x$$

You need to apply the rules of differentiation which you learned in your P1 and P2 courses to this work, so that you can build hyperbolic and inverse hyperbolic functions into your stock of skills and knowledge. The next two examples illustrate how these skills are used.

Example 12

Given that $y = \cos x \cosh x$, find $\dfrac{d^2 y}{dx^2}$.

Using the product formula $\dfrac{d}{dx}(uv) = v\dfrac{du}{dx} + u\dfrac{dv}{dx}$, you get

$$\frac{dy}{dx} = -\sin x \cosh x + \cos x \sinh x$$

Using the product formula again you get

$$\frac{d^2 y}{dx^2} = -\cos x \cosh x - \sin x \sinh x - \sin x \sinh x + \cos x \cosh x$$

$$= -2 \sin x \sinh x$$

Example 13

A curve is give by the equations $x = \cosh t$, $y = \sinh t$, where t is a parameter.

(a) Find the cartesian equation of the curve and sketch the curve.
(b) Find an equation of the tangent to the curve at the point where $t = \ln 2$.

(a) Since $\cosh^2 t - \sinh^2 t \equiv 1$, you have

$$x^2 - y^2 = 1$$

However, $\cosh t > 0$ (see page 68), so $x > 0$. The cartesian equation of the curve is:

$$x^2 - y^2 = 1, \quad x > 0$$

The curve is symmetrical about the x-axis and it looks like this:

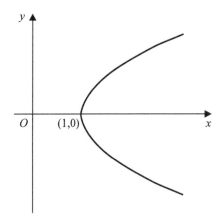

It is in fact one branch of a curve called a **hyperbola** which is where the name hyperbolic functions came from originally. You will meet this curve again in Book P4.

(b) Since $t = \ln 2$, $e^t = 2$ and $e^{-t} = (e^t)^{-1} = \frac{1}{2}$.

At this point:
$$x = \cosh t = \tfrac{1}{2}(e^t + e^{-t})$$
$$= \tfrac{1}{2}(2 + \tfrac{1}{2}) = \tfrac{5}{4}$$

and:
$$y = \sinh t = \tfrac{1}{2}(e^t - e^{-t})$$
$$= \tfrac{1}{2}(2 - \tfrac{1}{2}) = \tfrac{3}{4}$$

Also:
$$\frac{dx}{dt} = \sinh t, \quad \frac{dy}{dt} = \cosh t$$

$$\Rightarrow \quad \frac{dy}{dx} = \frac{dy}{dt} \cdot \frac{dt}{dx} = \frac{dy}{dt}\left(\frac{dx}{dt}\right)^{-1}$$

So: $\qquad\qquad \dfrac{dy}{dx} = \dfrac{\cosh t}{\sinh t}$, except where $\sinh t = 0$

and at $t = \ln 2$, $\dfrac{dy}{dx} = \dfrac{\frac{5}{4}}{\frac{3}{4}} = \dfrac{5}{3}$

The tangent at $(\frac{5}{4}, \frac{3}{4})$ to the curve has gradient $\frac{5}{3}$ and its equation is

$$y - \tfrac{3}{4} = \tfrac{5}{3}(x - \tfrac{5}{4})$$

which can be arranged as $3y - 5x + 4 = 0$.

4.7 The derivatives of inverse hyperbolic functions

If $y = \operatorname{arsinh} x$, then $\sinh y = x$. Differentiating with respect to x, you get

$$\cosh y \dfrac{dy}{dx} = 1$$

so: $\qquad\qquad \dfrac{dy}{dx} = \dfrac{1}{\cosh y}$

But you know that $\cosh^2 y - \sinh^2 y \equiv 1$ and therefore

$$\dfrac{dy}{dx} = \dfrac{1}{\sqrt{(1 + \sinh^2 y)}} = \dfrac{1}{\sqrt{(1 + x^2)}}$$

Remember that the function $\operatorname{arcosh} x$ has the domain $x \geqslant 0$ as we have defined it. If $y = \operatorname{arcosh} x$, $x \geqslant 0$, then

$$\cosh y = x, \quad x \geqslant 1$$

Differentiating with respect to x, you get

$$\sinh y \dfrac{dy}{dx} = 1$$

so: $\qquad\qquad \dfrac{dy}{dx} = \dfrac{1}{\sinh y} = \dfrac{1}{\sqrt{(x^2 - 1)}}$

So we have the results:

■ $\qquad \dfrac{d}{dx}(\mathbf{arsinh}\, x) = \dfrac{1}{\sqrt{(x^2 + 1)}}$ **and** $\dfrac{d}{dx}(\mathbf{arcosh}\, x) = \dfrac{1}{\sqrt{(x^2 - 1)}}$

Notice that at $x = 1$, the curve $y = \operatorname{arcosh} x$ (page 74) has a gradient that is parallel to the y-axis, since $\sqrt{(x^2 - 1)} = 0$, and hence $\dfrac{d}{dx}(\operatorname{arcosh} x) = \dfrac{1}{\sqrt{(x^2 - 1)}}$ is infinite.

Example 14

Find an equation of the tangent at the point where $x = -\frac{1}{2}$ to the curve with equation $y = \text{artanh}\, x$.

First you need to find $\dfrac{dy}{dx}$.

Since $y = \text{artanh}\, x$, $x = \tanh y$ and differentiating with respect to x gives

$$1 = \text{sech}^2 y \, \frac{dy}{dx}$$

That is:

$$\frac{dy}{dx} = \frac{1}{\text{sech}^2 y}$$

But $\qquad \text{sech}^2 y \equiv 1 - \tanh^2 y = 1 - x^2$, since $\tanh y = x$

So $\dfrac{dy}{dx} = \dfrac{1}{1 - x^2}$. That is to say:

■
$$\frac{d}{dx}(\text{artanh}\, x) = \frac{1}{1 - x^2}$$

At $x = -\frac{1}{2}$, $\dfrac{dy}{dx} = \dfrac{1}{1 - \frac{1}{4}} = \frac{4}{3}$

and $y = \text{artanh}(-\frac{1}{2}) = \frac{1}{2}\ln\left(\dfrac{1 - \frac{1}{2}}{1 + \frac{1}{2}}\right) = \frac{1}{2}\ln(\frac{1}{3})$.

But $\ln\frac{1}{3} = -\ln 3$, so $y = -\frac{1}{2}\ln 3$.

The tangent at $(-\frac{1}{2}, -\frac{1}{2}\ln 3)$ has gradient $\frac{4}{3}$ and its equation is

$$y + \tfrac{1}{2}\ln 3 = \tfrac{4}{3}(x + \tfrac{1}{2})$$

Exercise 4B

In questions 1–20, differentiate with respect to x:

1 $\cosh 2x$	**2** $\sinh \dfrac{x}{2}$	**3** $\tanh 3x$
4 $\text{sech}\, 2x$	**5** $\text{cosech}\, \dfrac{x}{3}$	**6** $e^x \cosh x$
7 $\sinh^2 3x$	**8** $\tanh^3 x$	**9** $\coth(\ln x)$
10 $\ln(\sinh x)$	**11** $x \sinh 2x$	**12** $x^3 \cosh 3x$
13 $\ln(\tanh x)$	**14** $e^{\sinh x}$	**15** $\dfrac{x}{\cosh x}$
16 $\dfrac{\cosh x}{x}$	**17** $e^{\cosh^3 x}$	**18** $\dfrac{\coth 2x}{x^3}$

19 $\dfrac{\text{cosech}(x^2)}{x}$ **20** $\ln(\tanh x - \text{sech}\, x)$

21 Given that $y = \text{arsinh}(x - 1)$, find the value of $\dfrac{dy}{dx}$ at $x = 2$.

22 Find the equation of the normal at the point where $x = \ln 2$ on the curve $y = \sinh x + 3 \cosh x$.

23 The curve $y = 5 \sinh x - 4 \cosh x$ crosses the x-axis at the point A. Determine the coordinates of A and the equation of the tangent to the curve at A.

24 Find the minimum value of y, where $y = 13 \cosh x + 12 \sinh x$ and the value of x where this occurs.

25 The tangent at the point P with x-coordinate $2c$ on the curve with equation $y = c \cosh \dfrac{x}{c}$, meets the y-axis at the point Q. Find the distance OQ in terms of c, where O is the origin.

26 Find to 2 decimal places the coordinates of the stationary points on the curve $y = 8 \sinh x - 27 \tanh x$ and determine the nature of these stationary points.

27 Given that $y = A \cosh 3x + B \sinh 3x$, where A and B are constants, show that $\dfrac{d^2y}{dx^2} - 9y = 0$.

28 Use successive differentiation and Maclaurin's expansion to show that:

- $\sinh x = x + \dfrac{x^3}{3!} + \dfrac{x^5}{5!} + \ldots$

- $\cosh x = 1 + \dfrac{x^2}{2!} + \dfrac{x^4}{4!} + \ldots$

29 Given that $y = \cosh 3x \sin x$, find $\dfrac{dy}{dx}$ and $\dfrac{d^2y}{dx^2}$.

30 Find the first two non-zero terms in the series expansion of $\tanh x$ in ascending powers of x.

31 Find an equation of the tangent and an equation of the normal at the point where $x = \frac{3}{2}$ on the curve with equation $y = \tanh x$.

In questions 32–47, differentiate with respect to x:

32 $\text{arsinh}\, x$ **33** $\text{arcosh}\, \dfrac{x}{2}$ **34** $\text{artanh}\, x^2$

35 $\text{arsech}\, x$ **36** $\text{arcosech}\, x$ **37** $\text{arcoth}\, 2x$

38 $\operatorname{arsech} x^{\frac{1}{2}}$ **39** $x \operatorname{arcosh} x$ **40** $\dfrac{x}{\operatorname{arsinh} x}$

41 $(\operatorname{artanh} x)^2$ **42** $(\operatorname{arsech} x)^{\frac{1}{2}}$ **43** $e^{x^2} \operatorname{arsinh} x$

44 $\dfrac{\ln x}{\operatorname{arcosh} x}$ **45** $\operatorname{artanh}(\sin x)$ **46** $\operatorname{artanh}(\sinh x)$

47 $\dfrac{\arcsin x}{\operatorname{arsinh} x}$

48 Find an equation of the tangent to the curve $y = \operatorname{arsinh} x$ at
   (i) the origin and
   (ii) the point where $x = 1$.

49 Given that $y = (\operatorname{arsinh} x)^2$, show that:

$$(1 + x^2)\frac{d^2 y}{dx^2} + x \frac{dy}{dx} = 2$$

50 Find an equation of the normal at the point where $x = \frac{3}{4}$ on the curve with equation $y = \operatorname{artanh} x$.

51 Given that $y = \operatorname{arsinh} x$, show that
   (a) $y = \ln[x + \surd(1 + x^2)]$
   (b) $(1 + x^2)\left(\dfrac{dy}{dx}\right)^2 = 1$
   (c) $(1 + x^2)\dfrac{d^3 y}{dx^3} + 3x \dfrac{d^2 y}{dx^2} + \dfrac{dy}{dx} = 0$

52 Show that the curve with equation $y = 3\cosh x - x \sinh x$ has a minimum point A on the y-axis. Find the coordinates of A. Show further that the curve has another stationary value between $x = 1.9$ and $x = 2$. Sketch the curve.

53 Show that $y = e^{\operatorname{arsinh} x}$ satisfies the relation

$$(1 + x^2)\frac{d^2 y}{dx^2} + x \frac{dy}{dx} - y = 0$$

54 Given that $y = \sinh x + k \cosh x$, show that the least value of y is $\surd(k^2 - 1)$ and that this occurs at $x = \frac{1}{2}\ln\left(\dfrac{k - 1}{k + 1}\right)$ where k is a constant and $|k| > 1$.

55 Show that $(\cosh x + \sinh x)^k + (\cosh x - \sinh x)^k \equiv 2\cosh kx$, where k is real.
Hence solve the equation

$$(\cosh x + \sinh x)^5 + (\cosh x - \sinh x)^5 = 5$$

giving your answers to 2 decimal places.

56 Find the coordinates of the minimum point on the curve
$y = 5 \cosh x - 3 \sinh x$.

57 Given that $y = \arctan(\mathrm{e}^x)$, show that $\dfrac{\mathrm{d}y}{\mathrm{d}x} = \frac{1}{2} \operatorname{sech} x$, and find $\dfrac{\mathrm{d}^2 y}{\mathrm{d}x^2}$.

58 Given that $\operatorname{artanh} x + \operatorname{artanh} y = \frac{1}{2} \ln 5$, show that $y = \dfrac{2 - 3x}{3 - 2x}$.

59 Given that $y = \ln\left[\tan\left(\dfrac{\pi}{4} + \dfrac{x}{2}\right)\right]$, show that $\sinh y = \tan x$ and $\cosh y = \sec x$.

60 For the curve $y = \operatorname{arsinh}(x + 1)$, find
   (a) the coordinates of its point of inflexion P
   (b) the equation of the normal to the curve at P.

SUMMARY OF KEY POINTS

1   $\sinh x = \frac{1}{2}(\mathrm{e}^x - \mathrm{e}^{-x})$, $\cosh x = \frac{1}{2}(\mathrm{e}^x + \mathrm{e}^{-x})$

2   $\tanh x = \dfrac{\sinh x}{\cosh x}$, $\operatorname{sech} x = \dfrac{1}{\cosh x}$,

   $\operatorname{cosech} x = \dfrac{1}{\sinh x}$, $\coth x = \dfrac{1}{\tanh x}$

3   $\cosh^2 x - \sinh^2 x \equiv 1$
   $\sinh 2x \equiv 2 \sinh x \cosh x$
   $\cosh 2x \equiv \cosh^2 x + \sinh^2 x \equiv 2 \cosh^2 x - 1 \equiv 1 + 2 \sinh^2 x$

4   **Osborn's rule**: In a trigonometric identity you can replace each trigonometric function by the corresponding hyperbolic function to form the corresponding hyperbolic identity *but* you must also change the sign of every product (or implied product) of two sines.

5   $\sinh(A \pm B) \equiv \sinh A \cosh B \pm \cosh A \sinh B$
   $\cosh(A \pm B) \equiv \cosh A \cosh B \pm \sinh A \sinh B$
   $\tanh(A \pm B) = \dfrac{\tanh A \pm \tanh B}{1 \pm \tanh A \tanh B}$

6   $\operatorname{arsinh} x = \ln[x + \surd(x^2 + 1)]$, $x \in \mathbb{R}$
   $\operatorname{arcosh} x = \ln[x + \surd(x^2 - 1)]$, $x \in \mathbb{R}$, $x \geqslant 1$
   $\operatorname{artanh} x = \frac{1}{2} \ln\left(\dfrac{1 + x}{1 - x}\right)$, $x \in \mathbb{R}$, $|x| < 1$

7 $\dfrac{d}{dx}(\sinh x) = \cosh x, \qquad \dfrac{d}{dx}(\cosh x) = \sinh x$

$\dfrac{d}{dx}(\tanh x) = \text{sech}^2\, x, \qquad \dfrac{d}{dx}(\coth x) = -\text{cosech}^2\, x$

$\dfrac{d}{dx}(\text{sech}\, x) = -\tanh x\,\text{sech}\, x,$

$\dfrac{d}{dx}(\text{cosech}\, x) = -\coth x\,\text{cosech}\, x$

8 $\dfrac{d}{dx}(\text{arsinh}\, x) = \dfrac{1}{\surd(x^2 + 1)}$

$\dfrac{d}{dx}(\text{arcosh}\, x) = \dfrac{1}{\surd(x^2 - 1)}$

$\dfrac{d}{dx}(\text{artanh}\, x) = \dfrac{1}{1 - x^2}$

Integration

5.1 More standard forms

Books P1 and P2 described integration as the inverse or the reverse process to differentiation. In chapters 3 and 4 you learned a number of important results in differentiation concerning inverse trigonometric functions, hyperbolic functions and inverse hyperbolic functions. Generally, if $\frac{d}{dx}(g(x)) = f(x)$

then:
$$\int f(x)\,dx = g(x) + C$$

where C is a constant.

Using this general result, you can add the following integrals to your list of standard forms as a direct consequence of the derivatives already found in chapters 3 and 4.

Derivative	**Integral**
■ $\frac{d}{dx}(\cosh x) = \sinh x$	$\int \sinh x\,dx = \cosh x + C$
■ $\frac{d}{dx}(\sinh x) = \cosh x$	$\int \cosh x\,dx = \sinh x + C$
■ $\frac{d}{dx}(\tanh x) = \operatorname{sech}^2 x$	$\int \operatorname{sech}^2 x\,dx = \tanh x + C$
■ $\frac{d}{dx}(\arcsin x) = \frac{1}{\sqrt{(1-x^2)}}$	$\int \frac{1}{\sqrt{(1-x^2)}}\,dx = \arcsin x + C, |x| < 1$
■ $\frac{d}{dx}(\arctan x) = \frac{1}{1+x^2}$	$\int \frac{1}{1+x^2}\,dx = \arctan x + C$
■ $\frac{d}{dx}(\operatorname{arsinh} x) = \frac{1}{\sqrt{(1+x^2)}}$	$\int \frac{1}{\sqrt{(1+x^2)}}\,dx = \operatorname{arsinh} x + C$
■ $\frac{d}{dx}(\operatorname{arcosh} x) = \frac{1}{\sqrt{(x^2-1)}}$	$\int \frac{1}{\sqrt{(x^2-1)}}\,dx = \operatorname{arcosh} x + C, (x > 1)$

You should note that in your ULEAC formula book the following are given (with the constants omitted):

$$\int \frac{1}{\sqrt{(a^2 - x^2)}} \, dx = \arcsin\left(\frac{x}{a}\right), \ |x| < a, \ a > 0$$

$$\int \frac{1}{\sqrt{(a^2 + x^2)}} \, dx = \operatorname{arsinh}\left(\frac{x}{a}\right), \ a > 0$$

$$\int \frac{1}{\sqrt{(x^2 - a^2)}} \, dx = \operatorname{arcosh}\left(\frac{x}{a}\right), \ x > a > 0$$

$$\int \frac{1}{a^2 + x^2} \, dx = \frac{1}{a} \arctan\left(\frac{x}{a}\right), \ a > 0$$

You can easily check these four results by differentiation using the chain rule.

Example 1
Show that

$$\int \frac{1}{a^2 + x^2} \, dx = \frac{1}{a} \arctan \frac{x}{a} + C$$

Let $y = \dfrac{1}{a} \arctan \dfrac{x}{a}$ and $t = \dfrac{x}{a}$,

then: $\qquad y = \dfrac{1}{a} \arctan t$ and $\dfrac{dy}{dt} = \dfrac{1}{a}\left(\dfrac{1}{1 + t^2}\right)$

also: $\qquad\qquad\qquad \dfrac{dt}{dx} = \dfrac{1}{a}$

Using the chain rule, $\dfrac{dy}{dx} = \dfrac{dy}{dt} \cdot \dfrac{dt}{dx}$, you get

$$\frac{dy}{dx} = \frac{1}{a}\left(\frac{1}{1 + t^2}\right)\frac{1}{a} \quad \text{and} \quad t^2 = \frac{x^2}{a^2}$$

So: $\qquad \dfrac{d}{dx}\left[\dfrac{1}{a} \arctan \dfrac{x}{a}\right] = \dfrac{1}{a^2}\left[\dfrac{1}{1 + \dfrac{x^2}{a^2}}\right] = \dfrac{1}{a^2 + x^2}$

That is: $\qquad \displaystyle\int \frac{1}{a^2 + x^2} \, dx = \frac{1}{a} \arctan \frac{x}{a} + C$

Example 2
Find (a) $\displaystyle\int \frac{1}{\sqrt{(x^2 - 9)}} \, dx, \ x > 3$ (b) $\displaystyle\int \frac{1}{\sqrt{(25 - 4x^2)}} \, dx, \ |x| < \frac{5}{2}$

In (a), use the result

$$\int \frac{1}{\sqrt{(x^2 - a^2)}}\, dx = \operatorname{arcosh} \frac{x}{a} + C$$

and take $a = 3$ to give

$$\int \frac{1}{\sqrt{(x^2 - 9)}}\, dx = \operatorname{arcosh} \frac{x}{3} + C$$

In (b) you need to rewrite $\sqrt{(25 - 4x^2)}$ in the form $2\sqrt{[(\frac{5}{2})^2 - x^2]}$ so that the result

$$\int \frac{1}{\sqrt{(a^2 - x^2)}}\, dx = \arcsin \frac{x}{a} + C$$

can be used with $a = \frac{5}{2}$.

Hence:
$$\int \frac{1}{\sqrt{(25 - 4x^2)}}\, dx = \frac{1}{2} \int \frac{1}{\sqrt{[(\frac{5}{2})^2 - x^2]}}\, dx$$

$$= \frac{1}{2} \arcsin \frac{x}{\frac{5}{2}} + C$$

$$= \frac{1}{2} \arcsin \frac{2x}{5} + C$$

Example 3

Evaluate $\displaystyle\int_1^2 \frac{1}{\sqrt{(1 + 4x^2)}}\, dx$, giving your answer to 3 significant figures.

Notice that $\sqrt{(1 + 4x^2)} = 2\sqrt{(\frac{1}{4} + x^2)}$, and so you can write the integral as

$$\frac{1}{2} \int_1^2 \frac{1}{\sqrt{(\frac{1}{4} + x^2)}}\, dx$$

Since $\displaystyle\int \frac{1}{\sqrt{(a^2 + x^2)}}\, dx = \operatorname{arsinh} \frac{x}{a}$, you have

$$\frac{1}{2} \int_1^2 \frac{1}{\sqrt{[(\frac{1}{2})^2 + x^2]}}\, dx = \frac{1}{2} \left[\operatorname{arsinh} \frac{x}{\frac{1}{2}} \right]_1^2$$

$$= \frac{1}{2} \left[\operatorname{arsinh} 2x \right]_1^2$$

$$= \frac{1}{2} (\operatorname{arsinh} 4 - \operatorname{arsinh} 2)$$

$$= \frac{1}{2} (2.0947 - 1.4436)$$

$$= 0.326 \text{ (3 significant figures)}$$

Example 4

The region R is bounded by the curve $y = \cosh x$ and the line $y = 3$, as shown in the diagram. Find the area of R, giving your answer to 3 significant figures.

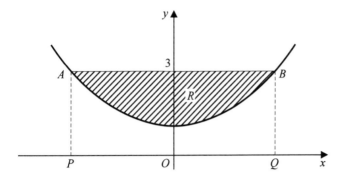

First you need to find values of x at A and at B, that is, at $\cosh x = 3$

$$\Rightarrow e^x + e^{-x} = 6 \quad \text{or} \quad e^{2x} - 6e^x + 1 = 0$$

Use the quadratic formula to find e^x:

$$e^x = \frac{6 \pm \sqrt{(36 - 4)}}{2} = 3 \pm 2\sqrt{2}$$

Then by taking natural logarithms you get

$$x = -1.763 \text{ or } 1.763$$

The points P and Q lie on the x-axis and have the same x-coordinates as A and B respectively.

Area of R = area of rectangle $APQB$ − area under curve between A and B and above x-axis

$$= AP \times PQ - \int_{-1.763}^{1.763} \cosh x \, dx$$
$$= 3 \times 3.526 - \left[\sinh x \right]_{-1.763}^{1.763}$$
$$= 10.578 - \sinh 1.763 + \sinh(-1.763)$$
$$= 4.92 \text{ (3 significant figures)}$$

5.2 Integration using identities

You can use hyperbolic identities to replace an expression that you cannot integrate directly by one that you can integrate. This was done with trigonometric identities in Book P2 (page 279).

Example 5

Find (a) $\displaystyle\int \cosh^2 2x \, dx$ (b) $\displaystyle\int \tanh^2 x \, dx$.

(a) There are two possible methods.

In the first you can use the identity

$$\cosh 2A \equiv 2\cosh^2 A - 1$$

and take $A = 2x$ so that:

$$\cosh^2 2x \equiv \tfrac{1}{2}(1 + \cosh 4x)$$

Hence:
$$\int \cosh^2 2x \, dx = \tfrac{1}{2}\int (1 + \cosh 4x) \, dx$$
$$= \tfrac{1}{2}x + \tfrac{1}{8}\sinh 4x + C$$

In the second, use the exponential form of

$$\cosh 2x \equiv \tfrac{1}{2}(e^{2x} + e^{-2x})$$

and square the identity to obtain:

$$\cosh^2 2x \equiv \tfrac{1}{4}(e^{4x} + 2 + e^{-4x})$$

Hence:
$$\int \cosh^2 2x \, dx = \tfrac{1}{4}\int (e^{4x} + 2 + e^{-4x}) \, dx$$
$$= \tfrac{1}{16}e^{4x} + \tfrac{1}{2}x - \tfrac{1}{16}e^{-4x} + C$$

which is equivalent to the first answer, since $\sinh 4x \equiv \tfrac{1}{2}(e^{4x} - e^{-4x})$.

(b) In the identity $\operatorname{sech}^2 A \equiv 1 - \tanh^2 A$, put $A = x$ and then

$$\tanh^2 x \equiv 1 - \operatorname{sech}^2 x$$

So:
$$\int \tanh^2 x \, dx = \int (1 - \operatorname{sech}^2 x) \, dx$$

But $\displaystyle\int \operatorname{sech}^2 x \, dx = \tanh x + C$ is a standard result, given on page 89.

So:
$$\int \tanh^2 x \, dx = x - \tanh x + C$$

Example 6

Find (a) $\displaystyle\int \tanh x \, dx$ (b) $\displaystyle\int \operatorname{sech} x \, dx$.

(a) Use the identity $\tanh x \equiv \dfrac{\sinh x}{\cosh x}$.

Then:
$$\int \tanh x \, dx = \int \frac{\sinh x}{\cosh x} \, dx$$

Let $\cosh x = t$; then, by differentiation, $\sinh x \dfrac{dx}{dt} = 1$.

So:
$$\int \frac{\sinh x}{\cosh x} \, dx = \int \frac{\sinh x}{\cosh x} \frac{dx}{dt} \, dt = \int \frac{1}{t} \, dt$$
$$= \ln t + C$$

That is:
$$\int \tanh x \, dx = \ln(\cosh x) + C$$

(b) Use the identity $\operatorname{sech} x \equiv \dfrac{1}{\cosh x}$. Then:

$$\int \operatorname{sech} x \, dx = \int \frac{1}{\cosh x} \, dx = \int \frac{\cosh x}{\cosh^2 x} \, dx$$

But $\cosh^2 x \equiv 1 + \sinh^2 x$, so you have

$$\int \operatorname{sech} x \, dx = \int \frac{\cosh x}{1 + \sinh^2 x} \, dx$$

Write $\sinh x = t$, then $\cosh x \dfrac{dx}{dt} = 1$ and the integral can be written as

$$\int \operatorname{sech} x \, dx = \int \frac{\cosh x}{1 + \sinh^2 x} \frac{dx}{dt} \, dt = \int \frac{1}{1 + t^2} \, dt$$

But $\displaystyle\int \frac{1}{1 + x^2} \, dx = \arctan x + C$ is a standard result given on page 89.

So: $\displaystyle\int \operatorname{sech} x \, dx = \arctan t + C = \arctan(\sinh x) + C$

Exercise 5A

Integrate each of the following with respect to x:

1 $\cosh 2x$

2 $\sinh 3x$

3 $-\sinh \dfrac{x}{2}$

4 $e^x \cosh x$

5 $e^{2x} \sinh x$

6 $\sinh x \cosh x$

7 $\cosh^2 x$

8 $\sinh^2 x$

9 $\operatorname{sech}^2 2x$

10 $\tanh^2 2x$

11 $\coth^2 \dfrac{x}{2}$

12 $\operatorname{cosech} 2x \coth 2x$

13 $\tanh 3x \operatorname{sech} 3x$

14 $\dfrac{1}{\sqrt{(4 - x^2)}}$

15 $\dfrac{1}{\sqrt{(4 + x^2)}}$

16 $\dfrac{1}{\sqrt{(x^2-4)}}$ **17** $\dfrac{1}{x^2+4}$ **18** $\dfrac{1}{x^2-4}$

19 $\dfrac{1}{\sqrt{(25-x^2)}}$ **20** $\dfrac{1}{\sqrt{(25-9x^2)}}$ **21** $\dfrac{1}{\sqrt{(16x^2-9)}}$

22 $\dfrac{1}{\sqrt{(64+9x^2)}}$ **23** $\dfrac{1}{9x^2+64}$ **24** $\dfrac{1}{\sqrt{(16x^2-1)}}$

25 $\dfrac{1}{\sqrt{(1+16x^2)}}$ **26** $\operatorname{sech} 2x$ **27** $\tanh 2x$

28 $\cosh^2 \dfrac{3x}{2}$ **29** $\sinh^2 \dfrac{2x}{5}$ **30** $\tanh^2 5x$

Evaluate, using integration, giving your final answer to 3 significant figures:

31 $\displaystyle\int_0^1 \cosh 2x \, dx$ **32** $\displaystyle\int_0^1 \sinh \dfrac{x}{2} \, dx$ **33** $\displaystyle\int_0^2 \tanh x \, dx$

34 $\displaystyle\int_0^3 \dfrac{1}{\sqrt{(9-x^2)}} \, dx$ **35** $\displaystyle\int_0^3 \dfrac{1}{\sqrt{(9+x^2)}} \, dx$ **36** $\displaystyle\int_2^3 \dfrac{1}{\sqrt{(x^2-1)}} \, dx$

37 $\displaystyle\int_1^2 \dfrac{1}{4+x^2} \, dx$ **38** $\displaystyle\int_0^1 e^x \sinh x \, dx$ **39** $\displaystyle\int_1^2 e^x \cosh 2x \, dx$

40 $\displaystyle\int_2^4 \dfrac{1}{\sqrt{(16-x^2)}} \, dx$

41 Find the area of the region bounded by the curve with equation $y\sqrt{(25+x^2)} = 25$, the x-axis and the lines $x = \pm 5$.

42 Find the area of the finite region bounded by the curve with equation $x^2 - y^2 = 4$ and the line $x = 5$.

43 Find, giving your answer to 2 decimal places, the area of the finite region bounded by the curve with equation $y = \operatorname{sech} x$, the x-axis and the lines $x = 1$ and $x = 4$.

44 Use the identity $\sinh x \equiv \tfrac{1}{2}(e^x - e^{-x})$ and the substitution $v = e^x$ to find $\displaystyle\int \operatorname{cosech} x \, dx$.

45 Show that $\dfrac{d}{dx}(\ln \sinh x) = \coth x$.

Hence find the area of the finite region bounded by the curve with equation $y = \coth x$, the x-axis and the lines $x = 2$ and $x = 4$.

46 The region R is bounded by the curve with equation

$$y = \frac{1}{\sqrt{(x^2 + 9)}}, \text{ the } x\text{-axis and the lines } x = \pm 2.$$

(a) Find the area of R.

The region R is rotated through $360°$ about the x-axis.

(b) Find the volume of the solid generated.

47 A curve is given by the equations $x = \sinh^2 t$, $y = \sinh t$, where t is a real parameter. The finite region R is bounded by part of the curve, the x-axis and the lines $x = 1$ and $x = 3$. Find, to 2 decimal places, the area of R.

48 Use the substitution $x = \sinh u$ to show that

$$\int_0^1 \sqrt{(1 + x^2)}\, dx = \tfrac{1}{2}\sqrt{2} + \tfrac{1}{2}\ln[1 + \sqrt{2}]$$

49 The finite region R is bounded by the curves $y = \cosh x$, $y = \sinh x$, the y-axis and the line $x = 1$. Find the area of R.

50 A curve C is given by $x = 2\cos t$, $y = \sin t$, $0 \leqslant t < 2\pi$, where t is a parameter. Find the area enclosed by C.

5.3 Some other methods of integration

Integrals of the types

$$\int \frac{1}{px^2 + qx + r}\, dx, \quad \int \frac{1}{\sqrt{(px^2 + qx + r)}}\, dx,$$

where p, q and r are constants can be integrated by using one of the standard forms, where C is an arbitrary constant and a is a positive constant.

1 $\displaystyle \int \frac{1}{x^2 + a^2}\, dx = \frac{1}{a} \arctan \frac{x}{a} + C$

2 $\displaystyle \int \frac{1}{x^2 - a^2}\, dx = \frac{1}{2a} \ln \left| \frac{x - a}{x + a} \right| + C, \text{ where } |x| > a$

3 $\displaystyle \int \frac{1}{a^2 - x^2}\, dx = \frac{1}{2a} \ln \left| \frac{a + x}{a - x} \right| + C, \text{ where } |x| < a$

4 $\displaystyle \int \frac{1}{\sqrt{(a^2 - x^2)}}\, dx = \arcsin \frac{x}{a} + C$

5 $\displaystyle \int \frac{1}{\sqrt{(x^2 + a^2)}}\, dx = \operatorname{arsinh} \frac{x}{a} + C$ **6** $\displaystyle \int \frac{1}{\sqrt{(x^2 - a^2)}}\, dx = \operatorname{arcosh} \frac{x}{a} + C$

Integrals 1, 4, 5, 6 have been discussed in section 5.1. Integrals 2 and 3 are obtained by first using **partial fractions** (Book P2, page 280).

It is important that you can complete the square in a quadratic expression with confidence.

The following examples illustrate the methods required.

Example 7

Find (a) $\int \dfrac{1}{x^2 - 2x - 3}\, dx$ (b) $\int \dfrac{1}{x^2 - 2x + 5}\, dx.$

(a) Notice that $x^2 - 2x - 3 = x^2 - 2x + 1 - 4 = (x - 1)^2 - 4$

So:
$$\int \frac{1}{x^2 - 2x - 3}\, dx = \int \frac{1}{(x - 1)^2 - 4}\, dx$$

Put $x - 1 = u$ and $\dfrac{dx}{du} = 1.$

Then:
$$\int \frac{1}{x^2 - 2x - 3}\, dx = \int \frac{1}{u^2 - 4} \frac{dx}{du}\, du = \int \frac{1}{u^2 - 4}\, du$$

If you compare this with the standard result for $\int \dfrac{1}{x^2 - a^2}\, dx$ you have:

$$\int \frac{1}{x^2 - 2x - 3}\, dx = \tfrac{1}{4}\ln\left|\frac{u - 2}{u + 2}\right| + C$$

$$= \tfrac{1}{4}\ln\left|\frac{x - 3}{x + 1}\right| + C$$

You could also get this result by factorising $x^2 - 2x - 3$ and using partial fractions.

(b) Notice that $x^2 - 2x + 5 = x^2 - 2x + 1 + 4 = (x - 1)^2 + 4$

So:
$$\int \frac{1}{x^2 - 2x + 5}\, dx = \int \frac{1}{(x - 1)^2 + 4}\, dx$$

Again, as in (a), put $x - 1 = u$ and $\dfrac{dx}{du} = 1.$

Then:
$$\int \frac{1}{x^2 - 2x + 5}\, dx = \int \frac{1}{u^2 + 4} \frac{dx}{du}\, du$$

$$= \int \frac{1}{u^2 + 4}\, du$$

$$= \tfrac{1}{2}\arctan \frac{u}{2} + C \text{ (see standard result 1 on page 89)}$$

$$= \tfrac{1}{2}\arctan\left(\frac{x - 1}{2}\right) + C$$

Example 8

Find $\int \dfrac{1}{\sqrt{(x^2 - x + 1)}}\, dx$.

Notice that
$$x^2 - x + 1 = x^2 - x + \tfrac{1}{4} + \tfrac{3}{4}$$
$$= (x - \tfrac{1}{2})^2 + (\tfrac{\sqrt{3}}{2})^2$$

Then:
$$\int \frac{1}{\sqrt{(x^2 - x + 1)}}\, dx = \int \frac{1}{\sqrt{[(x - \tfrac{1}{2})^2 + (\tfrac{\sqrt{3}}{2})^2]}}\, dx$$

Put $x - \tfrac{1}{2} = u$, then $\dfrac{dx}{du} = 1$.

So:
$$\int \frac{1}{\sqrt{(x^2 - x + 1)}}\, dx = \int \frac{1}{\sqrt{[u^2 + (\tfrac{\sqrt{3}}{2})^2]}}\frac{dx}{du}\, du = \int \frac{1}{\sqrt{[u^2 + (\tfrac{\sqrt{3}}{2})^2]}}\, du$$

$$= \operatorname{arsinh}\left(\frac{u}{\frac{\sqrt{3}}{2}}\right) + C \quad \text{(see standard result 5, page 96)}$$

$$= \operatorname{arsinh}\left(\frac{2u}{\sqrt{3}}\right) + C$$

$$= \operatorname{arsinh}\left(\frac{2x - 1}{\sqrt{3}}\right) + C$$

In examination questions, you will often be given a **substitution** to use when evaluating an integral.

Example 9

Use the substitution $x = 3(1 + \sin t)$ to evaluate the integral
$\displaystyle\int_3^{4.5} \dfrac{1}{(6x - x^2)^{\frac{1}{2}}}\, dx$.

For $x = 3 + 3\sin t$, $\dfrac{dx}{dt} = 3\cos t$

and:
$$6x - x^2 = 18 + 18\sin t - 9(1 + \sin t)^2$$
$$= 18 + 18\sin t - 9 - 18\sin t - 9\sin^2 t$$
$$= 9 - 9\sin^2 t$$
$$= 9(1 - \sin^2 t) = 9\cos^2 t$$

So:
$$(6x - x^2)^{\frac{1}{2}} = 3\cos t$$

At $x = 3$, $\sin t = 0 \Rightarrow t = 0$

At $x = 4.5$, $\sin t = \tfrac{1}{2} \Rightarrow t = \tfrac{\pi}{6}$

Hence:
$$\int_3^{4.5} \frac{1}{(6x-x^2)^{\frac{1}{2}}} \, dx = \int_0^{\frac{\pi}{6}} \frac{1}{(6x-x^2)^{\frac{1}{2}}} \frac{dx}{dt} \, dt$$

$$= \int_0^{\frac{\pi}{6}} \frac{1}{3\cos t}(3\cos t) \, dt$$

$$= \int_0^{\frac{\pi}{6}} 1 \, dt$$

$$= [t]_0^{\frac{\pi}{6}} = \frac{\pi}{6}$$

You will often need to do **integration by parts** to find the integrals of inverse trigonometric and inverse hyperbolic functions. Here are some examples of this.

Example 10

Use integration by parts to find $\int \text{arsinh}\, x \, dx$.

Book P2 (page 286) gave the integration by parts formula, which is

$$\int v \frac{du}{dx} \, dx = uv - \int u \frac{dv}{dx} \, dx$$

where u and v are functions of x.

You know also that $\dfrac{d}{dx}(\text{arsinh}\, x) = \dfrac{1}{\sqrt{(1+x^2)}}$, so in the integral $\int \text{arsinh}\, x \, dx$, you can take

$$v = \text{arsinh}\, x \qquad \text{and} \qquad \frac{du}{dx} = 1$$

Then:
$$\frac{dv}{dx} = \frac{1}{\sqrt{(1+x^2)}} \qquad \text{and} \qquad u = x$$

Using integration by parts:

$$\int \text{arsinh}\, x \, dx = x \, \text{arsinh}\, x - \int \frac{x}{\sqrt{(1+x^2)}} \, dx$$

Now you need to find $\int \dfrac{x}{\sqrt{(1+x^2)}} \, dx$ which can be done by writing $1+x^2 = t^2$, so that:

$$2x \frac{dx}{dt} = 2t \Rightarrow x \frac{dx}{dt} = t$$

Then:
$$\int \frac{x}{\sqrt{(1+x^2)}} \, dx = \int \frac{1}{t} t \, dt = t + C = \sqrt{(1+x^2)} + C$$

So:
$$\int \text{arsinh}\, x \, dx = x \, \text{arsinh}\, x - \sqrt{(1+x^2)} + C$$

Example 11

Giving your answer to 3 significant figures, find the area of the region bounded by the curve with equation $y = \text{artanh}\, x$, the x-axis and the line $x = \frac{1}{2}$.

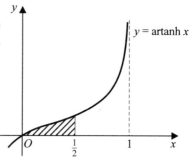

The diagram shows the region whose area is required. It is found by evaluating the integral $\displaystyle\int_0^{\frac{1}{2}} \text{artanh}\, x \, dx$.

You know that $\dfrac{d}{dx}(\text{artanh}\, x) = \dfrac{1}{1 - x^2}$ (page 88), so you take

$$v = \text{artanh}\, x \quad \text{and} \quad \frac{du}{dx} = 1$$

So: $$\frac{dv}{dx} = \frac{1}{1 - x^2} \quad \text{and} \quad u = x$$

Using integration by parts you obtain

$$\int \text{artanh}\, x \, dx = x \,\text{artanh}\, x - \int \frac{x}{1 - x^2} \, dx$$
$$= x \,\text{artanh}\, x + \tfrac{1}{2}\ln|1 - x^2| + C$$

(The integral $\displaystyle\int \frac{x}{1 - x^2} \, dx$ consists of a function and its derivative, the function being $(1 - x^2)$.)

$$\text{Area of region} = [x \,\text{artanh}\, x + \tfrac{1}{2}\ln|1 - x^2|]_0^{\frac{1}{2}}$$
$$= \tfrac{1}{2}\,\text{artanh}\,\tfrac{1}{2} + \tfrac{1}{2}\ln\tfrac{3}{4} - (0 + \tfrac{1}{2}\ln 1)$$
$$= 0.2747 - 0.1438$$
$$= 0.131 \text{ (3 significant figures)}$$

Exercise 5B

In questions 1–24 integrate the given expressions with respect to x:

1 $\dfrac{1}{x^2 - 2x}$ **2** $\dfrac{1}{\sqrt{(x^2 - 2x)}}$ **3** $\dfrac{1}{\sqrt{(2x - x^2)}}$

4 $\dfrac{1}{x^2 + x + 1}$ **5** $\dfrac{1}{\sqrt{(x^2 + x + 1)}}$ **6** $\dfrac{1}{x(x^2 + 1)}$

7 $\dfrac{\cosh x}{1 + \sinh x}$ **8** $\dfrac{\sinh x}{\cosh x - 1}$ **9** $\sinh^3 x \cosh x$

10 $\dfrac{2x+6}{x^2+6x+1}$ **11** $\dfrac{x-2}{x^2-4x-2}$ **12** $\dfrac{x}{(x^2+1)^{\frac{1}{2}}}$

13 $\dfrac{a+2bx}{ax+bx^2}$ **14** $\dfrac{\operatorname{arsinh} x}{(1+x^2)^{\frac{1}{2}}}$ **15** $\dfrac{\arcsin x}{(1-x^2)^{\frac{1}{2}}}$

16 $\dfrac{4x+7}{\sqrt{(2x^2+7x+3)}}$ **17** $\dfrac{1}{2x^2+7x+3}$ **18** $\dfrac{1}{x^2+8x+17}$

19 $\dfrac{2x-3}{\sqrt{(x^2-9)}}$ **20** $\dfrac{4x-1}{\sqrt{(x^2+16)}}$ **21** $\dfrac{1}{4x^2+4x+2}$

22 $\dfrac{1}{\sqrt{(1-x-x^2)}}$ **23** $\dfrac{1}{13-4x+x^2}$ **24** $\dfrac{1}{\sqrt{(5-4x-x^2)}}$

Use (a) differentiation (b) integration by parts to prove each of the following where C is a constant:

25 $\displaystyle\int \arcsin x\,\mathrm{d}x = x\arcsin x + (1-x^2)^{\frac{1}{2}} + C$

26 $\displaystyle\int \arccos x\,\mathrm{d}x = x\arccos x - (1-x^2)^{\frac{1}{2}} + C$

27 $\displaystyle\int \arctan x\,\mathrm{d}x = x\arctan x - \tfrac{1}{2}\ln(1+x^2) + C$

28 $\displaystyle\int \operatorname{arcsec} x\,\mathrm{d}x = x\operatorname{arcsec} x - \ln[x+\sqrt{(x^2-1)}] + C$

29 $\displaystyle\int x\arctan x\,\mathrm{d}x = \tfrac{1}{2}(x^2+1)\arctan x - \tfrac{1}{2}x + C$

30 $\displaystyle\int \operatorname{arcosh} x\,\mathrm{d}x = \tfrac{1}{4}(2x^2-1)\operatorname{arcosh} x - \tfrac{1}{4}x\sqrt{(x^2-1)} + C$

31 Use the substitution $\mathrm{e}^x = u$ to find

   (a) $\displaystyle\int \operatorname{sech} x\,\mathrm{d}x$ (b) $\displaystyle\int \operatorname{cosech} x\,\mathrm{d}x$

32 Show that $\displaystyle\int \sec x\,\mathrm{d}x = \ln(\sec x + \tan x) + C$, where you may assume that $\sec x + \tan x > 0$.

$$\left[\text{Hint: write } \sec x \text{ as } \frac{\sec^2 x + \sec x \tan x}{\sec x + \tan x} \text{ and use the substitution } u = \sec x + \tan x\right]$$

33 Use the substitution $\cos x = u$ to find

$$\int \frac{\sin x}{16 + 9 \cos^2 x} \, dx$$

34 Use the substitution $t = \tan x$ to find

$$\int \frac{1}{1 + 8 \sin^2 x} \, dx$$

35 Use the substitution $u = e^x$ to find

$$\int \frac{1}{5 \cosh x + 4 \sinh x} \, dx$$

In questions 36–50, evaluate the definite integrals using integration, giving answers to 3 significant figures.

36 $\displaystyle\int_{10}^{13} \frac{1}{x^2 - 4x} \, dx$ **37** $\displaystyle\int_{10}^{13} \frac{1}{\sqrt{(x^2 - 4x)}} \, dx$

38 $\displaystyle\int_{2}^{3} \frac{1}{\sqrt{(9 + x^2)}} \, dx$ **39** $\displaystyle\int_{1}^{4} \frac{x}{x^2 + 9} \, dx$

40 $\displaystyle\int_{1}^{4} \frac{1}{x^2 + 9} \, dx$ **41** $\displaystyle\int_{1}^{2} \frac{1}{x^2 + x + 1} \, dx$

42 $\displaystyle\int_{\frac{\pi}{12}}^{\frac{\pi}{6}} \sec 2x \, dx$ **43** $\displaystyle\int_{\frac{\pi}{6}}^{\frac{\pi}{3}} \operatorname{cosec} x \, dx$

44 $\displaystyle\int_{0}^{3} \operatorname{arsinh} 2x \, dx$ **45** $\displaystyle\int_{1}^{2} \operatorname{arcosh} x \, dx$

46 $\displaystyle\int_{0}^{\frac{1}{2}} \arcsin x \, dx$ **47** $\displaystyle\int_{1}^{\sqrt{3}} \arctan x \, dx$

48 $\displaystyle\int_{4}^{8} (x^2 - 16)^{\frac{1}{2}} \, dx$ **49** $\displaystyle\int_{1}^{\sqrt{3}} \frac{x^2}{1 + x^2} \, dx$

50 $\displaystyle\int_{0}^{1} \frac{1}{\sqrt{(3 + 2x - x^2)}} \, dx$

5.4 A strategy for systematic integration

You should make a list of all the standard integrals, often called **standard forms**, that you have met so far in your Pure Mathematics course. These standard forms include those given in Books P1 and P2 as well as those learned in this chapter. A list of standard forms is given in the Summary of key points at the end of this chapter. You should appreciate, however, that this list is not exhaustive.

You should learn and memorise standard forms. Only a few standard forms are given in the ULEAC formulae booklet provided in your examinations.

At this stage of your work, you should take stock of all the methods and results that you have studied. Any one of the integrals you have learned may be required in the examination, and so here is a clear strategy for you to use.

(a) Whenever it is possible, obtain an integral directly by comparing it with and using the appropriate standard form.

(b) Consider the replacement of the **integrand** (that is, the function to be integrated) by an identical function which you *know* you can integrate. Partial fractions in algebra and trigonometric and hyperbolic identities can be particularly effective in replacement strategies.

(c) Consider simplifying the integration by changing the variable using a substitution.

(d) Consider using integration by parts.

With regular practice you will find that you learn to choose quickly the most favourable method in each case. Here are some more examples.

Example 12

Find $\int \dfrac{2}{(x+1)(x^2+1)} \, \mathrm{d}x$.

First you need to express $\dfrac{2}{(x+1)(x^2+1)}$ in partial fractions like this:

$$\frac{2}{(x+1)(x^2+1)} \equiv \frac{A}{x+1} + \frac{Bx+C}{x^2+1}$$

where A, B and C are constants.

That is: $\qquad 2 \equiv A(x^2+1) + (Bx+C)(x+1)$

Put $x = -1$, then $A = 1$

Put $x = 0$, then $2 = A + C \Rightarrow C = 1$

Equating coefficients of x^2 gives: $0 = A + B \Rightarrow B = -1$

Hence you get:

$$\frac{2}{(x+1)(x^2+1)} \equiv \frac{1}{x+1} + \frac{1-x}{1+x^2}$$

and: $\int \frac{2}{(x+1)(x^2+1)}\,dx = \int \frac{1}{x+1}\,dx + \int \frac{1}{1+x^2}\,dx - \int \frac{x}{1+x^2}\,dx$

You should recognise at once that

$$\int \frac{1}{x+1}\,dx = \ln|x+1|$$

and

$$\int \frac{1}{1+x^2}\,dx = \arctan x$$

The third integral $\int \frac{x}{1+x^2}\,dx$ should be recognised as a function of x^2 and its derivative $2x$. So you write $u = x^2$ and $1 = 2x\,\dfrac{dx}{du}$. Then:

$$\int \frac{x}{1+x^2}\,dx = \int \frac{x}{1+x^2}\frac{dx}{du}\,du$$

$$= \tfrac{1}{2}\int \frac{1}{1+x^2}\left(2x\,\frac{dx}{du}\right)du$$

$$= \tfrac{1}{2}\int \frac{1}{1+u}\,du$$

$$= \tfrac{1}{2}\ln|1+u| = \tfrac{1}{2}\ln|1+x^2|$$

So you have:

$$\int \frac{2}{(x+1)(x^2+1)}\,dx = \ln|x+1| + \arctan x - \tfrac{1}{2}\ln|1+x^2| + C$$

Example 13

Given that $y = \dfrac{\cosh x}{1+\sinh x}$, find (a) $\int y\,dx$ (b) $\int y^{-1}\,dx$.

(a) $\int y\,dx = \int \dfrac{\cosh x}{1+\sinh x}\,dx$ and you should recognise a function of $\sinh x$ and its derivative $\cosh x$. So you substitute $\sinh x = u$ and then $\cosh x\,\dfrac{dx}{du} = 1$.

That is: $\qquad \int \dfrac{\cosh x}{1+\sinh x}\,dx = \int \dfrac{1}{1+\sinh x}\left(\cosh x\,\dfrac{dx}{du}\right)du$

$$= \int \frac{1}{1+u}\,du$$

$$= \ln|1+u| + C$$

$$= \ln|1+\sinh x| + C$$

(b) You have $y^{-1} = \dfrac{1+\sinh x}{\cosh x} = \dfrac{1}{\cosh x} + \dfrac{\sinh x}{\cosh x}$

$$= \operatorname{sech} x + \tanh x$$

So:
$$\int y^{-1}\,dx = \int \text{sech}\,x\,dx + \int \tanh x\,dx$$

both of which are standard forms.

∴
$$\int y^{-1}\,dx = 2\arctan(e^x) + \ln(\cosh x) + C$$

In examples 12 and 13 you met the integrals $\frac{1}{2}\int \dfrac{2x}{1+x^2}\,dx$ and $\int \dfrac{\cosh x}{1+\sinh x}\,dx$. These are known as 'a function and its derivative'. After practice, you will find that you can write down the answers $\frac{1}{2}\ln|1+x^2|$ and $\ln|1+\sinh x|$ without any working. When you have sufficient confidence, you should do this and mentally check by using differentiation of your answer.

Example 14

The diagram shows the curve C given by

$$x = \cosh t, \quad y = \sinh t, \quad t \geqslant 0$$

where t is a parameter.

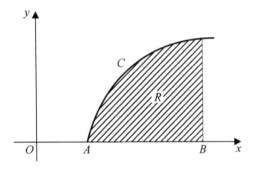

The finite region R is bounded by part of C, the x-axis and the line $x = \cosh 2$. At A, $t = 0$ and at B, $t = 2$. Find the area of R and the volume generated when R is rotated through $360°$ about the x-axis.

$$\text{Area of } R = \int y\,dx = \int_0^2 y\,\frac{dx}{dt}\,dt$$

So:
$$\text{Area of } R = \int_0^2 (\sinh t)(\sinh t)\,dt = \int_0^2 \sinh^2 t\,dt$$

The identity $\cosh 2t \equiv 2\sinh^2 t + 1$ is used to replace $\sinh^2 t$ by $\frac{1}{2}(\cosh 2t - 1)$.

Then: area of $R = \frac{1}{2}\int_0^2 (\cosh 2t - 1)\, dt$

$$= \left[\frac{1}{4}\sinh 2t - \frac{1}{2}t \right]_0^2$$
$$= \frac{1}{4}\sinh 4 - 1 \approx 5.82 \text{ (3 significant figures)}$$

Volume generated $= \pi \int y^2 \, dx = \pi \int_0^2 y^2 \frac{dx}{dt}\, dt$

$$= \pi \int_0^2 \sinh^2 t \sinh t \, dt$$

The identity $\cosh^2 t - \sinh^2 t \equiv 1$ is used to replace $\sinh^2 t$ by $\cosh^2 t - 1$.

Then: volume generated $= \pi \int_0^2 (\cosh^2 t - 1)\sinh t \, dt$

$$= \pi \int_0^2 \cosh^2 t \sinh t \, dt - \pi \int_0^2 \sinh t \, dt$$
$$= \pi \left[\frac{1}{3}\cosh^3 t \right]_0^2 - \pi \left[\cosh t \right]_0^2$$
$$= \pi \left[\frac{1}{3}\cosh^3 2 - \frac{1}{3} \right] - \pi \left[\cosh 2 - 1 \right]$$
$$= \frac{\pi}{3}\left[\cosh^3 2 + 2 - 3\cosh 2 \right]$$
$$\approx 46.0 \text{ (3 s.f.)}$$

Example 15

Given that $\tan \dfrac{x}{2} = t$, show that

(a) $\sin x = \dfrac{2t}{1 + t^2}$ and $\cos x = \dfrac{1 - t^2}{1 + t^2}$ (b) $\dfrac{dx}{dt} = \dfrac{2}{1 + t^2}$.

Hence find (c) $\displaystyle\int \operatorname{cosec} x \, dx$ (d) $\displaystyle\int \frac{1}{5 + 3\cos x}\, dx$.

(a)
$$\frac{2t}{1 + t^2} = \frac{2\tan \dfrac{x}{2}}{1 + \tan^2 \dfrac{x}{2}}$$

$$= \frac{\left(2\tan \dfrac{x}{2} \right) \cos^2 \dfrac{x}{2}}{\left(1 + \tan^2 \dfrac{x}{2} \right) \cos^2 \dfrac{x}{2}}$$

$$= \frac{2\sin \dfrac{x}{2}\cos \dfrac{x}{2}}{\cos^2 \dfrac{x}{2} + \sin^2 \dfrac{x}{2}}$$

$$= 2\sin \frac{x}{2}\cos \frac{x}{2} = \sin x$$

$$\frac{1-t^2}{1+t^2} = \frac{1-\tan^2\frac{x}{2}}{1+\tan^2\frac{x}{2}} = \frac{\left(1-\tan^2\frac{x}{2}\right)\cos^2\frac{x}{2}}{\left(1+\tan^2\frac{x}{2}\right)\cos^2\frac{x}{2}}$$

$$= \frac{\cos^2\frac{x}{2} - \sin^2\frac{x}{2}}{\cos^2\frac{x}{2} + \sin^2\frac{x}{2}}$$

$$= \cos^2\frac{x}{2} - \sin^2\frac{x}{2} = \cos x$$

(Notice how the identities $\cos^2 A + \sin^2 A \equiv 1$, $\dfrac{\sin A}{\cos A} \equiv \tan A$, $\sin 2A \equiv 2\sin A\cos A$, $\cos 2A \equiv \cos^2 A - \sin^2 A$, have been used here.)

(b) Differentiate $\tan\dfrac{x}{2} = t$, with respect to x:

$$\tfrac{1}{2}\sec^2\frac{x}{2}\frac{dx}{dt} = 1$$

But $\sec^2\dfrac{x}{2} \equiv 1 + \tan^2\dfrac{x}{2} = 1 + t^2 \Rightarrow \tfrac{1}{2}(1+t^2)\dfrac{dx}{dt} = 1$

So:

$$\frac{dx}{dt} = \frac{2}{1+t^2}$$

(c) Using the substitutions $t = \tan\dfrac{x}{2}$, $\sin x = \dfrac{2t}{1+t^2}$ and $\dfrac{dx}{dt} = \dfrac{2}{1+t^2}$ you have:

$$\int \operatorname{cosec} x \, dx = \int \frac{1}{\sin x}\frac{dx}{dt}\,dt$$

$$= \int \left(\frac{1+t^2}{2t}\right)\left(\frac{2}{1+t^2}\right)dt$$

$$= \int \frac{1}{t}\,dt$$

$$= \ln|t| + C$$

$$= \ln\left|\tan\frac{x}{2}\right| + C$$

(d) Using the substitutions $t = \tan\dfrac{x}{2}$, $\cos x = \dfrac{1-t^2}{1+t^2}$ and $\dfrac{dx}{dt} = \dfrac{2}{1+t^2}$

you have:

$$\int \frac{1}{5+3\cos x}\, dx = \int \left(\frac{1}{5 + \dfrac{3-3t^2}{1+t^2}}\right) \frac{dx}{dt}\, dt$$

$$= \int \left(\frac{1}{\dfrac{5+5t^2+3-3t^2}{1+t^2}}\right)\left(\frac{2}{1+t^2}\right) dt$$

$$= \int \left(\frac{1+t^2}{8+2t^2}\right)\left(\frac{2}{1+t^2}\right) dt$$

$$= \int \frac{1}{4+t^2}\, dt$$

$$= \tfrac{1}{2}\arctan\frac{t}{2} + C$$

$$= \tfrac{1}{2}\arctan\left(\tfrac{1}{2}\tan\frac{x}{2}\right) + C$$

Exercise 5C

In questions 1–50 integrate the given expressions with respect to x:

1 $\dfrac{1}{49+x^2}$ **2** $\dfrac{x}{4+x^2}$ **3** $\dfrac{1}{(x+3)^2}$

4 $\dfrac{1}{\sqrt{(5-2x^2)}}$ **5** $\dfrac{1}{1-4x^2}$ **6** $\dfrac{1}{\sqrt{(2x^2-5)}}$

7 $\dfrac{1}{2x^2+5}$ **8** $x(x-3)^4$ **9** $\sin^3 2x$

10 $\dfrac{x}{\sqrt{(x-2)}}$ **11** $\tan^2 2x$ **12** $e^x \cos 2x$

13 $\sqrt{x}\,e^{\sqrt{x}}$ **14** $\dfrac{e^{\sqrt{x}}}{\sqrt{x}}$ **15** $\dfrac{3-2x}{(3-x)^2}$

16 $\dfrac{1}{5x^2+13x-6}$ **17** $\dfrac{1}{\sqrt{(2-8x^2)}}$ **18** $\dfrac{1}{1+5x^2}$

19 $\dfrac{1}{\sqrt{(1+5x^2)}}$ **20** $\dfrac{1}{\sqrt{(4x^2-3)}}$ **21** $\dfrac{1}{x^2+4x+8}$

22 $\dfrac{1}{\sqrt{(35+4x-4x^2)}}$ **23** $\tanh 5x$ **24** $\tanh^2 5x$

25 $x^2 \ln x$

26 $(1 + \cos x)^2$

27 $\dfrac{\sin x}{(1 + \cos x)^2}$

28 $\dfrac{x + 4}{x - 4}$

29 $\dfrac{1}{e^x + 1}$

30 $e^{\sin x} \cos x$

31 $\sec^2 x \ln(\tan x)$

32 $\dfrac{x}{\sqrt{(1 + x)}}$

33 $\dfrac{2x + 1}{x^2 - 9}$

34 $\dfrac{x^2}{9x^2 + 1}$

35 $x \cos 5x$

36 $x^2 \sqrt{(1 - x^3)}$

37 $\operatorname{arsinh} \dfrac{x}{2}$

38 $\arctan 3x$

39 $e^x \cos x$

40 $\cosh^3 x$

41 $\cos^4 x$

42 $\dfrac{1}{9x^2 + 12x + 20}$

43 $\dfrac{1}{\sqrt{(9x^2 + 12x)}}$

44 $\sin^3 \dfrac{x}{2}$

45 $x \cosh x$

46 $\dfrac{x}{(2x^2 + 5)^3}$

47 $\coth \dfrac{3x}{2}$

48 $\operatorname{cosech} \dfrac{x}{3}$

49 $\tan^4 x$

50 $\operatorname{cosec}^4 2x$

In questions 51–60, evaluate the given definite integrals, giving answers exactly or to 3 significant figures, as appropriate.

51 $\displaystyle\int_0^{\sqrt{3}} \dfrac{1}{x^2 + 9}\, dx$

52 $\displaystyle\int_0^1 \cosh^2 x\, dx$

53 $\displaystyle\int_{\frac{\pi}{12}}^{\frac{\pi}{2}} \cos^2 x\, dx$

54 $\displaystyle\int_0^1 \arctan x\, dx$

55 $\displaystyle\int_1^8 \dfrac{1}{(x^2 - 2x + 2)^{\frac{1}{2}}}\, dx$

56 $\displaystyle\int_1^{1.5} \dfrac{1}{\sqrt{(2x - x^2)}}\, dx$

57 $\displaystyle\int_0^{\frac{\pi}{4}} (\sin x + \cos x)^2\, dx$

58 $\displaystyle\int_3^6 \dfrac{x}{\sqrt{(x - 2)}}\, dx$

59 $\displaystyle\int_2^4 \dfrac{1}{x^2 + 6x + 8}\, dx$

60 $\displaystyle\int_0^2 \dfrac{1}{\sqrt{(x^2 + 6x + 8)}}\, dx$

61 Use the substitution $u = \dfrac{1}{x}$ to evaluate $\displaystyle\int_{\frac{2}{\sqrt{3}}}^2 \dfrac{1}{x\sqrt{(x^2 - 1)}}\, dx$.

62 By differentiating $\dfrac{x^{\frac{1}{2}}}{x - 2}$, find the value of $\displaystyle\int_3^4 \dfrac{x + 2}{x^{\frac{1}{2}}(x - 2)^2}\, dx$.

63 Evaluate $\displaystyle\int_1^{\sqrt{3}}\left(\frac{1+x}{1+x^2}\right)dx$.

64 (a) Show that $\displaystyle\int_0^{\frac{\pi}{2}}\sin^2 x\,dx = \frac{\pi}{4}$.

    (b) Evaluate $\displaystyle\int_0^{\frac{\pi}{2}} x\sin^2 x\,dx$, giving your answer in terms of π.

65 Using the substitution $u^2 = 1 + x^2$, find $\displaystyle\int x^3\sqrt{(1+x^2)}\,dx$.

66 Use the substitution $x = 2\sin t$ to show that

$$\int_1^{\sqrt{3}}\frac{x+3}{\sqrt{(4-x^2)}}\,dx = \tfrac{\pi}{2} + \sqrt{3} - 1$$

67 Use the substitution $\tan x = t$ to evaluate $\displaystyle\int_{\frac{\pi}{4}}^{\frac{\pi}{3}}\operatorname{cosec} 2x\,dx$.

68 Find $\displaystyle\int\frac{x^n}{\sqrt{(x^2+1)}}\,dx$ in the cases when

    (a) $n = 0$ (b) $n = 1$ (c) $n = 2$.

69 Show that

$$\int(1-x^2)^{\frac{1}{2}}\,dx = \tfrac{1}{2}[\arcsin x + x\sqrt{(1-x^2)}] + C$$

    (a) by using differentiation
    (b) by using the substitution $x = \sin t$.

70 Show that

$$\int_0^1\left[\frac{7x-x^2}{(2-x)(x^2+1)}\right]dx = \tfrac{7}{2}\ln 2 - \tfrac{\pi}{4}$$

71 Show that $\displaystyle\int_1^2 x\ln x\,dx = \ln 4 - \tfrac{3}{4}$

72 The curve with equation $a^2y^2 = x^2(a^2 - x^2)$ has two loops, as shown.

Show, by integration, that the area enclosed by a loop is $\tfrac{2}{3}a^2$.

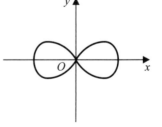

73 Show that $\displaystyle\int_{\frac{\pi}{3}}^{\frac{\pi}{2}}\sin x\left(\frac{1+\cos x}{1-\cos x}\right)dx = \ln 4 - \tfrac{1}{2}$.

74 Show that $\displaystyle\int_0^{\ln 2}\cosh^4 x\,dx = \tfrac{3}{8}\ln 2 + \tfrac{735}{1024}$.

75 Show that $\displaystyle\int_3^8\frac{(x+1)^{\frac{1}{2}}}{x+5}\,dx = \pi + 2 - 4\arctan\tfrac{3}{2}$.

76 Show that $\displaystyle\int_0^3 \operatorname{arsinh} x \, dx = 3 \operatorname{arsinh} 3 + 1 - \sqrt{10}$.

77 Use the substitution $x = \sin t$ to show that
$$\int_0^1 \frac{1}{x + \sqrt{(1 - x^2)}} \, dx = \frac{\pi}{4}.$$

78 Use the substitution $\tan \dfrac{x}{2} = t$ to integrate

(a) $\dfrac{1}{3 + 5 \cos x}$ (b) $\dfrac{1}{5 - 3 \cos x}$

SUMMARY OF KEY POINTS

1 Standard forms (to be memorised):

$$\int x^n \, dx = \frac{1}{n + 1} x^{n+1} + C \quad (n \neq -1)$$

$$\int x^{-1} \, dx = \ln |x| + C$$

$$\int e^{ax+b} \, dx = \frac{1}{a} e^{ax+b} + C$$

$$\int (ax + b)^{-1} \, dx = \frac{1}{a} \ln |ax + b| + C$$

$$\int \sin(ax + b) \, dx = -\frac{1}{a} \cos(ax + b) + C$$

$$\int \cos(ax + b) \, dx = \frac{1}{a} \sin(ax + b) + C$$

$$\int \tan(ax + b) \, dx = \frac{1}{a} \ln |\sec(ax + b)| + C$$

$$\int \cot(ax + b) \, dx = \frac{1}{a} \ln |\sin(ax + b)| + C$$

$$\int \operatorname{cosec} x \, dx = \ln \left| \tan \frac{x}{2} \right| + C$$

$$\int \sec x \, dx = \ln |\sec x + \tan x| + C$$

$$\int \ln x \, dx = x(\ln x - 1) + C$$

$$\int \sinh(ax + b) \, dx = \frac{1}{a} \cosh(ax + b) + C$$

$$\int \cosh(ax + b) \, dx = \frac{1}{a} \sinh(ax + b) + C$$

$$\int \tanh(ax + b) \, dx = \frac{1}{a} \ln |\cosh(ax + b)| + C$$

$$\int \coth(ax + b) \, dx = \frac{1}{a} \ln |\sinh(ax + b)| + C$$

$$\int \operatorname{cosech} x \, dx = \ln \left| \tanh \frac{x}{2} \right| + C$$

$$\int \operatorname{sech} x \, dx = 2 \arctan e^x + C \ (\text{or} \ \arctan(\sinh x) + C')$$

$$\int \frac{1}{a^2 + x^2} \, dx = \frac{1}{a} \arctan \frac{x}{a} + C$$

$$\int \frac{1}{\sqrt{(a^2 - x^2)}} \, dx = \arcsin \frac{x}{a} + C, \quad (|x| < a)$$

$$\int \frac{1}{\sqrt{(a^2 + x^2)}} \, dx = \operatorname{arsinh} \frac{x}{a} + C$$

$$(\text{or} \ \ln[x + \sqrt{(x^2 + a^2)}] + C)$$

$$\int \frac{1}{\sqrt{(x^2 - a^2)}} \, dx = \operatorname{arcosh} \frac{x}{a} + C, \quad (0 > x > a)$$

$$(\text{or} \ \ln[x + \sqrt{(x^2 - a^2)}] + C)$$

$$\int \frac{1}{x^2 - a^2} \, dx = \frac{1}{2a} \ln \left| \frac{x - a}{x + a} \right| + C, \quad |x| > a$$

$$\int \frac{1}{a^2 - x^2} \, dx = \frac{1}{2a} \ln \left| \frac{a + x}{a - x} \right| + C, \quad |x| < a$$

2   Integrations of sums and differences:

$$\int (u \pm v)\, \mathrm{d}x = \int u\, \mathrm{d}x \pm \int v\, \mathrm{d}x$$

3   Integration by parts:

$$\int v\, \frac{\mathrm{d}u}{\mathrm{d}x}\, \mathrm{d}x = uv - \int u\, \frac{\mathrm{d}v}{\mathrm{d}x}\, \mathrm{d}x$$

4   Integration by substitution, $x = \mathrm{g}(t)$:

$$\int \mathrm{f}(x)\, \mathrm{d}x = \int \mathrm{f}[\mathrm{g}(t)]\, \frac{\mathrm{d}x}{\mathrm{d}t}\, \mathrm{d}t$$

$$= \int \mathrm{f}\mathrm{g}(t)\mathrm{g}'(t)\, \mathrm{d}t$$

5

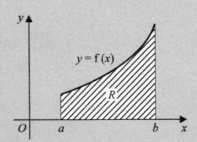

$$\text{Area of } R = \int_a^b \mathrm{f}(x)\, \mathrm{d}x$$

Volume generated when R is rotated completely about the x-axis is

$$\pi \int_a^b [\mathrm{f}(x)]^2\, \mathrm{d}x$$

Vectors

6

(a) The distance between P and Q is 200 m.

(b) The volume of the prism is 65 cm^3.

(c) The time taken to run round the block was 184 s.

(d) A man walks 2 km on a bearing of 062°.

(e) A horizontal force of 3 N was applied at right angles to the length of the book.

(f) The velocity of the aeroplane is 800 km h^{-1} on a bearing 158°.

These six sentences give examples of everyday quantities. The first three (distance, volume, time) are called **scalar** quantities and they only need a single number or *scalar* (200 m, 65 cm^3, 184 s) to specify them precisely.

However in (d), (e) and (f) the quantities need both a magnitude (2 km, 3 N, 800 km h^{-1}) *and* a direction to specify them precisely. These are examples of **vector** quantities.

■ **A vector is a quantity that has both magnitude and a direction in space.**

6.1 Some definitions

Directed line segment

A vector can be represented by a **directed line segment** whose direction is that of the vector and whose length represents the magnitude of the vector.

For example, this directed line segment represents the vector $\overrightarrow{AB}$ where the arrow on the diagram represents the *direction* from A to B and the length of the line AB represents the *magnitude* of the vector.

Such a vector can be written as $\overrightarrow{AB}$ where A and B are the endpoints of the directed line segment and the arrow above the letters indicates the direction of the vector. Alternatively, the vector is often denoted by a single lower case bold letter, for example, **p**.

When you need to use this alternative notation you should write the vector in *lower case* and *underline* it (i.e. p̲) since you will not be able to write it in bold print.

Displacement vector

A displacement is one of the most common types of vector. For example, a journey from P to Q of 90 km north east is a movement or displacement. You can write it as $\overrightarrow{PQ}$.

If the journey from P to Q is followed by a further journey from Q to R of 65 km south east, then the overall displacement is from P to R. The combination of the journey (displacement) from P to Q and the journey from Q to R results in the overall displacement of P to R:

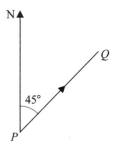

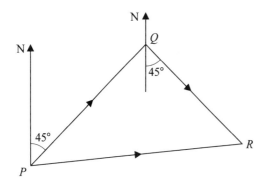

This is written as

$$\overrightarrow{PQ} + \overrightarrow{QR} = \overrightarrow{PR}$$

That is, the sum (or **resultant**) of the displacements $\overrightarrow{PQ}$ and $\overrightarrow{QR}$ is $\overrightarrow{PR}$.

Notice that if you want to add displacements, the end-point of one displacement vector must be the starting point of the next displacement vector. That is, $\overrightarrow{AC} + \overrightarrow{CQ} + \overrightarrow{QR} + \overrightarrow{RX} = \overrightarrow{AX}$, but $\overrightarrow{AB} + \overrightarrow{BE} + \overrightarrow{FH}$ can only be simplified to $\overrightarrow{AE} + \overrightarrow{FH}$ because the finishing point of the displacement $\overrightarrow{AE}$ is E and the starting point of the displacement $\overrightarrow{FH}$ is F, and these points are not the same.

Modulus of a vector

The **modulus** of a vector is its magnitude. The modulus of the vector $\overrightarrow{PQ}$ is written $|\overrightarrow{PQ}|$. The modulus of the vector **a** is written $|a|$ or a.

If $\overrightarrow{PQ}$ is a velocity of $200\,\text{km}\,\text{h}^{-1}$ north east, then

$$|\overrightarrow{PQ}| = 200\,\text{km}\,\text{h}^{-1}.$$

Equality of vectors

Two vectors are said to be equal if they have both the same magnitude and direction.

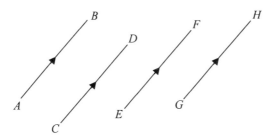

The four vectors $\overrightarrow{AB}$, $\overrightarrow{CD}$, $\overrightarrow{EF}$ and $\overrightarrow{GH}$ are each parallel to the others and all have the same magnitude. So the directed line segments used to represent them are parallel and of the same length. You can therefore write: $\overrightarrow{AB} = \overrightarrow{CD} = \overrightarrow{EF} = \overrightarrow{GH}$.

The zero vector

The **zero vector**, written **0**, has zero magnitude and indeterminate direction. Since the displacement vector $\overrightarrow{PQ}$ goes from P to Q and the displacement vector $\overrightarrow{QP}$ goes from Q to P you can write $\overrightarrow{PQ} + \overrightarrow{QP} = \mathbf{0}$, because a displacement from P to Q followed by a displacement from Q to P takes you back to where you started and so there is no overall displacement.

Negative vector

Since $\overrightarrow{PQ} + \overrightarrow{QP} = \mathbf{0}$, you can write $\overrightarrow{QP} = -\overrightarrow{PQ}$. That is, $\overrightarrow{QP}$ is the negative of the vector $\overrightarrow{PQ}$.

So the vector $\overrightarrow{QP}$ has the same magnitude as the vector $\overrightarrow{PQ}$ but its direction is exactly opposite to that of $\overrightarrow{PQ}$.

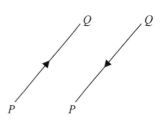

Example 1
Simplify: (a) $\overrightarrow{AB} + \overrightarrow{BC} - \overrightarrow{DC}$ (b) $\overrightarrow{AC} - \overrightarrow{BC} + \overrightarrow{BD}$.

(a)
$$\overrightarrow{AB} + \overrightarrow{BC} - \overrightarrow{DC} = \overrightarrow{AC} - \overrightarrow{DC}$$
$$= \overrightarrow{AC} + \overrightarrow{CD}$$
$$= \overrightarrow{AD}$$

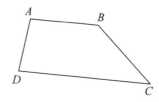

(b)
$$\overrightarrow{AC} - \overrightarrow{BC} + \overrightarrow{BD} = \overrightarrow{AC} + \overrightarrow{CB} + \overrightarrow{BD}$$
$$= \overrightarrow{AB} + \overrightarrow{BD}$$
$$= \overrightarrow{AD}$$

Example 2

If $\overrightarrow{AB} = \mathbf{a}$, $\overrightarrow{AC} = \mathbf{b}$ and $\overrightarrow{DC} = \mathbf{c}$, find, in terms of $\mathbf{a}$, $\mathbf{b}$ and $\mathbf{c}$:
(a) $\overrightarrow{BC}$ (b) $\overrightarrow{BD}$ (c) $\overrightarrow{AD}$.

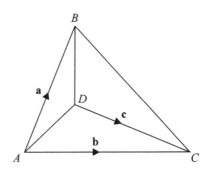

(a)
$$\overrightarrow{BC} = \overrightarrow{BA} + \overrightarrow{AC}$$
$$= -\overrightarrow{AB} + \overrightarrow{AC}$$
$$= -\mathbf{a} + \mathbf{b}$$

(b)
$$\overrightarrow{BD} = \overrightarrow{BC} + \overrightarrow{CD}$$
$$= \overrightarrow{BC} - \overrightarrow{DC}$$
$$= (-\mathbf{a} + \mathbf{b}) - \mathbf{c}$$
$$= -\mathbf{a} + \mathbf{b} - \mathbf{c}$$

(c)
$$\overrightarrow{AD} = \overrightarrow{AC} + \overrightarrow{CD}$$
$$= \overrightarrow{AC} - \overrightarrow{DC}$$
$$= \mathbf{b} - \mathbf{c}$$

Exercise 6A

1 Simplify:
   (a) $\overrightarrow{AB} + \overrightarrow{BC} + \overrightarrow{CF}$
   (b) $\overrightarrow{PQ} + \overrightarrow{ST} + \overrightarrow{QS} + \overrightarrow{TU}$
   (c) $\overrightarrow{LM} - \overrightarrow{PM} + \overrightarrow{QR}$
   (d) $\overrightarrow{AC} - \overrightarrow{FC} - \overrightarrow{HF}$
   (e) $\overrightarrow{PQ} + \overrightarrow{QR} + \overrightarrow{QS} + \overrightarrow{RQ}$

2 In the figure $\overrightarrow{AB} = \mathbf{p}$, $\overrightarrow{DC} = \mathbf{r}$, $\overrightarrow{DB} = \mathbf{q}$. Find, in terms of $\mathbf{p}$, $\mathbf{q}$
   and $\mathbf{r}$ expressions for
   (a) $\overrightarrow{BC}$ (b) $\overrightarrow{DA}$ (c) $\overrightarrow{AC}$.

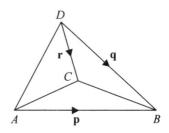

3 In the figure $\overrightarrow{EA} = \mathbf{a}$, $\overrightarrow{AB} = \mathbf{b}$, $\overrightarrow{CD} = \mathbf{c}$, $\overrightarrow{DA} = \mathbf{d}$.

Find, in terms of $\mathbf{a}$, $\mathbf{b}$, $\mathbf{c}$ and $\mathbf{d}$:

(a) $\overrightarrow{ED}$ (b) $\overrightarrow{BC}$ (c) $\overrightarrow{BE}$ (d) $\overrightarrow{DB}$.

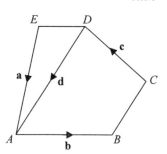

6.2 More definitions and operations on vectors

Unit vector

A **unit vector** is a vector whose magnitude (modulus) is 1.

The vector $\mathbf{a}$ has magnitude $|\mathbf{a}| = a$. So a unit vector in the same direction as $\mathbf{a}$ is $\dfrac{\mathbf{a}}{a}$.

Scalar multiplication of a vector

Scalar multiplication means multiplying a vector by a scalar, that is, a number. The result is another vector.

Vectors such as $2\mathbf{a}$, $5\mathbf{a}$, $-3\mathbf{a}$ can be defined as $2\mathbf{a} = \mathbf{a} + \mathbf{a}$, $5\mathbf{a} = \mathbf{a} + \mathbf{a} + \mathbf{a} + \mathbf{a} + \mathbf{a}$, $-3\mathbf{a} = -\mathbf{a} - \mathbf{a} - \mathbf{a}$, and so on. Now $\mathbf{a} + \mathbf{a}$ is a displacement of $\mathbf{a}$ followed by another displacement of $\mathbf{a}$. So $2\mathbf{a}$ is a vector in the same direction as $\mathbf{a}$ but which has twice the magnitude of $\mathbf{a}$. Similarly, $5\mathbf{a}$ is in the same direction as $\mathbf{a}$ but has five times its magnitude. The vector $-3\mathbf{a}$ is in the opposite direction to $\mathbf{a}$ and has three times its magnitude. (Here the scalar is -3.)

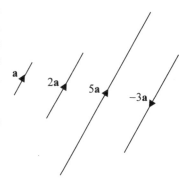

■ In general, the vector $\lambda\mathbf{a}$, where $\lambda > 0$, is in the same direction as $\mathbf{a}$ but its magnitude is λ times that of $\mathbf{a}$.

Parallel vectors

From the above you should be able to see that if two vectors $\mathbf{a}$ and $\mathbf{b}$ are parallel then one is a scalar multiple of the other, that is: $\mathbf{a} = \lambda\mathbf{b}$.

If λ is positive then $\mathbf{a}$ is in the same direction as $\mathbf{b}$. If λ is negative then $\mathbf{a}$ is in the opposite direction to $\mathbf{b}$.

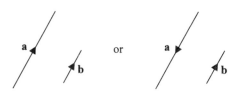

Adding vectors

Vectors are added in the same way as journeys.

It is clear that a journey from *A* to *B* followed by a journey from *B* to *C* is equivalent to a journey from *A* to *C*.

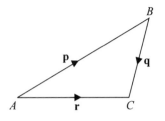

That is: $$\overrightarrow{AB} + \overrightarrow{BC} = \overrightarrow{AC}$$

or $$\mathbf{p} + \mathbf{q} = \mathbf{r}$$

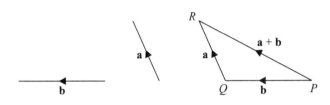

If **a** and **b** are two vectors $\overrightarrow{QR}$ and $\overrightarrow{PQ}$ then **a** + **b** is the vector $\overrightarrow{PR}$. This is known as the **triangle law** for the addition of vectors. You must be sure that when you try to add two vectors **a** and **b** by the triangle law, the arrows of the line segments representing **a** and **b** on the diagram go in the same sense round the triangle. That is, they must both go round clockwise or both go round anticlockwise. You should also notice that the arrow of the line segment representing the resultant **a** + **b** goes in the *opposite* sense to **a** and **b**.

Another way to add the two vectors is to complete a parallelogram *PQRS*, where $\overrightarrow{RQ} = \mathbf{a}$ and $\overrightarrow{RS} = \mathbf{b}$. Remember that opposite sides of a parallelogram are equal and parallel. So $\overrightarrow{SP} = \overrightarrow{RQ} = \mathbf{a}$ and $\overrightarrow{QP} = \overrightarrow{RS} = \mathbf{b}$.

By using the triangle law in triangle *PQR*, as before

$$\overrightarrow{RQ} + \overrightarrow{QP} = \overrightarrow{RP}$$

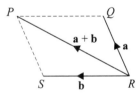

that is: $$\overrightarrow{RQ} + \overrightarrow{RS} = \overrightarrow{RP}$$

This is sometimes called the **parallelogram law** of addition.

When you use the parallelogram law of addition to add two vectors $\overrightarrow{RQ}$ and $\overrightarrow{RS}$ you should note that it is the *diagonal* $\overrightarrow{RP}$ of the parallelogram that represents the vector **a** + **b**.

The commutative law

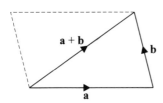 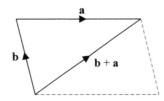

From the left-hand diagram you can see that the diagonal of the parallelogram represents $\mathbf{a} + \mathbf{b}$. From the right-hand diagram you can see that the diagonal represents $\mathbf{b} + \mathbf{a}$. But the vectors $\mathbf{a} + \mathbf{b}$ and $\mathbf{b} + \mathbf{a}$ are parallel and of equal magnitude. That is, they are equal.

■ So: $$\mathbf{a} + \mathbf{b} = \mathbf{b} + \mathbf{a}$$

That is, *it does not matter which way round you add two vectors.*

This is known as the **commutative law**.

The associative law

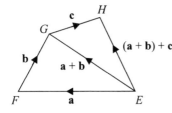 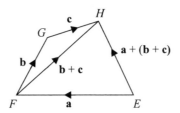

In the left-hand diagram, from $\triangle EFG$:

$$\overrightarrow{EG} = \mathbf{a} + \mathbf{b}$$

From $\triangle EGH$: $$\overrightarrow{EH} = (\mathbf{a} + \mathbf{b}) + \mathbf{c}$$

In the right-hand diagram, from $\triangle FGH$:

$$\overrightarrow{FH} = \mathbf{b} + \mathbf{c}$$

From $\triangle EFH$: $$\overrightarrow{EH} = \mathbf{a} + (\mathbf{b} + \mathbf{c})$$

■ So: $$(\mathbf{a} + \mathbf{b}) + \mathbf{c} = \mathbf{a} + (\mathbf{b} + \mathbf{c})$$

That is, *it does not matter in which order you add vectors.*

This is known as the **associative law**.

Subtracting vectors

If, once again, $\overrightarrow{RQ} = \mathbf{a}$ and $\overrightarrow{RS} = \mathbf{b}$ then:

$$\overrightarrow{SQ} = \overrightarrow{SR} + \overrightarrow{RQ}$$

But

$$\overrightarrow{SR} = -\overrightarrow{RS} = -\mathbf{b}$$

So

$$\overrightarrow{SQ} = -\mathbf{b} + \mathbf{a}$$

or:

$$\overrightarrow{SQ} = \mathbf{a} - \mathbf{b}$$

So the diagonal $\overrightarrow{SQ}$ of the parallelogram represents the vector $\mathbf{a} - \mathbf{b}$.

Non-parallel vectors

If $\mathbf{a}$ and $\mathbf{b}$ are *not* parallel and $\lambda\mathbf{a} + \mu\mathbf{b} = \alpha\mathbf{a} + \beta\mathbf{b}$, where λ, μ, α, β are scalars, then:

$$\lambda\mathbf{a} - \alpha\mathbf{a} = \beta\mathbf{b} - \mu\mathbf{b}$$

that is:

$$(\lambda - \alpha)\mathbf{a} = (\beta - \mu)\mathbf{b}$$

Since $\mathbf{a}$ and $\mathbf{b}$ are not parallel then $(\lambda - \alpha)$ cannot be a scalar multiple of $(\beta - \mu)$. So the only way they can be equal is if $\lambda - \alpha = 0$ and $\beta - \mu = 0$.

That is:

$$\lambda = \alpha \quad \text{and} \quad \beta = \mu$$

■ $\lambda\mathbf{a} + \mu\mathbf{b} = \alpha\mathbf{a} + \beta\mathbf{b}$ where $\mathbf{a}$ and $\mathbf{b}$ are non-parallel $\Rightarrow \lambda = \alpha$ and $\mu = \beta$.

Example 3

$ABCD$ is a trapezium with AB parallel to DC.

$\overrightarrow{DA} = \mathbf{a}$, $\overrightarrow{AB} = 2\mathbf{b}$, $\overrightarrow{DM} = \overrightarrow{AB}$.

The point M is such that $DM : MC = 2 : 1$ and N is the mid-point of BC. Find, in terms of $\mathbf{a}$ or $\mathbf{b}$ or both $\mathbf{a}$ and $\mathbf{b}$,

(a) $\overrightarrow{DC}$ (b) $\overrightarrow{AM}$ (c) $\overrightarrow{BC}$ (d) $\overrightarrow{MN}$.

(a)

$$\overrightarrow{DM} = \overrightarrow{AB} = 2\mathbf{b}$$

$$DM : MC = 2 : 1$$

Thus:

$$\overrightarrow{MC} = \mathbf{b} \quad \text{and} \quad \overrightarrow{DC} = 3\mathbf{b}$$

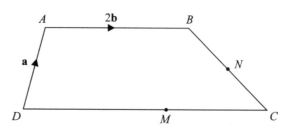

(b)
$$\overrightarrow{AM} = \overrightarrow{AD} + \overrightarrow{DM} = -\mathbf{a}+2\mathbf{b}$$

(c)
$$\overrightarrow{BC} = \overrightarrow{BA} + \overrightarrow{AD} + \overrightarrow{DC}$$
$$= -\overrightarrow{AB} - \overrightarrow{DA} + \overrightarrow{DC}$$
$$= -2\mathbf{b} - \mathbf{a}+3\mathbf{b}$$
$$= \mathbf{b} - \mathbf{a}$$

(d)
$$\overrightarrow{MN} = \overrightarrow{MC} + \overrightarrow{CN} = \mathbf{b} - \overrightarrow{NC}$$

Since N is the mid-point of BC,

$$\overrightarrow{NC} = \tfrac{1}{2}(\mathbf{b} - \mathbf{a})$$

So:
$$\overrightarrow{MN} = \mathbf{b} - \tfrac{1}{2}(\mathbf{b} - \mathbf{a})$$
$$= \mathbf{b} - \tfrac{1}{2}\mathbf{b} + \tfrac{1}{2}\mathbf{a}$$
$$= \tfrac{1}{2}\mathbf{b} + \tfrac{1}{2}\mathbf{a}$$

Example 4

The vectors $\mathbf{a}$ and $\mathbf{b}$ are not parallel and

$$(\lambda - \mu)\mathbf{a} + (\mu + 1)\mathbf{b} = 7\mathbf{a} - (\lambda + 2)\mathbf{b}$$

where λ and μ are scalars. Find the value of λ and the value of μ.

Since
$$(\lambda - \mu)\mathbf{a} + (\mu + 1)\mathbf{b} = 7\mathbf{a} - (\lambda + 2)\mathbf{b}$$

and $\mathbf{a}$ and $\mathbf{b}$ are not parallel, then:

$$\lambda - \mu = 7 \qquad\qquad (1)$$

and
$$\mu + 1 = -(\lambda + 2) \qquad\qquad (2)$$

(2) can be written
$$\lambda + \mu = -3 \qquad\qquad (3)$$

So (1) $+$ (3) gives: $2\lambda = 4 \Rightarrow \lambda = 2$

Substituting in (1) gives: $2 - \mu = 7 \Rightarrow \mu = -5$

Exercise 6B

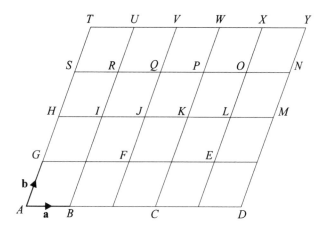

1 These two sets of lines are equally spaced and $\overrightarrow{AB} = \mathbf{a}$, $\overrightarrow{AG} = \mathbf{b}$.
   Find, in terms of $\mathbf{a}$ and $\mathbf{b}$:
   (a) $\overrightarrow{AC}$ (b) $\overrightarrow{CD}$ (c) $\overrightarrow{FV}$ (d) $\overrightarrow{YM}$ (e) $\overrightarrow{UB}$
   (f) $\overrightarrow{AF}$ (g) $\overrightarrow{IX}$ (h) $\overrightarrow{XN}$ (i) $\overrightarrow{WJ}$ (j) $\overrightarrow{AX}$
   (k) $\overrightarrow{LV}$ (l) $\overrightarrow{EU}$ (m) $\overrightarrow{DT}$

2 State which of the following vectors are parallel to $2\mathbf{a} - 5\mathbf{b}$:
   (a) $6\mathbf{a} - 15\mathbf{b}$ (b) $-2\mathbf{a} + 5\mathbf{b}$
   (c) $\mathbf{a} - 3\mathbf{b}$ (d) $-\mathbf{a} + 2\mathbf{b}$
   (e) $\frac{2}{5}\mathbf{a} - \mathbf{b}$

3 $ABCD$ is a parallelogram with $\overrightarrow{AB} = \mathbf{a}$ and $\overrightarrow{AD} = \mathbf{b}$. The point
   E is such that $\overrightarrow{DE} = 2\mathbf{b}$. Draw a sketch to illustrate this and
   express the vectors $\overrightarrow{AE}$, $\overrightarrow{AC}$ and $\overrightarrow{EC}$ in terms of $\mathbf{a}$ and $\mathbf{b}$.   [L]

4 In the triangle PQR, $\overrightarrow{PR} = \mathbf{a}$ and $\overrightarrow{PQ} = \mathbf{b}$. The point N lies on
   QR and is such that $QN : NR = 1 : 4$. Find, in terms of $\mathbf{a}$ and $\mathbf{b}$:
   (a) $\overrightarrow{QR}$ (b) $\overrightarrow{RN}$ (c) $\overrightarrow{PN}$.

5 $ABCD$ is a trapezium with BC parallel to AD. If $\overrightarrow{AB} = \mathbf{a}$,
   $\overrightarrow{BC} = \mathbf{b}$, $BC = \frac{1}{3}AD$ and E is the mid-point of BC, find, in
   terms of $\mathbf{a}$ and $\mathbf{b}$:
   (a) $\overrightarrow{CD}$ (b) $\overrightarrow{AE}$ (c) $\overrightarrow{DB}$ (d) $\overrightarrow{DE}$.

6 $ABCD$ is a parallelogram with $\overrightarrow{AB} = \mathbf{a}$ and $\overrightarrow{AD} = \mathbf{b}$. The point
   P lies on AD and is such that $AP : PD = 1 : 2$ and the point Q
   lies on BD and is such that $BQ : QD = 2 : 1$. Show that PQ is
   parallel to AC.

7 In the quadrilateral $OABC$, D is the mid-point of BC and G is the point on AD such that $AG : GD = 2 : 1$. Given that $\overrightarrow{OA} = \mathbf{a}$, $\overrightarrow{OB} = \mathbf{b}$ and $\overrightarrow{OC} = \mathbf{c}$, express $\overrightarrow{OD}$ and $\overrightarrow{OG}$ in terms of $\mathbf{a}$, $\mathbf{b}$ and $\mathbf{c}$.

[L]

8 In the regular hexagon $PQRSTU$, $\overrightarrow{PQ} = \mathbf{a}$ and $\overrightarrow{QR} = \mathbf{b}$. Find in terms of $\mathbf{a}$ and $\mathbf{b}$:

   (a) $\overrightarrow{PR}$ (b) $\overrightarrow{RS}$ (c) $\overrightarrow{RT}$ (d) $\overrightarrow{RP}$.

9 ABC is a triangle in which P and Q are the mid-points of AC and BC respectively. Prove that $\overrightarrow{BQ} + \overrightarrow{PQ} = \overrightarrow{AP}$.

10 In $\triangle OAB$, $\overrightarrow{OA} = 6\mathbf{a}$ and $\overrightarrow{OB} = 6\mathbf{b}$. The mid-point of OA is M and the point P lies on AB such that $AP : PB = 2 : 1$. The mid-point of OP is N.

   (a) Calculate, in terms of $\mathbf{a}$ and $\mathbf{b}$, the vectors $\overrightarrow{AB}$, $\overrightarrow{OP}$ and $\overrightarrow{MN}$.

   (b) Show that the area of the quadrilateral $AMNP$ is half the area of $\triangle OAB$.

   The line AN produced meets OB at C.

   (c) Given that $\overrightarrow{OC} = k\mathbf{b}$, find the value of k.   [L]

11 Find the values of λ and μ given that $\mathbf{a}$ and $\mathbf{b}$ are not parallel:

   (a) $5\mathbf{a} + \lambda\mathbf{b} = (6 - \mu)\mathbf{a} + 7\mathbf{b}$

   (b) $(8 + \lambda)\mathbf{a} + (\mu - 2)\mathbf{b} = \mathbf{0}$

   (c) $2\mathbf{a} + 3\mathbf{b} - (\lambda - 4)\mathbf{a} + (2 - \mu)\mathbf{b} = \mathbf{0}$

   (d) $(2\lambda - 3)\mathbf{a} + 7\mathbf{b} = (5 - \lambda)\mathbf{a} + (2 - \mu)\mathbf{b}$

   (e) $7\lambda\mathbf{a} + 5\lambda\mathbf{b} + 3\mu\mathbf{a} - \mu\mathbf{b} = 5\mathbf{a} + 2\mathbf{b}$

   (f) $2\lambda\mathbf{a} + 3\lambda\mathbf{b} + 3\mu\mathbf{a} - 5\mu\mathbf{b} = 21\mathbf{b} - 5\mathbf{a}$

   (g) $2\lambda\mathbf{a} + 3\mu\mathbf{b} = 7\mu\mathbf{a} + 11\lambda\mathbf{b} + 57\mathbf{a} + 6\mathbf{b}$

   (h) $\lambda\mathbf{a} + 3\lambda\mathbf{b} + \mu\mathbf{b} = 2\mu\mathbf{a} + 8\mathbf{b} + 5\mathbf{a}$

12 In the figure, $\overrightarrow{OA} = \mathbf{a}$, $\overrightarrow{OB} = \mathbf{b}$ and C divides AB in the ratio $5 : 1$.

   (a) Write down, in terms of $\mathbf{a}$ and $\mathbf{b}$, expressions for $\overrightarrow{AB}$, $\overrightarrow{AC}$ and $\overrightarrow{OC}$.

   Given that $\overrightarrow{OE} = \lambda\mathbf{b}$, where λ is a scalar,

   (b) write down, in terms of $\mathbf{a}$, $\mathbf{b}$ and λ, an expression for $\overrightarrow{CE}$.

   Given that $\overrightarrow{OD} = \mu(\mathbf{b} - \mathbf{a})$, where μ is a scalar,

   (c) write down, in terms of $\mathbf{a}$, $\mathbf{b}$, λ and μ, an expression for $\overrightarrow{ED}$.

   Given also that E is the mid-point of CD,

   (d) deduce the values of λ and μ.   [L]

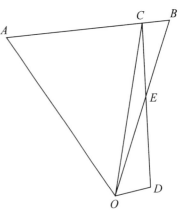

13 In the figure the points A and B are such that $\overrightarrow{OA} = \mathbf{a}$ and
   $\overrightarrow{OB} = \mathbf{b}$. The point C lies on OB and is such that
   $OC : CB = 2 : 1$. The point M is the mid-point of BC and the
   point N is the mid-point of AC.

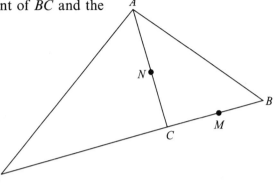

   Find, in terms of $\mathbf{a}$, $\mathbf{b}$, or $\mathbf{a}$ and $\mathbf{b}$,
   (a) $\overrightarrow{OC}$ (b) $\overrightarrow{OM}$ (c) $\overrightarrow{ON}$.
   The point X lies on AM and is
   such that $\overrightarrow{AX} = t\overrightarrow{AM}$, where $0 < t < 1$.
   (d) Find $\overrightarrow{OX}$, in terms of $\mathbf{a}$, $\mathbf{b}$ and t.
   The point Y lies on BN and is such
   that $\overrightarrow{BY} = s\overrightarrow{BN}$, where $0 < s < 1$.
   (e) Find $\overrightarrow{OY}$, in terms of $\mathbf{a}$, $\mathbf{b}$ and s.
   P is the point of intersection of AM and BN.
   (f) Find $\overrightarrow{OP}$, in terms of $\mathbf{a}$ and $\mathbf{b}$ only.
   Q is the mid-point of AB.
   (g) Show that C, P and Q are collinear and determine the ratio
       $CP : CQ$.   [L]

14 In the figure $\overrightarrow{OA} = \mathbf{a}$, $\overrightarrow{OB} = \mathbf{b}$, $\overrightarrow{OC} = 2\overrightarrow{OA}$, $\overrightarrow{OD} = 3\overrightarrow{OB}$,
   $\overrightarrow{BE} = \lambda\overrightarrow{BC}$, $\overrightarrow{DE} = \mu\overrightarrow{DA}$ and $\overrightarrow{DF} = k\overrightarrow{DC}$, where λ, μ and k are
   constants.

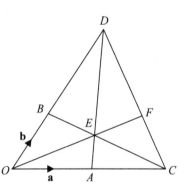

   (a) Find, in terms of $\mathbf{a}$ and $\mathbf{b}$, (i) $\overrightarrow{BC}$ (ii) $\overrightarrow{DA}$ (iii) $\overrightarrow{DC}$.
   (b) Find $\overrightarrow{OE}$, in terms of $\mathbf{a}$, $\mathbf{b}$ and λ.
   (c) Show that $\overrightarrow{OE} = \mu\mathbf{a} + (3 - 3\mu)\mathbf{b}$.
   (d) Using your answers to (b) and (c), show that
       $\overrightarrow{OE} = \frac{1}{5}(4\mathbf{a} + 3\mathbf{b})$.
   (e) Show that $\overrightarrow{OF} = 2k\mathbf{a} + (3 - 3k)\mathbf{b}$.
   (f) Using your answers to (d) and (e), find $\overrightarrow{OF}$, in terms of $\mathbf{a}$
       and $\mathbf{b}$ only.   [L]

15 In the figure $\overrightarrow{OA} = \mathbf{a}$, $\overrightarrow{OB} = \mathbf{b}$, $3\overrightarrow{OC} = 2\overrightarrow{OA}$ and $4\overrightarrow{OD} = 7\overrightarrow{OB}$.
   The line DC meets the line AB at E.

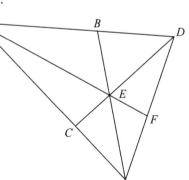

   (a) Write down, in terms of $\mathbf{a}$ and $\mathbf{b}$, expressions for
       (i) $\overrightarrow{AB}$ and (ii) $\overrightarrow{DC}$.
   Given that $\overrightarrow{DE} = \lambda\overrightarrow{DC}$ and $\overrightarrow{EB} = \mu\overrightarrow{AB}$ where λ and μ are
   constants
   (b) use $\triangle EBD$ to form an equation relating $\mathbf{a}$, $\mathbf{b}$, λ and μ.
   Hence
   (c) show that $\lambda = \frac{9}{13}$

(d) find the exact value of μ

(e) express $\overrightarrow{OE}$ in terms of **a** and **b**.

The line OE produced meets the line AD at F.

Given that $\overrightarrow{OF} = k\overrightarrow{OE}$ where k is a constant and that $\overrightarrow{AF} = \frac{1}{10}(7\mathbf{b} - 4\mathbf{a})$

(f) find the value of k. [L]

16 In $\triangle OAB$, P is the mid-point of AB and Q is the point on OP such that $OQ = \frac{3}{4}OP$. Given that $\overrightarrow{OA} = \mathbf{a}$ and $\overrightarrow{OB} = \mathbf{b}$, find, in terms of **a** and **b**

(a) $\overrightarrow{AB}$ (b) $\overrightarrow{OP}$ (c) $\overrightarrow{OQ}$ (d) $\overrightarrow{AQ}$.

The point R on OB is such that $OR = kOB$, where $0 < k < 1$.

(e) Find, in terms of **a**, **b** and k, the vector $\overrightarrow{AR}$.

Given that AQR is a straight line

(f) find the ratio in which Q divides AR and the value of k.

[L]

17 In the figure the points A and B are such that $\overrightarrow{OA} = \mathbf{a}$ and $\overrightarrow{OB} = \mathbf{b}$. The point M is the mid-point of OA. The point X is on OB such that X divides OB in the ratio $3 : 1$ and the point Y is on AX such that Y divides AX in the ratio $4 : 1$.

(a) Write down in terms of **a**, **b**, or **a** and **b**, expressions for $\overrightarrow{OM}$, $\overrightarrow{OX}$ and $\overrightarrow{OY}$.

(b) Show that $\overrightarrow{BY} = \frac{1}{5}(\mathbf{a} - 2\mathbf{b})$.

(c) Deduce that B, Y and M are collinear.

(d) Calculate the ratio $BY : YM$. [L]

18 In the figure $OE : EA = 1 : 2$, $AF : FB = 3 : 1$ and $OG : OB = 3 : 1$. The vector $\overrightarrow{OA} = \mathbf{a}$ and the vector $\overrightarrow{OB} = \mathbf{b}$.

Find, in terms of **a**, **b** or **a** and **b**, expressions for

(a) $\overrightarrow{OE}$ (b) $\overrightarrow{OF}$ (c) $\overrightarrow{EF}$ (d) $\overrightarrow{BG}$ (e) $\overrightarrow{FB}$ (f) $\overrightarrow{FG}$.

(g) Use your results in (c) and (f) to show that the points E, F and G are collinear and find the ratio $EF : FG$.

(h) Find $\overrightarrow{EB}$ and $\overrightarrow{AG}$ and hence prove that EB is parallel to AG.

[L]

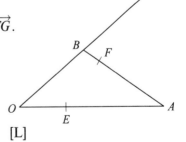

19 In the figure, $\overrightarrow{OA} = 5\mathbf{a}$, $\overrightarrow{AB} = 3\mathbf{b}$, $\overrightarrow{OC} = \frac{3}{2}\overrightarrow{OB}$ and $\overrightarrow{OD} = \frac{3}{5}\overrightarrow{OA}$.

The line DC meets AB at F.

(a) Write down, in terms of $\mathbf{a}$ and $\mathbf{b}$, expressions for $\overrightarrow{OB}$, $\overrightarrow{OC}$ and $\overrightarrow{DC}$.

Given that $\overrightarrow{DF} = \lambda(\mathbf{a} + \mathbf{b})$ and $\overrightarrow{AF} = \mu\mathbf{b}$

(b) use the triangle ADF to form an equation relating to $\mathbf{a}$, $\mathbf{b}$, λ and μ.

(c) Use your equation from part (b) to find the values of λ and μ.

(d) Deduce the ratios

  (i) $AF : FB$ (ii) $DF : FC$.

A line is drawn through F parallel to AO to meet OB at G.

(e) Write down an expression, in terms of $\mathbf{a}$ and $\mathbf{b}$, for $\overrightarrow{OG}$.

[L]

20

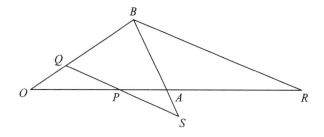

In the figure, $\overrightarrow{OA} = \mathbf{a}$ and $\overrightarrow{OB} = \mathbf{b}$. The points P and Q lie on OA and OB respectively, so that $OP : PA = 2 : 1$ and $OQ : QB = 1 : 2$.

(a) Find, in terms of $\mathbf{a}$, $\mathbf{b}$ or $\mathbf{a}$ and $\mathbf{b}$, the vectors

  (i) $\overrightarrow{OP}$ (ii) $\overrightarrow{OQ}$ (iii) $\overrightarrow{PQ}$.

The point R is such that $OR : AR = 2 : 1$.

(b) Find, in terms of $\mathbf{a}$ and $\mathbf{b}$, the vector $\overrightarrow{RB}$.

(c) Show that RB is parallel to PQ and find the ratio $RB : PQ$.

The line segment QP is produced to a point S so that $QP = PS$.

(d) Find, in terms of $\mathbf{a}$ and $\mathbf{b}$, the vectors $\overrightarrow{PS}$ and $\overrightarrow{AS}$.

(e) Show that the points B, A and S are collinear.   [L]

6.3 Position vectors

If you have a fixed origin O and a point A, then the vector $\overrightarrow{OA}$ is defined to be the **position vector** of the point A. The line segment representing $\overrightarrow{OA}$ starts at O and ends at A, so the vector $\overrightarrow{OA}$ uniquely defines the position of A.

Suppose you have two points A and B. The position vector of A is $\overrightarrow{OA} = \mathbf{a}$. The position vector of B is $\overrightarrow{OB} = \mathbf{b}$. From the vector triangle, you can see that the vector $\overrightarrow{AB}$ is $\mathbf{b} - \mathbf{a}$. Likewise, the vector $\overrightarrow{BA}$ is $\mathbf{a} - \mathbf{b}$.

Position vector of the mid-point of a line

Let the position vector of a point A be $\mathbf{a}$ (that is, $\overrightarrow{OA} = \mathbf{a}$).

Let the position vector of B be $\mathbf{b}$.

Let M be the mid-point of AB.

Then:
$$\overrightarrow{BA} = \mathbf{a} - \mathbf{b}$$

So:
$$\overrightarrow{OM} = \overrightarrow{OB} + \overrightarrow{BM}$$
$$= \overrightarrow{OB} + \tfrac{1}{2}\overrightarrow{BA}$$
$$= \mathbf{b} + \tfrac{1}{2}(\mathbf{a} - \mathbf{b})$$
$$= \tfrac{1}{2}(\mathbf{a} + \mathbf{b})$$

■ So the position vector of the mid-point of the line AB is $\tfrac{1}{2}(\mathbf{a} + \mathbf{b})$.

6.4 Cartesian components of a vector in two dimensions

Consider the point $P(5, 2)$ referred to cartesian axes:

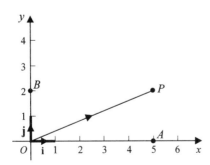

The vector $\overrightarrow{OP}$ is the position vector of P.

■ The vector $\mathbf{i}$ is defined to be a unit vector in the direction of x increasing parallel to the x-axis.

■ The vector **j** is defined to be a unit vector in the direction of y increasing parallel to the y-axis.

So if A is the point on the x-axis with coordinates $(5, 0)$ then A has position vector $5\mathbf{i}$. Similarly, $B(0, 2)$ has position vector $2\mathbf{j}$.

Now: $\qquad \overrightarrow{OP} = \overrightarrow{OA} + \overrightarrow{AP} = \overrightarrow{OA} + \overrightarrow{OB} = 5\mathbf{i} + 2\mathbf{j}$

So the point P, with coordinates $(5, 2)$, has position vector $5\mathbf{i} + 2\mathbf{j}$.

This result can be generalised.

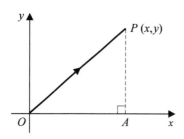

Any point $P(x, y)$ has position vector $\overrightarrow{OP}$. Now the distance $OA = x$ and $AP = y$.

Also: $\qquad \overrightarrow{OP} = \overrightarrow{OA} + \overrightarrow{AP} = x\mathbf{i} + y\mathbf{j}$

■ So the position vector of any point $P(x, y)$ is $x\mathbf{i} + y\mathbf{j}$.

x and y are called the **cartesian components** of $\overrightarrow{OP}$.

Now the length of the line OP which joins $(0, 0)$ to (x, y) is $\sqrt{(x^2 + y^2)}$. (This was shown in Book P1, page 96.)

■ So the modulus of $\overrightarrow{OP}$ is:

$$|\overrightarrow{OP}| = |x\mathbf{i} + y\mathbf{j}| = \sqrt{(x^2 + y^2)}$$

Since a unit vector in the direction of $\overrightarrow{OP}$ is defined as $\dfrac{\overrightarrow{OP}}{|\overrightarrow{OP}|}$, a unit vector in the direction of $x\mathbf{i} + y\mathbf{j}$ is $\dfrac{x\mathbf{i} + y\mathbf{j}}{\sqrt{(x^2 + y^2)}}$.

■ A unit vector in the direction $x\mathbf{i} + y\mathbf{j}$ is $\dfrac{x\mathbf{i} + y\mathbf{j}}{\sqrt{(x^2 + y^2)}}$.

Example 5
If $\mathbf{a} = 2\mathbf{i} + 7\mathbf{j}$, find $|\mathbf{a}|$.

$|\mathbf{a}| = \sqrt{(2^2 + 7^2)} = \sqrt{53}$.

Example 6

Given that $\mathbf{a} = -3\mathbf{i} + 2\mathbf{j}$ and $\mathbf{b} = 4\mathbf{i} - 7\mathbf{j}$, find: (a) $\mathbf{a} + \mathbf{b}$ (b) $\mathbf{a} - \mathbf{b}$ (c) $|\mathbf{a} - \mathbf{b}|$.

(a) $$\mathbf{a} + \mathbf{b} = (-3\mathbf{i} + 2\mathbf{j}) + (4\mathbf{i} - 7\mathbf{j}) = \mathbf{i} - 5\mathbf{j}$$

(b) $$\mathbf{a} - \mathbf{b} = (-3\mathbf{i} + 2\mathbf{j}) - (4\mathbf{i} - 7\mathbf{j})$$
$$= -3\mathbf{i} + 2\mathbf{j} - 4\mathbf{i} + 7\mathbf{j}$$
$$= -7\mathbf{i} + 9\mathbf{j}$$

(c) $$|\mathbf{a} - \mathbf{b}| = |-7\mathbf{i} + 9\mathbf{j}| = \sqrt{(49 + 81)} = \sqrt{130}$$

Example 7

Find a unit vector in the direction of $-2\mathbf{i} + 5\mathbf{j}$.

$$|-2\mathbf{i} + 5\mathbf{j}| = \sqrt{(2^2 + 5^2)} = \sqrt{29}$$

So a unit vector in the direction of $-2\mathbf{i} + 5\mathbf{j}$ is

$$\frac{1}{\sqrt{29}}(-2\mathbf{i} + 5\mathbf{j}) = -\frac{2}{\sqrt{29}}\mathbf{i} + \frac{5}{\sqrt{29}}\mathbf{j}$$

6.5 Cartesian components of a vector in three dimensions

If you assume that the vectors $\mathbf{i}$ and $\mathbf{j}$ are as previously defined and that the vector $\mathbf{k}$ is defined to be a unit vector in the direction of z increasing parallel to the z-axis, similar results apply in three dimensions as in two.

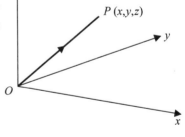

- If P has coordinates (x, y, z)

    then: $$\overrightarrow{OP} = x\mathbf{i} + y\mathbf{j} + z\mathbf{k}$$

- The modulus of $\overrightarrow{OP}$ is $\sqrt{(x^2 + y^2 + z^2)}$.

- A unit vector in the direction of $\overrightarrow{OP}$ is $\dfrac{x\mathbf{i} + y\mathbf{j} + z\mathbf{k}}{\sqrt{(x^2 + y^2 + z^2)}}$.

Exercise 6C

1 Find the modulus of:
   (a) $-5\mathbf{i} + 12\mathbf{j}$
   (b) $-24\mathbf{i} + 7\mathbf{j}$
   (c) $-\mathbf{i} - 5\mathbf{j}$
   (d) $3\mathbf{i} - 2\mathbf{j} + 6\mathbf{k}$
   (e) $-2\mathbf{i} - 2\mathbf{j} + \mathbf{k}$
   (f) $5\mathbf{i} - 2\mathbf{j} - 5\mathbf{k}$

2 Find a unit vector in the direction of:
   (a) $-5\mathbf{i} + 12\mathbf{j}$ (b) $-\mathbf{i} - 5\mathbf{j}$
   (c) $4\mathbf{i} - 7\mathbf{j}$ (d) $3\mathbf{i} - 2\mathbf{j} + 6\mathbf{k}$
   (e) $8\mathbf{i} - \mathbf{j} - 4\mathbf{k}$ (f) $7\mathbf{i} - 5\mathbf{j} + \mathbf{k}$

3 Find a vector of magnitude 27 units which is parallel to $3\mathbf{i} + 4\mathbf{j}$.

4 Find a vector of magnitude 3 units which is parallel to $\mathbf{i} - 3\mathbf{j} + 2\mathbf{k}$.

5 Given that $\mathbf{a} = \mathbf{i} + 2\mathbf{j} - 3\mathbf{k}$ and $\mathbf{b} = 2\mathbf{i} - 4\mathbf{j} - 5\mathbf{k}$, find
   (a) $\mathbf{a} + \mathbf{b}$ (b) $\mathbf{a} - \mathbf{b}$ (c) $|\mathbf{a} - \mathbf{b}|$ (d) $|-\mathbf{a} + 2\mathbf{b}|$.

6 Given that $\mathbf{a} = 2\mathbf{i} - 6\mathbf{j} + 3\mathbf{k}$ and $\mathbf{b} = -\mathbf{i} + 7\mathbf{j} - 5\mathbf{k}$, find
   (a) $|\mathbf{a} - \mathbf{b}|$ (b) $|2\mathbf{a} + 3\mathbf{b}|$
   (c) a unit vector in the direction of $2\mathbf{a} - \mathbf{b}$.

7 The point P has position vector $2\mathbf{i} - 4\mathbf{j} + 5\mathbf{k}$ and $\overrightarrow{PQ} = 3\mathbf{i} + 6\mathbf{j} - 2\mathbf{k}$. Find the position vector of the point Q.

8 Given that $\mathbf{a} = 2\lambda\mathbf{i} + 3\mathbf{j} - \lambda\mathbf{k}$ and that $|\mathbf{a}| = 5$ find the possible values of λ.

9 Given that $\mathbf{a} = 2\lambda\mathbf{i} - \mathbf{j} + 3\lambda\mathbf{k}$ and that $|\mathbf{a}| = \sqrt{27}$, find the possible values of λ.

10 Given that $\mathbf{a} = 3\mathbf{i} - 2\lambda\mathbf{j} + 5\lambda\mathbf{k}$ and that $|\mathbf{a}| = \sqrt{67}$, find the possible values of λ.

6.6 The scalar product of two vectors

The **scalar** (or **dot**) **product** of two vectors $\mathbf{a}$ and $\mathbf{b}$ is defined as $|\mathbf{a}||\mathbf{b}| \cos \theta$ where θ is the angle between $\mathbf{a}$ and $\mathbf{b}$. The result of this calculation is a *scalar*, which is why it is called the scalar product.

You must note very carefully that this formula only works when the directions of the vectors $\mathbf{a}$ and $\mathbf{b}$ are either both towards their point of intersection or both away from their point of intersection and θ is the angle between their directions.

The scalar product is written $\mathbf{a} \cdot \mathbf{b}$ and you read it as '$\mathbf{a}$ dot $\mathbf{b}$'.

             $$\mathbf{a} \cdot \mathbf{b} = |\mathbf{a}||\mathbf{b}| \cos \theta$$

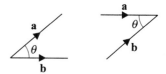

Notice the following properties of the scalar product:

1. For two perpendicular vectors:

$$\mathbf{a} \cdot \mathbf{b} = 0$$

In particular, $$\mathbf{i} \cdot \mathbf{j} = \mathbf{j} \cdot \mathbf{k} = \mathbf{k} \cdot \mathbf{i} = 0$$

If **a** and **b** are perpendicular

then: $$\mathbf{a.b} = |\mathbf{a}||\mathbf{b}|\cos 90°$$

But $\cos 90° = 0$

So: $$\mathbf{a.b} = 0$$

2. $$\mathbf{a.a} = a^2$$

In particular, $\mathbf{i.i} = \mathbf{j.j} = \mathbf{k.k} = 1$

$$\mathbf{a.a} = |\mathbf{a}||\mathbf{a}|\cos\theta$$

But since they are the same vector the angle between them is zero.

So $$\mathbf{a.a} = |\mathbf{a}||\mathbf{a}|\cos 0 = a.a.1 = a^2$$

3. $$\mathbf{a.b} = \mathbf{b.a}$$

$$\mathbf{a.b} = |\mathbf{a}||\mathbf{b}|\cos\theta = |\mathbf{b}||\mathbf{a}|\cos\theta = \mathbf{b.a}$$

4. $$\lambda(\mathbf{a.b}) = (\lambda\mathbf{a}).\mathbf{b} = \mathbf{a}.(\lambda\mathbf{b})$$

$$\lambda(\mathbf{a.b}) = \lambda(|\mathbf{a}||\mathbf{b}|\cos\theta) = \lambda|\mathbf{a}||\mathbf{b}|\cos\theta$$

Since $$|\lambda\mathbf{a}| = \lambda|\mathbf{a}| \text{ and } |\lambda\mathbf{b}| = \lambda|\mathbf{b}|$$

then: $$(\lambda\mathbf{a}).\mathbf{b} = |\lambda\mathbf{a}||\mathbf{b}|\cos\theta = \lambda|\mathbf{a}||\mathbf{b}|\cos\theta = \lambda(\mathbf{a.b})$$

You can show that $\lambda(\mathbf{a.b}) = \mathbf{a}.(\lambda\mathbf{b})$ in a similar way.

5. $$\mathbf{a}.(\mathbf{b}+\mathbf{c}) = \mathbf{a.b} + \mathbf{a.c}$$

In the diagram $$\mathbf{d} = \mathbf{b}+\mathbf{c}$$

So $$\mathbf{a}.(\mathbf{b}+\mathbf{c}) = \mathbf{a.d}$$

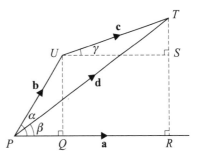

Now $$PQ + QR = PR$$

Since $\dfrac{PQ}{|\mathbf{b}|} = \cos\alpha$, $\dfrac{SU}{|\mathbf{c}|} = \cos\gamma = \dfrac{QR}{|\mathbf{c}|}$ and $\dfrac{PR}{|\mathbf{d}|} = \cos\beta$, then:

$$|\mathbf{b}|\cos\alpha + |\mathbf{c}|\cos\gamma = |\mathbf{d}|\cos\beta$$

Multiply through by $|\mathbf{a}|$:

$$|\mathbf{a}||\mathbf{b}|\cos\alpha + |\mathbf{a}||\mathbf{c}|\cos\gamma = |\mathbf{a}||\mathbf{d}|\cos\beta$$

that is: $$\mathbf{a.b} + \mathbf{a.c} = \mathbf{a.d}$$

or: $$\mathbf{a.b} + \mathbf{a.c} = \mathbf{a}.(\mathbf{b}+\mathbf{c})$$

The scalar product in terms of cartesian coordinates

If the vectors **a** and **b** are given in terms of their cartesian components as $\mathbf{a} = x_1\mathbf{i} + y_1\mathbf{j} + z_1\mathbf{k}$ and $\mathbf{b} = x_2\mathbf{i} + y_2\mathbf{j} + z_2\mathbf{k}$, then

$$\mathbf{a}.\mathbf{b} = (x_1\mathbf{i} + y_1\mathbf{j} + z_1\mathbf{k}).(x_2\mathbf{i} + y_2\mathbf{j} + z_2\mathbf{k})$$
$$= x_1x_2\mathbf{i}.\mathbf{i} + x_1y_2\mathbf{i}.\mathbf{j} + x_1z_2\mathbf{i}.\mathbf{k}$$
$$+ y_1x_2\mathbf{j}.\mathbf{i} + y_1y_2\mathbf{j}.\mathbf{j} + y_1z_2\mathbf{j}.\mathbf{k}$$
$$+ z_1x_2\mathbf{k}.\mathbf{i} + z_1y_2\mathbf{k}.\mathbf{j} + z_1z_2\mathbf{k}.\mathbf{k}$$

Now since $\mathbf{i}.\mathbf{i} = |\mathbf{i}||\mathbf{i}| \cos 0 = 1$, and likewise $\mathbf{j}.\mathbf{j}$ and $\mathbf{k}.\mathbf{k}$, and since $\mathbf{i}.\mathbf{j} = |\mathbf{i}||\mathbf{j}| \cos 90° = 0$, and likewise $\mathbf{i}.\mathbf{k} = \mathbf{j}.\mathbf{i} = \mathbf{j}.\mathbf{k} = \mathbf{k}.\mathbf{i} = \mathbf{k}.\mathbf{j} = 0$, then

■ $$\mathbf{a}.\mathbf{b} = x_1x_2 + y_1y_2 + z_1z_2$$

Putting the two results for the scalar product together you get:

■ $$x_1x_2 + y_1y_2 + z_1z_2 = |\mathbf{a}||\mathbf{b}| \cos \theta$$

Example 8

Find the angle between the vectors $\mathbf{a} = 2\mathbf{i} - 3\mathbf{j} + \mathbf{k}$ and $\mathbf{b} = -\mathbf{i} + 5\mathbf{j} + 4\mathbf{k}$, giving your answer to the nearest tenth of a degree.

$\mathbf{a}.\mathbf{b} = |\mathbf{a}||\mathbf{b}| \cos \theta$, where θ is the required angle

$$|\mathbf{a}| = \sqrt{(4 + 9 + 1)} = \sqrt{14}$$
$$|\mathbf{b}| = \sqrt{(1 + 25 + 16)} = \sqrt{42}$$

Also
$$\mathbf{a}.\mathbf{b} = (2\mathbf{i} - 3\mathbf{j} + \mathbf{k}).(-\mathbf{i} + 5\mathbf{j} + 4\mathbf{k})$$
$$= -2 - 15 + 4$$
$$= -13$$

So:
$$\sqrt{14}\sqrt{42} \cos \theta = -13$$

$$\cos \theta = \frac{-13}{\sqrt{588}} = -0.5361$$

and:
$$\theta = 122.4°$$

Example 9

The points A, B and C have position vectors $\mathbf{a} = 4\mathbf{i} - \mathbf{k}$, $\mathbf{b} = \mathbf{i} + 2\mathbf{j} - 2\mathbf{k}$ and $\mathbf{c} = 3\mathbf{i} + 3\mathbf{j} - 6\mathbf{k}$ respectively referred to an origin O. Show that $\angle ABC = 90°$.

To use the scalar product you must have both vectors $\overrightarrow{BC}$ and $\overrightarrow{BA}$ in the directions away from the angle. Then:

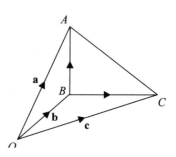

$$\overrightarrow{BC} = \overrightarrow{OC} - \overrightarrow{OB} = \mathbf{c} - \mathbf{b} = 2\mathbf{i} + \mathbf{j} - 4\mathbf{k} \text{ (see p. 129)}$$

$$\overrightarrow{BA} = \overrightarrow{OA} - \overrightarrow{OB} = \mathbf{a} - \mathbf{b} = 3\mathbf{i} - 2\mathbf{j} + \mathbf{k}$$

So:

$$\overrightarrow{BC} \cdot \overrightarrow{BA} = (2 \times 3) + (1 \times -2) + (-4 \times 1)$$
$$= 6 - 2 - 4 = 0$$

Thus $\angle ABC = 90°$.

The projection of a vector on to another vector

You have already seen that a vector can be expressed in terms of its cartesian components. This is a special case. In fact, you can find the component of a vector in *any* direction. Remember that a component of a vector is a scalar quantity not a vector quantity.

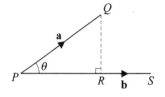

Let θ be the angle between $\mathbf{a}$ and $\mathbf{b}$ where $\overrightarrow{PQ} = \mathbf{a}$ and $\overrightarrow{PS} = \mathbf{b}$. Consider the vector $\mathbf{a}$ and its **projection** PR in the direction of $\mathbf{b}$.

Now

$$PR = PQ \cos \theta$$

But

$$\mathbf{a} \cdot \mathbf{b} = (PQ)(PS) \cos \theta$$

So:

$$PQ \cos \theta = \frac{\mathbf{a} \cdot \mathbf{b}}{PS}$$

But PS is the magnitude of $\mathbf{b}$:

$$PS = |\mathbf{b}|$$

■ So the projection of $\mathbf{a}$ on $\mathbf{b}$ is $\dfrac{\mathbf{a} \cdot \mathbf{b}}{|\mathbf{b}|}$.

Example 10
Find the projection of $\mathbf{a} = 2\mathbf{i} + \mathbf{j} - 5\mathbf{k}$ in the direction of $\mathbf{b} = -\mathbf{i} + 7\mathbf{j} + 2\mathbf{k}$.

$$\mathbf{a} \cdot \mathbf{b} = -2 + 7 - 10 = -5$$

$$|\mathbf{b}| = \sqrt{(1 + 49 + 4)} = \sqrt{54}$$

So the projection is $\dfrac{-5}{\sqrt{54}} = \dfrac{-5}{3\sqrt{6}}$.

Notice that in this example the projection is negative. This means that the angle θ between the vectors $\mathbf{a}$ and $\mathbf{b}$ is obtuse, so the projection is in the *opposite* direction to $\mathbf{b}$.

Exercise 6D

1 Find $\mathbf{a} \cdot \mathbf{b}$ where:
   (a) $\mathbf{a} = 2\mathbf{i} - \mathbf{j} + 5\mathbf{k}$, $\mathbf{b} = -3\mathbf{i} + 5\mathbf{j} - 7\mathbf{k}$
   (b) $\mathbf{a} = 5\mathbf{i} - \mathbf{k}$, $\mathbf{b} = -2\mathbf{i} + 6\mathbf{j} - 2\mathbf{k}$
   (c) $\mathbf{a} = -3\mathbf{i} + 4\mathbf{j} + 6\mathbf{k}$, $\mathbf{b} = \mathbf{k} - 2\mathbf{i}$
   (d) $\mathbf{a} = 6\mathbf{i} - 3\mathbf{k}$, $\mathbf{b} = 4\mathbf{j} + 7\mathbf{k}$
   (e) $\mathbf{a} = -5\mathbf{i} + 7\mathbf{j} - 8\mathbf{k}$, $\mathbf{b} = 2\mathbf{i} - 5\mathbf{j} + 11\mathbf{k}$

2 Find, in degrees to 1 decimal place, the angle between the
   vectors $\mathbf{a}$ and $\mathbf{b}$ where:
   (a) $\mathbf{a} = 2\mathbf{i} - \mathbf{j} - 2\mathbf{k}$, $\mathbf{b} = 3\mathbf{i} + \mathbf{j} - 5\mathbf{k}$
   (b) $\mathbf{a} = -\mathbf{i} + 4\mathbf{j} - 2\mathbf{k}$, $\mathbf{b} = 5\mathbf{i} + \mathbf{j} - 3\mathbf{k}$
   (c) $\mathbf{a} = -2\mathbf{i} + 6\mathbf{j} - \mathbf{k}$, $\mathbf{b} = \mathbf{i} - \mathbf{j} - 2\mathbf{k}$
   (d) $\mathbf{a} = -\mathbf{i} - 2\mathbf{j} + \mathbf{k}$, $\mathbf{b} = 3\mathbf{i} - 4\mathbf{k}$
   (e) $\mathbf{a} = \mathbf{i} + 3\mathbf{j} + \mathbf{k}$, $\mathbf{b} = 3\mathbf{i} - \mathbf{j} - \mathbf{k}$
   (f) $\mathbf{a} = -5\mathbf{i} - 2\mathbf{j} - \mathbf{k}$, $\mathbf{b} = 2\mathbf{i} - 3\mathbf{j} + 4\mathbf{k}$
   (g) $\mathbf{a} = -3\mathbf{i} + 6\mathbf{j} - \mathbf{k}$, $\mathbf{b} = 2\mathbf{i} - 2\mathbf{j} + 3\mathbf{k}$
   (h) $\mathbf{a} = 2\mathbf{i} - 6\mathbf{j} + 3\mathbf{k}$, $\mathbf{b} = 2\mathbf{i} - \mathbf{j} + 2\mathbf{k}$
   (i) $\mathbf{a} = 2\mathbf{i} + \mathbf{j} - 3\mathbf{k}$, $\mathbf{b} = \mathbf{i} + 2\mathbf{j} + \mathbf{k}$
   (j) $\mathbf{a} = 5\mathbf{i} - 3\mathbf{j} + 7\mathbf{k}$, $\mathbf{b} = -3\mathbf{i} - 4\mathbf{j} + 2\mathbf{k}$

3 Find the value of λ for which the vectors $2\mathbf{i} - 3\mathbf{j} + \mathbf{k}$ and
   $3\mathbf{i} + 6\mathbf{j} + \lambda\mathbf{k}$ are perpendicular. [L]

4 Given that $\mathbf{u} = 3\mathbf{i} + 2\mathbf{j}$ and $\mathbf{v} = 2\mathbf{i} + \lambda\mathbf{j}$, determine the value of λ
   such that:
   (a) $\mathbf{u}$ and $\mathbf{v}$ are at right angles
   (b) $\mathbf{u}$ and $\mathbf{v}$ are parallel
   (c) the acute angle between $\mathbf{u}$ and $\mathbf{v}$ is $\frac{\pi}{4}$. [L]

5 The angle between $\mathbf{i} + \mathbf{j}$ and $\mathbf{i} + \mathbf{j} + p\mathbf{k}$ is $\frac{\pi}{4}$. Find the possible
   values of p. [L]

6 Find the angle, in degrees to 1 decimal place, which the vector
   $\mathbf{a}$ makes with the positive (i) x-axis (ii) y-axis (iii) z-axis,
   where $\mathbf{a} =$
   (a) $5\mathbf{i} + 2\mathbf{j} + 4\mathbf{k}$
   (b) $8\mathbf{i} + \mathbf{j} - 4\mathbf{k}$
   (c) $2\mathbf{i} - 3\mathbf{j} + 4\mathbf{k}$
   (d) $-\mathbf{i} - \mathbf{j} - 3\mathbf{k}$
   (e) $4\mathbf{i} - 2\mathbf{j} - \mathbf{k}$

7 Find a vector which is perpendicular to both **a** and **b** where:
   (a) $\mathbf{a} = \mathbf{i} + 3\mathbf{j} - \mathbf{k}$, $\mathbf{b} = 3\mathbf{i} - \mathbf{j} - \mathbf{k}$
   (b) $\mathbf{a} = 2\mathbf{i} - 3\mathbf{j} - 5\mathbf{k}$, $\mathbf{b} = \mathbf{i} - 2\mathbf{j} - 3\mathbf{k}$
   (c) $\mathbf{a} = 2\mathbf{i} + 10\mathbf{j} + 3\mathbf{k}$, $\mathbf{b} = \mathbf{i} + 6\mathbf{j} + 2\mathbf{k}$
   (d) $\mathbf{a} = 3\mathbf{i} + 2\mathbf{j} + \mathbf{k}$, $\mathbf{b} = -3\mathbf{i} + 4\mathbf{j} + 3\mathbf{k}$
   (e) $\mathbf{a} = 2\mathbf{i} - 3\mathbf{j} - 4\mathbf{k}$, $\mathbf{b} = 4\mathbf{i} - 3\mathbf{j} + \mathbf{k}$

8 Find the values of λ for which the vectors $2\lambda\mathbf{i} + \lambda\mathbf{j} - 4\mathbf{k}$ and $\lambda\mathbf{i} - 2\mathbf{j} + \mathbf{k}$ are perpendicular.

9 Find the projection of **a** in the direction of **b** where:
   (a) $\mathbf{a} = \mathbf{i} - 2\mathbf{j} + \mathbf{k}$, $\mathbf{b} = 4\mathbf{i} - 4\mathbf{j} + 7\mathbf{k}$
   (b) $\mathbf{a} = 2\mathbf{i} - 3\mathbf{j} + 6\mathbf{k}$, $\mathbf{b} = \mathbf{i} + 2\mathbf{j} + 2\mathbf{k}$
   (c) $\mathbf{a} = \mathbf{i} - \mathbf{j} + 2\mathbf{k}$, $\mathbf{b} = 2\mathbf{i} + 3\mathbf{j} - \mathbf{k}$
   (d) $\mathbf{a} = -\mathbf{i} - 3\mathbf{j} + 5\mathbf{k}$, $\mathbf{b} = 2\mathbf{i} - 5\mathbf{j} + 4\mathbf{k}$
   (e) $\mathbf{a} = 3\mathbf{i} - 5\mathbf{j} - 2\mathbf{k}$, $\mathbf{b} = 5\mathbf{i} + 4\mathbf{j} - \mathbf{k}$

10 The vectors **F** and **u** are $\mathbf{i} - 2\mathbf{j} + 3\mathbf{k}$ and $8\mathbf{i} + 9\mathbf{j} + 12\mathbf{k}$ respectively. Find the projection of **F** in the direction of **u**.

11 Prove the cosine rule by vector methods.

12 Prove Pythagoras' theorem by vector methods.

13 Prove that the angle in a semi-circle is a right angle by vector methods.

14 Show that any one of $2\mathbf{i} - 2\mathbf{j} + \mathbf{k}$, $\mathbf{i} + 2\mathbf{j} + 2\mathbf{k}$, $2\mathbf{i} + \mathbf{j} - 2\mathbf{k}$ is perpendicular to the other two.

15 Simplify $(\mathbf{a} + \mathbf{b}) \cdot \mathbf{c} - (\mathbf{a} - \mathbf{b}) \cdot \mathbf{c}$.

16 Points A and B have position vectors $\mathbf{a} = 2\mathbf{i} - 3\mathbf{j} + \mathbf{k}$, $\mathbf{b} = -4\mathbf{i} - \mathbf{j} + 3\mathbf{k}$ referred to an origin O. Calculate the sizes of the angles of $\triangle AOB$, giving your answers to the nearest tenth of a degree.

17 Given $A(2, 1, 7)$, $B(-3, 1, 4)$, $C(2, -1, 5)$, use a vector method to find the cosine of $\angle ABC$.

18 Given $A(-1, 2, -1)$, $B(2, 0, 5)$, $C(1, 5, -1)$, use a vector method to find the cosine of $\angle BCA$ and the area of $\triangle ABC$.

19 The vectors **a** and **b** are $2\mathbf{i} - \mathbf{j} + 3\mathbf{k}$ and $3\mathbf{i} + 2\mathbf{j} - 2\mathbf{k}$ respectively. Find the projection of **a** in the direction of **b**. Find also the projection of **a** in a direction perpendicular to **b**.

20 Find the angle between the vectors **a** and **b** given that $|\mathbf{a}| = 3$, $|\mathbf{b}| = 5$ and $|\mathbf{a} - \mathbf{b}| = 7$. [L]

6.7 The vector equation of a straight line

Think of a line that passes through the point A and is parallel to the vector **b**. The point A has position vector **a** referred to the origin O. Let R be any other point on the line and let it have position vector **r**. Since the line is parallel to **b**, then:

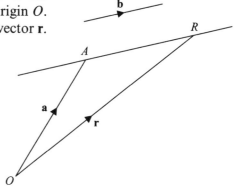

$$\overrightarrow{AR} = \lambda\mathbf{b}, \text{ where } \lambda \text{ is a scalar}$$

However:

$$\overrightarrow{AR} = \mathbf{r} - \mathbf{a}$$

So:

$$\mathbf{r} - \mathbf{a} = \lambda\mathbf{b}$$

or

$$\mathbf{r} = \mathbf{a} + \lambda\mathbf{b}$$

This is a vector equation of the straight line. The vector **b** is in the same direction as the line and is sometimes called the **direction vector of the line**. The vector **a** is the position vector of a point on the line and λ is a scalar taking all real values.

Example 11
Find a vector equation of the line that passes through the point with position vector $2\mathbf{i} + \mathbf{j} - \mathbf{k}$ and is parallel to the vector $-5\mathbf{i} - 2\mathbf{j} - \mathbf{k}$.

The equation of the line is

$$\mathbf{r} = 2\mathbf{i} + \mathbf{j} - \mathbf{k} + \lambda(-5\mathbf{i} - 2\mathbf{j} - \mathbf{k})$$

This could also be rearranged as:

$$\mathbf{r} = (2 - 5\lambda)\mathbf{i} + (1 - 2\lambda)\mathbf{j} - (1 + \lambda)\mathbf{k}$$

Example 12
Find a vector equation of the line that passes through the points A and B with position vectors $\mathbf{a} = 2\mathbf{i} - 2\mathbf{j} + 3\mathbf{k}$ and $\mathbf{b} = -4\mathbf{i} + 5\mathbf{j} - \mathbf{k}$ respectively.

Since the line passes through the points A and B a direction vector for the line is $\overrightarrow{AB}$. (Notice that $\overrightarrow{BA}$ is also a direction vector for the line.) Then:

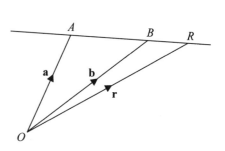

$$\overrightarrow{AB} = \mathbf{b} - \mathbf{a} = -4\mathbf{i} + 5\mathbf{j} - \mathbf{k} - (2\mathbf{i} - 2\mathbf{j} + 3\mathbf{k})$$
$$= -6\mathbf{i} + 7\mathbf{j} - 4\mathbf{k}$$

So a vector equation of the line is:

$$\mathbf{r} = 2\mathbf{i} - 2\mathbf{j} + 3\mathbf{k} + \lambda(-6\mathbf{i} + 7\mathbf{j} - 4\mathbf{k})$$

Notice that since B lies on the line, another form of the vector equation of the line is:

$$\mathbf{r} = -4\mathbf{i} + 5\mathbf{j} - \mathbf{k} + \mu(-6\mathbf{i} + 7\mathbf{j} - 4\mathbf{k})$$

Example 13

Find a vector equation of the line that passes through the points $A(1, 2, 1)$ and $B(2, -1, -1)$.

Show that the point $C(0, 5, 3)$ also lies on the line.

A direction vector for the line is:

$$\overrightarrow{AB} = 2\mathbf{i} - \mathbf{j} - \mathbf{k} - (\mathbf{i} + 2\mathbf{j} + \mathbf{k}) = \mathbf{i} - 3\mathbf{j} - 2\mathbf{k}$$

So an equation of the line is:

$$\mathbf{r} = \mathbf{i} + 2\mathbf{j} + \mathbf{k} + \lambda(\mathbf{i} - 3\mathbf{j} - 2\mathbf{k})$$

If $\lambda = -1$, then:

$$\mathbf{r} = 0\mathbf{i} + 5\mathbf{j} + 3\mathbf{k}$$

So the line passes through the point $(0, 5, 3)$.

Example 14

Show that the lines with equations

$$\mathbf{r} = 7\mathbf{i} - 3\mathbf{j} + 3\mathbf{k} + \lambda(3\mathbf{i} - 2\mathbf{j} + \mathbf{k})$$

and
$$\mathbf{r} = 7\mathbf{i} - 2\mathbf{j} + 4\mathbf{k} + \mu(-2\mathbf{i} + \mathbf{j} - \mathbf{k})$$

intersect and find the position vector of their point of intersection.

You can rewrite the first equation as:

$$\mathbf{r} = (7 + 3\lambda)\mathbf{i} + (-3 - 2\lambda)\mathbf{j} + (3 + \lambda)\mathbf{k}$$

and the second as:

$$\mathbf{r} = (7 - 2\mu)\mathbf{i} + (-2 + \mu)\mathbf{j} + (4 - \mu)\mathbf{k}$$

If these intersect then:

$$(7 + 3\lambda)\mathbf{i} + (-3 - 2\lambda)\mathbf{j} + (3 + \lambda)\mathbf{k} = (7 - 2\mu)\mathbf{i} + (-2 + \mu)\mathbf{j} + (4 - \mu)\mathbf{k}$$

Since $\mathbf{i}$, $\mathbf{j}$ and $\mathbf{k}$ are non-parallel,

$$7 + 3\lambda = 7 - 2\mu \qquad \qquad (1)$$
$$-3 - 2\lambda = -2 + \mu \qquad \qquad (2)$$
$$3 + \lambda = 4 - \mu \qquad \qquad (3)$$

From (1): $\qquad \qquad 3\lambda = -2\mu$ or $\mu = -\frac{3}{2}\lambda$

Substituting in (2): $\qquad -3 - 2\lambda = -2 - \frac{3}{2}\lambda$

$$\Rightarrow \qquad -1 = \frac{1}{2}\lambda$$

$$\lambda = -2 \text{ so } \mu = 3$$

Check in (3): $\qquad 3 + \lambda = 3 - 2 = 1$

$$4 - \mu = 4 - 3 = 1$$

Notice that it is essential to check in the third equation, because if the values of λ and μ do not satisfy all *three* equations then it means that the lines do *not* intersect.

Using $\lambda = -2$ in the equation

$$\mathbf{r} = 7\mathbf{i} - 3\mathbf{j} + 3\mathbf{k} + \lambda(3\mathbf{i} - 2\mathbf{j} + \mathbf{k})$$

gives: $\qquad \mathbf{r} = \mathbf{i} + \mathbf{j} + \mathbf{k}$

where $\mathbf{r}$ is the position vector of the point of intersection of the two lines, as required.

Notice that using $\mu = 3$ in

$$\mathbf{r} = 7\mathbf{i} - 2\mathbf{j} + 4\mathbf{k} + \mu(-2\mathbf{i} + \mathbf{j} - \mathbf{k})$$

also gives $\mathbf{r} = \mathbf{i} + \mathbf{j} + \mathbf{k}$ and this in itself could be a sufficient check, since you have shown $\mathbf{i} + \mathbf{j} + \mathbf{k}$ to be on both lines.

6.8 Deriving cartesian equations of a straight line from a vector equation

From the vector equation of a straight line you have

$$\mathbf{r} = \mathbf{a} + \lambda\mathbf{b}$$

If $\qquad \mathbf{r} = x\mathbf{i} + y\mathbf{j} + z\mathbf{k}$

$$\mathbf{a} = a_1\mathbf{i} + a_2\mathbf{j} + a_3\mathbf{k}$$

and $\qquad \mathbf{b} = b_1\mathbf{i} + b_2\mathbf{j} + b_3\mathbf{k}$

then: $\qquad x\mathbf{i} + y\mathbf{j} + z\mathbf{k} = a_1\mathbf{i} + a_2\mathbf{j} + a_3\mathbf{k} + \lambda(b_1\mathbf{i} + b_2\mathbf{j} + b_3\mathbf{k})$

So: $\qquad x\mathbf{i} + y\mathbf{j} + z\mathbf{k} = (a_1 + \lambda b_1)\mathbf{i} + (a_2 + \lambda b_2)\mathbf{j} + (a_3 + \lambda b_3)\mathbf{k}$

Since **i**, **j**, **k** are not parallel:

$$x = a_1 + \lambda b_1 \Rightarrow \lambda = \frac{x - a_1}{b_1}$$

$$y = a_2 + \lambda b_2 \Rightarrow \lambda = \frac{y - a_2}{b_2}$$

$$z = a_3 + \lambda b_3 \Rightarrow \lambda = \frac{z - a_3}{b_3}$$

Putting these values of λ together gives

$$\frac{x - a_1}{b_1} = \frac{y - a_2}{b_2} = \frac{z - a_3}{b_3}$$

which are the equations of a straight line in cartesian form.

■ So the cartesian equations of the line that passes through the point (a_1, a_2, a_3) and has direction vector $b_1\mathbf{i} + b_2\mathbf{j} + b_3\mathbf{k}$ are

$$\frac{x - a_1}{b_1} = \frac{y - a_2}{b_2} = \frac{z - a_3}{b_3}$$

Example 15

Find cartesian equations for the line that is parallel to the vector $2\mathbf{i} - 5\mathbf{j} + 4\mathbf{k}$ and passes through the point A with position vector $-\mathbf{i} + 7\mathbf{j} - 2\mathbf{k}$.

A vector equation of the line is:

$$\mathbf{r} = -\mathbf{i} + 7\mathbf{j} - 2\mathbf{k} + \lambda(2\mathbf{i} - 5\mathbf{j} + 4\mathbf{k})$$

or $\qquad \mathbf{r} = (-1 + 2\lambda)\mathbf{i} + (7 - 5\lambda)\mathbf{j} + (-2 + 4\lambda)\mathbf{k}$

So: $\qquad x = -1 + 2\lambda, \ y = 7 - 5\lambda, \ z = -2 + 4\lambda$

The cartesian equations are therefore:

$$\frac{x + 1}{2} = \frac{y - 7}{-5} = \frac{z + 2}{4}$$

Example 16

Find the vector equation of the line which has cartesian equations

$$\frac{x - 1}{5} = \frac{y + 1}{2} = \frac{z}{-5}$$

Let $\lambda = \dfrac{x - 1}{5} = \dfrac{y + 1}{2} = \dfrac{z}{-5}$

Then $x = 5\lambda + 1, \ y = 2\lambda - 1, \ z = -5\lambda$

So the vector equation is

$$\mathbf{r} = \mathbf{i} - \mathbf{j} + \lambda(5\mathbf{i} + 2\mathbf{j} - 5\mathbf{k})$$

Example 17

Find cartesian equations for the line that passes through the points $(3, 1, -2)$ and $(4, 3, 4)$.

A direction vector of the line is:

$$(4 - 3)\mathbf{i} + (3 - 1)\mathbf{j} + (4 + 2)\mathbf{k} = \mathbf{i} + 2\mathbf{j} + 6\mathbf{k}$$

So a vector equation of the line is:

$$\mathbf{r} = 3\mathbf{i} + \mathbf{j} - 2\mathbf{k} + \lambda(\mathbf{i} + 2\mathbf{j} + 6\mathbf{k})$$

Thus: $\qquad x = 3 + \lambda, \; y = 1 + 2\lambda, \; z = -2 + 6\lambda$

and cartesian equations of the line are

$$\frac{x - 3}{1} = \frac{y - 1}{2} = \frac{z + 2}{6}$$

Example 18

The cartesian equations of two straight lines L_1 and L_2 are

$$L_1: \quad \frac{x - 1}{5} = \frac{y + 2}{4} = \frac{z}{6}$$

$$L_2: \quad \frac{x + 3}{2} = \frac{y - 5}{7} = \frac{z + 1}{-1}$$

Find the acute angle between the two lines.

For L_1: $\qquad x = 1 + 5\lambda, \; y = -2 + 4\lambda, \; z = 6\lambda$

So the vector equation of L_1 is

$$\mathbf{r} = \mathbf{i} - 2\mathbf{j} + \lambda(5\mathbf{i} + 4\mathbf{j} + 6\mathbf{k})$$

For L_2: $\qquad x = -3 + 2\mu, \; y = 5 + 7\mu, \; z = -1 - \mu$

So the vector equation of L_2 is

$$\mathbf{r} = -3\mathbf{i} + 5\mathbf{j} - \mathbf{k} + \mu(2\mathbf{i} + 7\mathbf{j} - \mathbf{k})$$

The angle between the lines is the angle between their direction vectors. The scalar product of the direction vectors is:

$$(5\mathbf{i} + 4\mathbf{j} + 6\mathbf{k}) \cdot (2\mathbf{i} + 7\mathbf{j} - \mathbf{k}) = 10 + 28 - 6 = 32$$

Also: $\qquad |5\mathbf{i} + 4\mathbf{j} + 6\mathbf{k}| = \sqrt{(25 + 16 + 36)} = \sqrt{77}$

and: $\qquad |2\mathbf{i} + 7\mathbf{j} - \mathbf{k}| = \sqrt{(4 + 49 + 1)} = \sqrt{54}$

So: $\qquad\qquad \sqrt{77}\,\sqrt{54}\cos\theta = 32$

$$\cos\theta = \frac{32}{\sqrt{77}\sqrt{54}} = 0.4963$$

So: $\qquad\qquad\qquad \theta = 60.2°$

Exercise 6E

1 Find a vector equation of the line that passes through the point with position vector **a** and is parallel to the vector **b** where:
   (a) $\mathbf{a} = -\mathbf{i} + \mathbf{j} + \mathbf{k}$, $\mathbf{b} = 2\mathbf{i} - 3\mathbf{j} + \mathbf{k}$
   (b) $\mathbf{a} = 2\mathbf{i} - 7\mathbf{j} - 11\mathbf{k}$, $\mathbf{b} = -3\mathbf{i} + 9\mathbf{j} + 17\mathbf{k}$
   (c) $\mathbf{a} = -3\mathbf{i} + 9\mathbf{j} - 15\mathbf{k}$, $\mathbf{b} = 2\mathbf{i} + \mathbf{j}$
   (d) $\mathbf{a} = 3\mathbf{i} - \mathbf{k}$, $\mathbf{b} = -\mathbf{i} - 5\mathbf{j} + 2\mathbf{k}$
   (e) $\mathbf{a} = 5\mathbf{i} - \mathbf{j} + 4\mathbf{k}$, $\mathbf{b} = \mathbf{i} - 2\mathbf{j} + \mathbf{k}$

2 Find a vector equation of the line that passes through the point $(-1, 7, 4)$ and is parallel to the y-axis.

3 Find a vector equation of the line which passes through the point $(2, -1, 6)$ and is perpendicular to the yz-plane.

4 Find vector equations of the lines passing through the following points:
   (a) $(1, -1, 2)$ and $(-5, 2, 2)$ (b) $(2, -1, 7)$ and $(7, 0, -3)$
   (c) $(-3, -1, 2)$ and $(8, 1, -3)$ (d) $(2, -6, 4)$ and $(-1, -2, -3)$
   (e) $(3, 1, 4)$ and $(-1, 2, 5)$

5 Show that the point $(11.5, 20.5, -28)$ lies on the line with equation

$$\mathbf{r} = \mathbf{i} - 4\mathbf{j} + 7\mathbf{k} + \lambda(-3\mathbf{i} - 7\mathbf{j} + 10\mathbf{k})$$

   and state the value of λ at this point.

6 Find cartesian equations of the lines with vector equations:
   (a) $\mathbf{r} = -3\mathbf{i} + 2\mathbf{j} - 5\mathbf{k} + \lambda(2\mathbf{i} - 4\mathbf{j} + \mathbf{k})$
   (b) $\mathbf{r} = \mathbf{i} - 3\mathbf{j} + 2\mathbf{k} + \lambda(-\mathbf{i} + \mathbf{j} - 2\mathbf{k})$
   (c) $\mathbf{r} = -\mathbf{i} + 3\mathbf{j} + 4\mathbf{k} + \lambda(-6\mathbf{i} + 4\mathbf{j} - 9\mathbf{k})$
   (d) $\mathbf{r} = 2\mathbf{i} - 3\mathbf{j} + 4\mathbf{k} + \lambda(-2\mathbf{i} + 6\mathbf{j} - \mathbf{k})$
   (e) $\mathbf{r} = -3\mathbf{i} + 4\mathbf{j} - \mathbf{k} + \lambda(2\mathbf{i} - 3\mathbf{j} - \mathbf{k})$

7 Find a vector equation of the line with cartesian equations:

(a) $\dfrac{x-1}{2} = \dfrac{y+1}{4} = \dfrac{z-1}{3}$

(b) $\dfrac{x-1}{3} = \dfrac{y+1}{-4} = \dfrac{z-3}{-1}$

(c) $\dfrac{1-x}{2} = \dfrac{y+2}{4} = \dfrac{z+3}{5}$

(d) $\dfrac{1-x}{3} = \dfrac{4-y}{2} = \dfrac{z+3}{-1}$

(e) $\dfrac{2x-1}{4} = \dfrac{2-y}{3} = \dfrac{1-3z}{2}$

8 The lines with vector equations

$$\mathbf{r} = \mathbf{i} + 3\mathbf{j} - 2\mathbf{k} + \lambda(4\mathbf{i} + \mathbf{k})$$

and $$\mathbf{r} = 5\mathbf{i} + 3\mathbf{j} + 8\mathbf{k} + \mu(-\mathbf{i} + 2\mathbf{k})$$

intersect. Find the position vector of the point of intersection.

9 Find the coordinates of the point of intersection of the lines L_1 and L_2 with cartesian equations:

L_1: $x - 6 = \dfrac{2+y}{5} = \dfrac{z-8}{7}$

L_2: $\dfrac{x-1}{3} = \dfrac{y-3}{5} = \dfrac{2-z}{8}$

10 Determine whether the lines with the given equations intersect. If they do, state the coordinates of the point of intersection.

(a) $\dfrac{x}{4} = \dfrac{2-y}{2} = \dfrac{z+1}{3}$ and $4 - x = \dfrac{y-1}{3} = \dfrac{z+2}{4}$

(b) $\mathbf{r} = -3\mathbf{j} + 5\mathbf{k} + \lambda(2\mathbf{i} + 4\mathbf{j} + 2\mathbf{k})$ and

$\mathbf{r} = \mathbf{i} + 8\mathbf{j} + 3\mathbf{k} + \mu(-\mathbf{i} + \mathbf{j} - 2\mathbf{k})$

(c) $\mathbf{r} = 2\mathbf{i} - \mathbf{k} + \lambda(3\mathbf{i} + \tfrac{1}{2}\mathbf{j} + 4\mathbf{k})$ and

$\mathbf{r} = -4\mathbf{i} + 5\mathbf{j} + \tfrac{5}{3}\mathbf{k} + \mu(3\mathbf{i} + \mathbf{j} + \tfrac{4}{3}\mathbf{k})$

(d) $\dfrac{x-14}{5} = y - 3 = \dfrac{z+2}{2}$ and $\dfrac{x-2}{3} = \dfrac{y+5}{2} = 2 - z$

11 Find, in degrees to 1 decimal place, the acute angle between the lines with equations:

(a) $\mathbf{r} = \mathbf{i} + 2\mathbf{j} - \mathbf{k} + \lambda(-\mathbf{i} + 3\mathbf{j} - \mathbf{k})$ and
$\mathbf{r} = -\mathbf{i} + 2\mathbf{j} - \mathbf{k} + \mu(3\mathbf{i} - \mathbf{j} + 2\mathbf{k})$

(b) $\mathbf{r} = -\mathbf{i} + 3\mathbf{j} + 5\mathbf{k} + \lambda(-3\mathbf{i} + 4\mathbf{j} + \mathbf{k})$ and
$\mathbf{r} = 3\mathbf{i} - 2\mathbf{j} + \mathbf{k} + \mu(4\mathbf{i} - 2\mathbf{j} + 6\mathbf{k})$

(c) $\mathbf{r} = \mathbf{i} - 2\mathbf{k} + \lambda(-2\mathbf{i} + 3\mathbf{j} - \mathbf{k})$ and
$\mathbf{r} = 2\mathbf{j} - 4\mathbf{k} + \mu(3\mathbf{i} - \mathbf{j} + 6\mathbf{k})$

(d) $\dfrac{x-1}{2} = \dfrac{y+2}{1} = 3 - z$ and $\dfrac{x+1}{-2} = y - 3 = \dfrac{z-7}{2}$

(e) $\dfrac{x-2}{5} = \dfrac{3-y}{3} = \dfrac{z+1}{2}$ and $\dfrac{9-x}{3} = \dfrac{y-2}{5} = 2 - z$

12 Points A, B, C, D in a plane have position vectors $\mathbf{a} = 6\mathbf{i} + 8\mathbf{j}$, $\mathbf{b} = \frac{3}{2}\mathbf{a}$, $\mathbf{c} = 6\mathbf{i} + 3\mathbf{j}$, $\mathbf{d} = \frac{5}{3}\mathbf{c}$ respectively. Write down vector equations of the lines AD and BC and find the position vector of their point of intersection. [L]

13 State a vector equation of the line passing through the points A and B whose position vectors are $\mathbf{i} - \mathbf{j} + 3\mathbf{k}$ and $\mathbf{i} + 2\mathbf{j} + 2\mathbf{k}$ respectively. Determine the position vector of the point C which divides the line segment AB internally such that $AC = 2CB$. [L]

14 Show that the lines

$$\mathbf{r} = (-2\mathbf{i} + 5\mathbf{j} - 11\mathbf{k}) + \lambda(3\mathbf{i} + \mathbf{j} + 3\mathbf{k})$$
$$\mathbf{r} = 8\mathbf{i} + 9\mathbf{j} + \mu(4\mathbf{i} + 2\mathbf{j} + 5\mathbf{k})$$

intersect and find the position vector of their common point. [L]

15 Find the point of intersection of the line through the points $(2, 0, 1)$ and $(-1, 3, 4)$ and the line through the points $(-1, 3, 0)$ and $(4, -2, 5)$. Calculate the acute angle between the two lines. [L]

16 The point P lies on the line which is parallel to the vector $2\mathbf{i} + \mathbf{j} - \mathbf{k}$ and which passes through the point with position vector $\mathbf{i} + \mathbf{j} + 2\mathbf{k}$. The point Q lies on another line which is parallel to the vector $\mathbf{i} + \mathbf{j} - 2\mathbf{k}$ and which passes through the point with position vector $\mathbf{i} + \mathbf{j} + 4\mathbf{k}$. The line PQ is perpendicular to both these lines. Find the vector equation of the line PQ and the coordinates of the mid-point of PQ. [L]

17 The position vectors of three points A, B and C with respect to a fixed origin O are

$$(2\mathbf{i} - 2\mathbf{j} + \mathbf{k}), \quad (4\mathbf{i} + 2\mathbf{j} + \mathbf{k}) \text{ and } (\mathbf{i} + \mathbf{j} + 3\mathbf{k})$$

respectively.

(a) Write down unit vectors in the direction of the lines CA and CB and calculate the size of $\angle ACB$, in degrees, to 1 decimal place.

The mid-point of AB is M.

(b) Find a vector equation of the straight line passing through C and M.

(c) Show that AB and CM are perpendicular.

(d) Find the position vector of the point N on the line CM such that $\angle ONC = 90°$. [L]

18 Show that the lines L_1 and L_2 which have cartesian equations

$$L_1: \quad \frac{x - 9}{2} = -y - 4 = z - 5$$

$$L_2: \quad x - 2 = \frac{y + 8}{2} = \frac{12 - z}{3}$$

meet in a point P. Find the coordinates of P. The point A is on the line L_1 and has y-coordinate zero. Find the x and z coordinates of A.

19 The lines L_1 and L_2 intersect at the point B. Given that the equations of the lines are

$$L_1: \quad \mathbf{r} = (2 + 3t)\mathbf{i} + (3 + 4t)\mathbf{j} + (4 + 2t)\mathbf{k}$$
$$L_2: \quad \mathbf{r} = (1 + 2s)\mathbf{i} + (1 + 3s)\mathbf{j} + (4s - 2)\mathbf{k}$$

where t and s are scalar parameters, find

(a) the coordinates of B

(b) the acute angle, in degrees to 1 decimal place, between the lines.

20 Referred to an origin O, the points A, B, C and D are $(3, 1, -1)$, $(6, 7, 8)$, $(2, 5, 0)$ and $(0, 7, -2)$ respectively.

(a) Find vector equations for AB and CD.

(b) Show that AB and CD intersect at the point $(4, 3, 2)$.

(c) Calculate the size of $\angle ACD$ to the nearest degree.

SUMMARY OF KEY POINTS

1 A vector is a quantity which has both magnitude and a direction in space.

2 A unit vector is a vector with magnitude (modulus) 1.

3 If **a** and **b** are parallel then $\mathbf{a} = \lambda\mathbf{b}$ for some scalar λ.

4 Vectors are added by the triangle law.

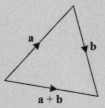

They can also be added or subtracted by the parallelogram law:

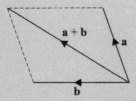 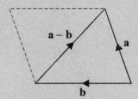

5 The vector $-\mathbf{a}$ has the same magnitude but opposite direction to **a**.

6 If **a** and **b** are non-parallel vectors and

$$\lambda\mathbf{a} + \mu\mathbf{b} = \alpha\mathbf{a} + \beta\mathbf{b}$$

where λ, μ, α, β are scalars, then:

$$\lambda = \alpha \text{ and } \mu = \beta$$

7 If the points A and B have position vectors **a** and **b** respectively, then M, the mid-point of AB, has position vector $\frac{1}{2}(\mathbf{a} + \mathbf{b})$.

8 The modulus of $\mathbf{a} = x\mathbf{i} + y\mathbf{j} + z\mathbf{k}$ is

$$|\mathbf{a}| = \sqrt{(x^2 + y^2 + z^2)}$$

9 If P has coordinates (x, y, z) then a unit vector in the direction of $\overrightarrow{OP}$, where O is the origin, is:

$$\frac{x\mathbf{i} + y\mathbf{j} + z\mathbf{k}}{\sqrt{(x^2 + y^2 + z^2)}}$$

10 The scalar (or dot) product of $\mathbf{a} = x_1\mathbf{i} + y_1\mathbf{j} + z_1\mathbf{k}$ and $\mathbf{b} = x_2\mathbf{i} + y_2\mathbf{j} + z_2\mathbf{k}$ is

$$\mathbf{a} \cdot \mathbf{b} = x_1 x_2 + y_1 y_2 + z_1 z_2 = |\mathbf{a}||\mathbf{b}| \cos \theta$$

where θ is the angle between $\mathbf{a}$ and $\mathbf{b}$.

11 If $\mathbf{a}$ and $\mathbf{b}$ are perpendicular then $\mathbf{a} \cdot \mathbf{b} = 0$ and vice versa.

12 The length of the projection of $\mathbf{a}$ on $\mathbf{b}$ is $\dfrac{\mathbf{a} \cdot \mathbf{b}}{|\mathbf{b}|}$.

13 The vector equation of the straight line passing through the point with position vector $\mathbf{a}$ and parallel to the vector $\mathbf{b}$ is

$$\mathbf{r} = \mathbf{a} + \lambda \mathbf{b}$$

14 Cartesian equations of the straight line passing through the point (a_1, a_2, a_3) and parallel to the vector $b_1\mathbf{i} + b_2\mathbf{j} + b_3\mathbf{k}$ are

$$\frac{x - a_1}{b_1} = \frac{y - a_2}{b_2} = \frac{z - a_3}{b_3}$$

Review exercise 2

1 Find the value of x for which

$$4\tanh x - \operatorname{sech} x = 1$$

giving your solution in terms of natural logarithms. [L]

2 With respect to a fixed origin O, the point A has position vector $2\mathbf{i} - \mathbf{j} + 3\mathbf{k}$. The line l passes through A and is parallel to the vector $-\mathbf{i} + 2\mathbf{j} - 2\mathbf{k}$.

(a) Giving your answer to the nearest degree, calculate the acute angle between OA and l.

The point B with position vector $3\mathbf{i} + u\mathbf{j} + v\mathbf{k}$ lies on l.

(b) Calculate the values of u and v. [L]

3 Given that $t = \tan\theta$, show that

(a) $\sin 2\theta = \dfrac{2t}{1 + t^2}$

(b) $\dfrac{\mathrm{d}\theta}{\mathrm{d}t} = \dfrac{1}{1 + t^2}$

Hence, or otherwise, evaluate

$$\int_{\frac{\pi}{6}}^{\frac{\pi}{3}} \left(\frac{1}{\sin 2\theta}\right) \mathrm{d}\theta$$

giving your answer in the form $p\ln q$, where p and q are numbers to be found. [L]

4 Referred to a fixed origin O, the points A, B and C are given by

$$\overrightarrow{OA} = 9\mathbf{i}, \ \overrightarrow{OB} = 3\mathbf{j} \text{ and } \overrightarrow{OC} = 2\mathbf{k}$$

(a) Obtain $\overrightarrow{CA}$ and $\overrightarrow{CB}$.

(b) Calculate the size of $\angle ACB$, giving your answer to the nearest tenth of a degree. [L]

5 Evaluate

$$I = \int_0^1 \sqrt{(4 - x^2)}\, dx$$

On a sketch, indicate a region R which has area I.   [L]

6 Starting from the definitions of $\cosh x$ and $\sinh x$ in terms of e^x, show that

$$\cosh^2 x - \sinh^2 x \equiv 1$$ [L]

7 By use of the substitution $u^2 = 1 + x$, or otherwise, find the exact value of

$$\int_3^8 \frac{dx}{x\sqrt{(1 + x)}}$$ [L]

8 (a) Starting from the definition of $\tanh x$ in terms of e^x, show that

$$\operatorname{artanh} x = \tfrac{1}{2}\ln\left(\frac{1 + x}{1 - x}\right)$$

and sketch the graph of $y = \operatorname{artanh} x$.
   (b) Solve the equation $x = \tanh[\ln \sqrt{(6x)}]$ for $0 < x < 1$.   [L]

9 With respect to an origin O, the position vectors of the points L and M are $2\mathbf{i} - 3\mathbf{j} + 3\mathbf{k}$ and $5\mathbf{i} + \mathbf{j} + c\mathbf{k}$ respectively, where c is a constant. The point N is such that $OLMN$ is a rectangle.
   (a) Find the value of c.
   (b) Write down the position vector of N.
   (c) Find, in the form $\mathbf{r} = \mathbf{p} + t\mathbf{q}$, an equation of the line MN.

          [L]

10          $$f(x) \equiv \frac{1}{(x + 2)(x^2 + 4)}$$

Express $f(x)$ in partial fractions.
Show that

$$\int_0^2 f(x)\, dx = \frac{(\pi + 2\ln 2)}{32}$$ [L]

11 With respect to an origin O, the position vectors of the points L, M and N are $(4\mathbf{i} + 7\mathbf{j} + 7\mathbf{k})$, $(\mathbf{i} + 3\mathbf{j} + 2\mathbf{k})$ and $(2\mathbf{i} + 4\mathbf{j} + 6\mathbf{k})$ respectively.
    (a) Find the vectors $\overrightarrow{ML}$ and $\overrightarrow{MN}$.
    (b) Prove that $\cos \angle LMN = \frac{9}{10}$.   [L]

12 Using the substitution $t = \tan x$, evaluate

$$\int_0^{\frac{\pi}{4}} \frac{1}{3\cos^2 x + \sin^2 x}\,dx$$

giving your answer in terms of π.   [L]

13 Write down an expression for $\tanh x$ in terms of exponentials. Hence, or otherwise, find the exact value of x for which $\tanh x = \frac{1}{2}$.   [L]

14 The vectors $\mathbf{u}$ and $\mathbf{v}$ are given by

$$\mathbf{u} = 5\mathbf{i} - 4\mathbf{j} + s\mathbf{k}, \quad \mathbf{v} = 2\mathbf{i} + t\mathbf{j} - 3\mathbf{k}$$

    (a) Given that the vectors $\mathbf{u}$ and $\mathbf{v}$ are perpendicular, find a relation between the scalars s and t.
    (b) Given instead that the vectors $\mathbf{u}$ and $\mathbf{v}$ are parallel, find the values of the scalars s and t.   [L]

15

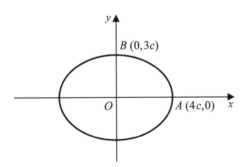

The figure shows a sketch of the ellipse given parametrically by the equations

$$x = 4c\cos t, \quad y = 3c\sin t, \quad -\pi < t \leqslant \pi,$$

where c is a positive constant.
    (a) Write down the value of t at the point $A(4c, 0)$ and at the point $B(0, 3c)$.
    (b) By considering the integral $\displaystyle\int y\,\frac{dx}{dt}\,dt$ find, in terms of c, the area of the region enclosed by the ellipse.   [L]

16 Write down, in vector form, an equation of the line l which passes through $L(-3, 1, -7)$ and $M(5, 3, 5)$.

Find the position vector of the point P on the line for which OP is perpendicular to l, where O is the origin.

Hence find the shortest distance from O to the line l.   [L]

17 Show that

$$\int_0^{\ln 3} x \sinh x \, dx = \tfrac{5}{3} \ln 3 - \tfrac{4}{3}$$ [L]

18 (a) Express $x^2 + 6x - 7$ in the form $(x + a)^2 - b$, where a and b are integers.

(b) Using a suitable hyperbolic substitution, or otherwise, obtain

$$\int_1^2 \frac{1}{\sqrt{(x^2 + 6x - 7)}} \, dx$$

giving your answer in terms of natural logarithms.   [L]

19 Vectors $\mathbf{r}$ and $\mathbf{s}$ are given by

$$\mathbf{r} = \lambda \mathbf{i} + (2\lambda - 1)\mathbf{j} - \mathbf{k}$$
$$\mathbf{s} = (1 - \lambda)\mathbf{i} + 3\lambda \mathbf{j} + (4\lambda - 1)\mathbf{k}$$

where λ is a scalar.

(a) Find the values of λ for which $\mathbf{r}$ and $\mathbf{s}$ are perpendicular.

When $\lambda = 2$, $\mathbf{r}$ and $\mathbf{s}$ are the position vectors of the points A and B respectively, referred to an origin O.

(b) Find $\overrightarrow{AB}$.

(c) Use a scalar product to find the size of $\angle BAO$, giving your answer to the nearest degree.   [L]

20 Evaluate

(a) $\displaystyle \int_{-1}^0 \frac{1}{\sqrt{(3 - 2x - x^2)}} \, dx$

(b) $\displaystyle \int_{-1}^0 \frac{x}{\sqrt{(3 - 2x - x^2)}} \, dx$ [L]

21 Find the values of x for which

$$4 \tanh^2 x - 1 = 0$$

giving your answers in the form $a \ln b$, where $a \in \mathbb{Q}$ and $b \in \mathbb{Z}^+$.   [L]

22 (a) Using the same axes, sketch the graphs given by the equations

$$y = \sinh x, \quad x \in \mathbb{R}$$
$$y = \cosh x, \quad x \in \mathbb{R}$$

(b) Show that the area of the finite region bounded by these curves and the lines $x = a$, $x = b$, $0 < a < b$, is $e^{-a} - e^{-b}$.

(c) Find the limiting value of this area as both $a \to 0$ and $b \to \infty$.   [L]

23 The point A has coordinates $(7, -1, 3)$ and the point B has coordinates $(10, -2, 2)$. The line l has vector equation

$$\mathbf{r} = \mathbf{i} + \mathbf{j} + \mathbf{k} + \lambda(3\mathbf{i} - \mathbf{j} + \mathbf{k}), \text{where } \lambda \text{ is a real parameter.}$$

(a) Show that the point A lies on the line l.

(b) Find the length of AB.

(c) Find the size of the acute angle between the line l and the line segment AB, giving your answer to the nearest degree.

(d) Hence, or otherwise, calculate the perpendicular distance from B to the line l, giving your answer to 2 significant figures.   [L]

24 (a) Express $\sinh t$ and $\cosh t$ in terms of e^t and hence show that, if $x = \sinh t$, then

  (i) $\dfrac{\mathrm{d}x}{\mathrm{d}t} = \cosh t$

  (ii) $t = \ln[x + \sqrt{(x^2 + 1)}]$.

(b) Using the substitution $x = \sinh t$, or otherwise, evaluate the integral

$$I = \int_0^1 \sqrt{(x^2 + 1)} \, \mathrm{d}x$$

(c) Evaluate $\displaystyle\int_0^1 \operatorname{arsinh} x \, \mathrm{d}x$.   [L]

25 A line l_1 passes through the point A, with position vector $5\mathbf{i} + 3\mathbf{j}$, and the point B, with position vector $-2\mathbf{i} - 4\mathbf{j} + 7\mathbf{k}$.

(a) Write down an equation of the line l_1.

A second line l_2 has equation $\mathbf{r} = \mathbf{i} - 3\mathbf{j} - 4\mathbf{k} + \mu(\mathbf{i} + 2\mathbf{j} + 3\mathbf{k})$ where μ is a parameter.

(b) Show that l_1 and l_2 are perpendicular to each other.

    (c) Show that the two lines meet, and find the position vector of the point of intersection.

The point C has position vector $2\mathbf{i} - \mathbf{j} - \mathbf{k}$.

    (d) Show that C lies on l_2.

The point D is the image of C after reflection in the line l_1.

    (e) Find the position vector of D.   [L]

26 Express $\tanh x$ in terms of (a) e^x (b) e^{2x}.

Hence, or otherwise, prove that

$$\tanh (x+y) \equiv \frac{\tanh x + \tanh y}{1 + \tanh x \tanh y}$$

Determine whether $\tanh x$ is an even function, an odd function or neither.

Starting from the expression for $\tanh x$ in terms of e^x show that

$$\frac{\mathrm{d}}{\mathrm{d}x} (\tanh x) = \operatorname{sech}^2 x$$

Show that the volume of the solid generated when the finite region enclosed by the curve with equation $y = \tanh x$, the line $x = +1$ and the x-axis is rotated through 2π radians about the x-axis is $\dfrac{2\pi}{1 + e^2}$.

        [L]

27 Referred to the origin O, the points A and B have position vectors $(4\mathbf{i} - 11\mathbf{j} + 4\mathbf{k})$ and $(7\mathbf{i} + \mathbf{j} + 7\mathbf{k})$ respectively.

    (a) Find a vector equation for the line passing through A and B in terms of a parameter t.

    (b) Find the position vector of the point P on AB such that OP is perpendicular to AB.   [L]

28 (a) Sketch the graphs of (i) $y = \sinh x$ (ii) $y = \tanh x$.

Starting from the definitions of $\sinh x$ and $\cosh x$ in terms of e^x, show that $\cosh^2 x - \sinh^2 x \equiv 1$.

Given that $\operatorname{cosech} x = -\frac{9}{40}$, find the exact values of (iii) $\cosh x$ (iv) $\tanh 2x$.

    (b) Find

    (i) $\displaystyle\int \frac{1}{\sqrt{(x^2 + 2x + 10)}}\, \mathrm{d}x$ (ii) $\displaystyle\int \tanh 3x \operatorname{sech} 3x\, \mathrm{d}x$.   [L]

29 Using the definitions of sinh and cosh, prove that

$$\text{artanh}\, x = \tfrac{1}{2} \ln \frac{1+x}{1-x}$$

for $-1 < x < 1$.

(a) Find $\dfrac{\mathrm{d}}{\mathrm{d}x}(\text{artanh}\, x)$.

(b) Sketch the graph of $y = \text{artanh}\, x$ for $-1 < x < 1$.

(c) Calculate, to 3 decimal places, the area of the finite region bounded by the curve with equation $y = \text{artanh}\, x$, the x-axis, and the line $x = \tfrac{1}{2}$. [L]

30 Use the substitution $x = \dfrac{a}{\sinh \theta}$, where a is a constant, to show that, for $x > 0$, $a > 0$,

$$\int \frac{1}{x\sqrt{(x^2 + a^2)}}\, \mathrm{d}x = -\frac{1}{a}\,\text{arsinh}\left(\frac{a}{x}\right) + \text{constant} \qquad [L]$$

31 Show that the curve with equation $y = \text{sech}\, x$ has $\dfrac{\mathrm{d}^2 y}{\mathrm{d}x^2} = 0$ at points where $x = \pm \ln p$ and state a value for p.

Sketch the curve with equation $y = \text{sech}\, x$. [L]

32 Use the substitution $t = \sinh x$ to prove that

$$\int_0^a (1 + t^2)^{\frac{1}{2}}\, \mathrm{d}t = \tfrac{1}{2} a(1 + a^2)^{\frac{1}{2}} + \tfrac{1}{2}\ln[a + (1 + a^2)^{\frac{1}{2}}] \qquad [L]$$

33 Referred to an origin O, the points A and B have position vectors given by

$$\overrightarrow{OA} = 7\mathbf{i} + 3\mathbf{j} + 8\mathbf{k}$$
$$\overrightarrow{OB} = 5\mathbf{i} + 4\mathbf{j} + 6\mathbf{k}$$

(a) Show that the point P with position vector given by

$$\overrightarrow{OP} = (5 - 2\lambda)\mathbf{i} + (4 + \lambda)\mathbf{j} + (6 - 2\lambda)\mathbf{k}$$

where λ is a parameter, lies on the straight line L passing through the points A and B.

(b) Find the value of λ for which OP is perpendicular to L.

With centre O and radius OA, a circle is drawn to cut the line L at the points A and C.

(c) Determine the position vector of C. [L]

34 Starting from the definition of $\cosh x$ in terms of e^x, find, in terms of natural logarithms, the values of x for which

$$5 = 3\cosh x \qquad\qquad\text{[L]}$$

35 Find the minimum value of $(5\cosh x + 3\sinh x)$. [L]

36 In the diagram, M is the mid-point of OA and $ON : NB = 3 : 1$. The lines AN and BM intersect at the point X. $\overrightarrow{OA} = \mathbf{a}$ and $\overrightarrow{OB} = \mathbf{b}$.

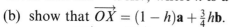

(a) Write down, in terms of $\mathbf{a}$ and $\mathbf{b}$, expressions for $\overrightarrow{AN}$ and $\overrightarrow{BM}$.

Given that $\overrightarrow{AX} = h\,\overrightarrow{AN}$, where h is a scalar,

(b) show that $\overrightarrow{OX} = (1 - h)\mathbf{a} + \frac{3}{4}h\mathbf{b}$.

Given that $\overrightarrow{BX} = k\,\overrightarrow{BM}$, where k is a scalar,

(c) find an expression for $\overrightarrow{OX}$ in terms of $\mathbf{a}$, $\mathbf{b}$ and k.

Using the expressions for $\overrightarrow{OX}$ found in (b) and (c),

(d) calculate the values of h and k.

(e) Write down the value of the ratio $AX : XN$. [L]

37 The position vectors of the points A and B relative to an origin O are $5\mathbf{i} + 4\mathbf{j} + \mathbf{k}$, $-\mathbf{i} + \mathbf{j} - 2\mathbf{k}$ respectively. Find the position vector of the point P which lies on AB produced such that $AP = 2BP$. [L]

38 Show that $\displaystyle\int_1^{\sqrt{3}} \frac{x + 3}{\sqrt{(4 - x^2)}}\,\mathrm{d}x = \frac{\pi}{2} + \sqrt{3} - 1.$ [L]

39 Solve the equation

$$4\tanh x - \operatorname{sech} x = 1$$

giving your solution in logarithmic form. [L]

40 Evaluate

(a) $\displaystyle\int_1^3 \frac{1}{\sqrt{(x^2 - 2x + 5)}}\,\mathrm{d}x$

(b) $\displaystyle\int_0^1 \operatorname{arsinh} x\,\mathrm{d}x$ [L]

41 Prove that $\cosh^2 x - \sinh^2 x \equiv 1$.

Solve the equation

$$3\sinh^2 x - 2\cosh x - 2 = 0$$

Give the values of x as natural logarithms. [L]

42 Referred to a fixed origin O, the points A and B have position vectors $(5\mathbf{i} - \mathbf{j} - \mathbf{k})$ and $(\mathbf{i} - 5\mathbf{j} + 7\mathbf{k})$ respectively.

(a) Find an equation of the line AB.

(b) Show that the point C with position vector $4\mathbf{i} - 2\mathbf{j} + \mathbf{k}$ lies on AB.

(c) Show that OC is perpendicular to AB.

(d) Find the position vector of the point D, where $D \not\equiv A$, on AB such that $|\overrightarrow{OD}| = |\overrightarrow{OA}|$.　　　　　　[L]

43 (a) Find $\displaystyle\int \frac{\mathrm{d}x}{\sqrt{(x^2 - 2x + 10)}}$

(b) Find $\displaystyle\int \frac{\mathrm{d}x}{x^2 - 2x + 10}$

(c) By using the subsitution $x = \sin\theta$, show that

$$\int_0^{\frac{1}{2}} \frac{x^4 \,\mathrm{d}x}{\sqrt{(1 - x^2)}} = \frac{(4\pi - 7\sqrt{3})}{64}$$　　　[L]

44 Evaluate:

(a) $\displaystyle\int_0^1 \frac{1}{\sqrt{(4 + x^2)}} \,\mathrm{d}x$

(b) $\displaystyle\int_0^1 \frac{1}{\sqrt{(4 - x^2)}} \,\mathrm{d}x$　　　　　　[L]

45 (a) Evaluate

$$\int_{\frac{\pi}{3}}^{\frac{\pi}{2}} \frac{1}{1 + \cos\theta} \,\mathrm{d}\theta$$

(b) Show that

$$\int_1^3 \frac{3(x + 1)}{x^2(x^2 + 3)} \,\mathrm{d}x = \frac{1}{2}\ln 3 + \frac{2}{3} - \frac{\pi}{6\sqrt{3}}$$　　　[L]

46 If x and y satisfy the equations

$$\cosh x \cosh y = 2$$
$$\sinh x \sinh y = -1$$

show that $x = -y = \pm\ln(1 + \sqrt{2})$.　　　　　　[L]

47 Using the subsitution $u^2 = x^2 - 1$, or otherwise, evaluate

$$\int_{\sqrt{2}}^{\sqrt{5}} \frac{x^3}{\sqrt{(x^2-1)}}\,dx \qquad\qquad [L]$$

48 Use the substitution $t = \tan\left(\dfrac{x}{2}\right)$ and the formula

$$\cos x = \frac{1-t^2}{1+t^2}$$

to evaluate

$$\int_0^{\frac{\pi}{2}} \frac{1}{(1+3\cos x)}\,dx$$

giving your answer in terms of natural logarithms. [L]

49 Differentiate with respect to x:

(a) $\ln\cosh x$

(b) $\sinh(x^2)$

(c) $\arcsin(2x)$ [L]

50 (a) Show that $\displaystyle\int_1^2 \ln x\,dx = \ln\left(\dfrac{4}{e}\right)$.

(b) By using the substitution $x = \tan\theta$, or otherwise, show that

$$\int_0^1 \frac{dx}{(1+x^2)^2} = \frac{\pi+2}{8} \qquad\qquad [L]$$

51 Starting from the definitions of cosh and sinh in terms of exponentials, show that

(a) $\cosh^2 x - \sinh^2 x \equiv 1$

(b) $\operatorname{arcoth} x = \frac{1}{2}\ln\left(\dfrac{x+1}{x-1}\right)$, $x > 1$.

(c) Solve the equation

$$\operatorname{cosech}^2 x - 2\coth x = 2$$

giving your answer in terms of natural logarithms.

(d) Find $\displaystyle\int_2^3 \operatorname{arcoth} x\,dx$, giving your answer in terms of natural logarithms. [L]

52 Find (a) $\displaystyle\int x\sqrt{(4-x^2)}\,dx$

(b) $\displaystyle\int \sqrt{(4-x^2)}\,dx$. [L]

53 Write down the value of $\displaystyle\int \frac{x}{\sqrt{(1-x^2)}}\,dx$.

Hence, or otherwise, find $\displaystyle\int \arcsin x\,dx$.   [L]

54 Show that $\displaystyle\int_0^{\frac{\pi}{4}} \frac{2}{3\sin 2x + 4\cos 2x}\,dx = \tfrac{1}{5}\ln 6$.   [L]

55 Solve the simultaneous equations:

$$\cosh x + \cosh y = 4$$
$$\sinh x + \sinh y = 2$$

giving your answers in terms of natural logarithms.   [L]

56 $ORST$ is a parallelogram, U is the mid-point of RS and V is the mid-point of ST. Relative to the origin O, $\mathbf{r}$, $\mathbf{s}$, $\mathbf{t}$, $\mathbf{u}$ and $\mathbf{v}$ are the position vectors of R, S, T, U and V respectively.

(a) Express $\mathbf{s}$ in terms of $\mathbf{r}$ and $\mathbf{t}$.

(b) Express $\mathbf{v}$ in terms of $\mathbf{s}$ and $\mathbf{t}$.

(c) Hence, or otherwise, show that

$$4(\mathbf{u}+\mathbf{v}) = 3(\mathbf{r}+\mathbf{s}+\mathbf{t})$$ [L]

57 (a) Find $\displaystyle\int \frac{1}{\sinh x + 2\cosh x}\,dx$.

(b) Show that

$$\int_1^4 \frac{3x-1}{(x^2-2x+10)^{\frac{1}{2}}}\,dx = 9(\sqrt{2}-1) + 2\,\mathrm{arsinh}\,1$$ [L]

58 Two points A and B have position vectors $\mathbf{a}$ and $\mathbf{b}$ respectively. Show that the point which divides AB internally in the ratio $m:n$ has position vector

$$\frac{n\mathbf{a} + m\mathbf{b}}{n+m}$$

Three non-collinear points A, B and C have position vectors $\mathbf{a}$, $\mathbf{b}$ and $\mathbf{c}$ respectively. The point D divides AB internally in the ratio $2:1$. The point E divides BC internally in the ratio $2:1$. Show that DE produced meets AC produced at the point with position vector

$$\tfrac{4}{3}\mathbf{c} - \tfrac{1}{3}\mathbf{a}$$ [L]

59 (a) Show that $\displaystyle\int_0^{\frac{\pi}{2}} \frac{1}{3+5\cos x}\,dx = \frac{1}{4}\ln 3$.

   (b) Use the substitution $x = \dfrac{1}{u}$ to find the value of $\displaystyle\int_{\frac{1}{2}}^2 \frac{\ln x}{1+x^2}\,dx$.

   [L]

60 Use the substitution $t = \tan x$ to evaluate

$$\int_0^{\frac{\pi}{4}} \frac{1}{3\sin 2x + 3}\,dx$$

giving your answer in the form $\dfrac{p}{q}$, where p and q are integers.

   [L]

Complex numbers

7

Chapter 2 of Book P1 explained how to solve quadratic equations. One method of doing this was by using the quadratic formula. So for the equation

$$ax^2 + bx + c = 0$$

the solutions are:

$$x = \frac{-b \pm \sqrt{(b^2 - 4ac)}}{2a}$$

This is fine so long as $b^2 - 4ac$ is positive or equal to zero. However, you meet a big problem if $b^2 - 4ac$ is negative.

For example, consider the equation

$$x^2 + 2x + 5 = 0$$

Applying the formula gives:

$$x = \frac{-2 \pm \sqrt{(4 - 20)}}{2} = \frac{-2 \pm \sqrt{(-16)}}{2}$$

So you need the square root of -16. This is the problem. The square root of -16 is not 4, since $4^2 = +16$, and it is not -4 since $(-4)^2 = +16$. Thus you cannot solve this equation at the moment because you cannot find the square root of -16.

7.1 Imaginary numbers

In order to overcome the problem, you need to invent a new number. So mathematicians define the square root of -1 as:

■ $\sqrt{(-1)} = i$

With this definition you can now find $\sqrt{(-16)}$, because

$$\sqrt{(-16)} = \sqrt{(16 \times -1)}$$
$$= \sqrt{16} \times \sqrt{(-1)}$$
$$= 4 \times i = 4i$$

Similarly, $\quad \sqrt{(-81)} = \sqrt{81} \times \sqrt{(-1)} = 9 \times i = 9i$

Also: $\quad \sqrt{(-53)} = \sqrt{53} \times \sqrt{(-1)} = 7.280i$ (4 s.f.)

A number of the form bi is called an **imaginary number**. The numbers that you have dealt with in mathematics up until now, for example 7, -4, $\sqrt{17}$, π, e, are called **real numbers** and the complete set of real numbers is usually denoted by the symbol $\mathbb{R}$. So $5 \in \mathbb{R}$, $-\sqrt{17} \in \mathbb{R}$, $\pi \in \mathbb{R}$, and so on.

Going back to the quadratic equation

$$x^2 + 2x + 5 = 0$$

you can now solve it:

$$\begin{aligned}
x &= \frac{-2 \pm (-16)}{2} \\
&= \frac{-2 \pm \sqrt{16}\sqrt{(-1)}}{2} \\
&= \frac{-2 \pm 4i}{2} \\
&= -1 \pm 2i
\end{aligned}$$

So the roots of $x^2 + 2x + 5 = 0$ are $x = -1 + 2i$ and $x = -1 - 2i$.

You could also solve this equation by completing the square:

$$x^2 + 2x + 5 = 0$$

so: $$\begin{aligned}
x^2 + 2x &= -5 \\
(x+1)^2 - 1 &= -5 \\
(x+1)^2 &= -4
\end{aligned}$$

Now since $i = \sqrt{(-1)}$ then $i^2 = -1$.

So: $$(x+1)^2 = -4 = 4 \times -1 = 4i^2$$

Thus: $$\begin{aligned}
(x+1) &= \pm\sqrt{(4i^2)} \\
(x+1) &= \pm 2i
\end{aligned}$$

So $x = -1 \pm 2i$, as before.

Example 1

Solve the equation $x^2 + 25 = 0$.

$$x^2 + 25 = 0$$

$$\Rightarrow \quad x^2 = -25$$

$$x = \pm\sqrt{(-25)} = \pm 5i$$

Example 2

Solve the equation $5x^2 - 2x + 2 = 0$.

$$x = \frac{2 \pm \sqrt{(4 - 40)}}{10}$$

$$= \frac{2 \pm \sqrt{(-36)}}{10}$$

$$= \frac{2 \pm 6i}{10}$$

$$= \tfrac{1}{5} \pm \tfrac{3}{5}i$$

Example 3

Solve the equation $2x^2 + 3x + 6 = 0$.

$$x = \frac{-3 \pm \sqrt{(9 - 48)}}{4}$$

$$= \frac{-3 \pm \sqrt{(-39)}}{4}$$

$$= \frac{-3 \pm 6.245i}{4}$$

So: $$x = -0.75 \pm 1.56i$$

7.2 Complex numbers and their manipulation

You will notice from the four quadratic equations solved above that the solutions are all of the form $a \pm bi$, where $a, b \in \mathbb{R}$. The first solution was $-1 \pm 2i$, the second $0 \pm 5i$, then $\tfrac{1}{5} \pm \tfrac{3}{5}i$ and finally $-0.75 \pm 1.56i$.

■ **Any number of the form $a + ib$ where $a, b \in \mathbb{R}$ is called a *complex number*.**

a is called the **real part** of the number and b is called the **imaginary part** of the number. You write

$$\mathrm{Re}(a + ib) = a \quad \text{and} \quad \mathrm{Im}(a + ib) = b$$

Of course, if $b = 0$ the number has no imaginary part (for example $7 + 0i = 7$) and so it is a real number. Real numbers, then, are a subset of complex numbers.

Likewise, if $a = 0$ the number has no real part and is called a **pure imaginary number**. So pure imaginary numbers are also a subset of the set of complex numbers. The set of complex numbers is denoted by $\mathbb{C}$.

Adding and subtracting complex numbers

You can add complex numbers together by adding the real parts and then adding the imaginary parts.

You can subtract one complex number from another by subtracting the real parts and then subtracting the imaginary parts.

So: $$(a + ib) + (c + id) = (a + c) + i(b + d)$$

and: $$(a + ib) - (c + id) = (a - c) + i(b - d)$$

Example 4
Simplify: (a) $(2 + 3i) + (7 - 6i)$ (b) $(25 - 7i) - (13 - 4i)$.

(a) $(2 + 3i) + (7 - 6i) = (2 + 7) + (3 - 6)i = 9 - 3i$

(b) $(25 - 7i) - (13 - 4i) = (25 - 13) + (-7 + 4)i$
$$= 12 - 3i$$

Multiplying one complex number by another

If you wish to multiply two complex numbers together you must apply the rules of algebra. (These were demonstrated in Book P1, chapter 1.)

So: $(a + ib)(c + id) = ac + iad + ibc + i^2 bd$
$$= ac + i(ad + bc) - bd \text{ (using } i^2 = -1)$$
$$= (ac - bd) + i(ad + bc)$$

Example 5
Multiply $(4 - 3i)$ by $(-7 + 5i)$.

$$(4 - 3i)(-7 + 5i) = -28 + 20i + 21i - 15i^2$$
$$= -28 + 20i + 21i + 15$$
$$= -13 + 41i$$

Dividing one complex number by another

If you have a complex number $a + ib$ then the complex number $a - ib$ is called the **complex conjugate** of the first, and vice versa. So $(-2 + 5i)$ and $(-2 - 5i)$ are complex conjugates. $-2 + 5i$ is the complex conjugate of $-2 - 5i$ and $-2 - 5i$ is the complex conjugate of $-2 + 5i$.

■ **If z is a complex number, its complex conjugate is denoted by z^*.**

When you multiply a complex number by its conjugate the result is always a *real* number. For example:

$$\begin{aligned} (a + ib)(a - ib) &= a^2 - abi + abi - i^2b^2 \\ &= a^2 - abi + abi + b^2 \\ &= a^2 + b^2 \end{aligned}$$

Complex conjugates are useful when you need to divide one complex number by another.

Example 6

Express $\dfrac{2 + 3i}{1 - 2i}$ in the form $a + bi$ where $a, b \in \mathbb{R}$.

Multiplying both the numerator and the denominator by the complex conjugate of $1 - 2i$ gives:

$$\begin{aligned} \frac{2 + 3i}{1 - 2i} \times \frac{1 + 2i}{1 + 2i} &= \frac{2 + 4i + 3i + 6i^2}{1 + 2i - 2i - 4i^2} \\ &= \frac{2 + 7i - 6}{1 + 4} \\ &= \frac{-4 + 7i}{5} \\ &= -\tfrac{4}{5} + \tfrac{7}{5}i \end{aligned}$$

So the technique with division is to multiply both the numerator and the denominator by the complex conjugate of the denominator.

Example 7

Show that $\dfrac{1 + 2i}{3 - i} + \dfrac{1 - 2i}{3 + i}$ is real.

$$\frac{1 + 2i}{3 - i} + \frac{1 - 2i}{3 + i} = \left(\frac{1 + 2i}{3 - i} \times \frac{3 + i}{3 + i} \right) + \left(\frac{1 - 2i}{3 + i} \times \frac{3 - i}{3 - i} \right)$$

$$= \left(\frac{3 + 6i + i + 2i^2}{9 - i^2} \right) + \left(\frac{3 - 6i - i + 2i^2}{9 - i^2} \right)$$

$$= \frac{3 + 7i + 2i^2 + 3 - 7i + 2i^2}{9 - i^2}$$

$$= \frac{6 + 4i^2}{9 - i^2}$$

$$= \frac{6 - 4}{9 + 1}$$

$$= \tfrac{2}{10} = \tfrac{1}{5}, \text{ which is real.}$$

Exercise 7A

1 Express in terms of i:
   (a) $\sqrt{(-64)}$ (b) $\sqrt{(-7)}$ (c) $\sqrt{16} - \sqrt{(-81)}$
   (d) $3 - \sqrt{(-25)}$ (e) $\sqrt{(-100)} - \sqrt{(-49)}$

2 Simplify:
   (a) i^3 (b) i^7 (c) i^{-9}
   (d) $i(2i - 3i^3)$ (e) $(i + 2i^2)(3 - i)$

3 Write in the form $a + ib$, where $a, b \in \mathbb{R}$:
   (a) $2i(5 - 2i)$ (b) $(2 + i)^2$ (c) $(4 - i)^5$
   (d) $(1 + 2i)^2 + (3 - i)^3$ (e) $(1 + i)^2 - 3(2 - i)^3$

4 Find z^* given that $z =$
   (a) $2 + 4i$ (b) $3 - 6i$ (c) $-5 + 2i$
   (d) $-7 - 3i$ (e) $2i - 4$ (f) 6
   (g) $3i$ (h) $-3i + 7$

5 Simplify:
   (a) $(2 + 3i) + (4 - 7i)$ (b) $(-3 + 5i) + (-6 - 7i)$
   (c) $(-7 - 10i) + (2 - 3i)$ (d) $(2 + 4i) - (3 - 6i)$
   (e) $(-3 + 5i) - (-7 + 4i)$ (f) $(-9 - 6i) - (-8 - 9i)$
   (g) $(6 - 3i) - (8 - 5i)$

6 Express in the form $a + ib$, where $a, b \in \mathbb{R}$:

(a) $(2 + i)(3 - i)$

(b) $(-3 - 4i)(2 - 7i)$

(c) $(5 + 2i)(-3 + 4i)$

(d) $(1 - 5i)^2$

(e) $(2 - i)^3$

(f) $(1 + i)(2 - i)(i + 3)$

(g) $i(3 - 7i)(2 - i)$

7 Express in the form $a + ib$, where $a, b \in \mathbb{R}$:

(a) $\dfrac{2 - 7i}{1 + 2i}$

(b) $\dfrac{1 + 2i}{3 - i}$

(c) $\dfrac{1 + 2i}{3 + 4i}$

(d) $\dfrac{1}{1 + 2i}$

(e) $\dfrac{2 + 3i}{2 - 3i}$

(f) $\dfrac{5 + i}{i - 3}$

(g) $\dfrac{6}{4i - 3}$

(h) $\dfrac{1}{(i + 2)(1 - 2i)}$

8 Solve:

(a) $x^2 + 25 = 0$

(b) $x^3 + 64x = 0$

(c) $x^2 - 4x + 5 = 0$

(d) $x^2 + 6x + 10 = 0$

(e) $x^2 + 29 = 4x$

(f) $2x^2 + 3x + 7 = 0$

(g) $3x^2 + 2x + 1 = 0$

(h) $3x^2 - 2x + 2 = 0$

9 Express in the form $a + ib$, where $a, b \in \mathbb{R}$:

(a) $\dfrac{1}{1 + 2i} + \dfrac{1}{1 - 2i}$

(b) $\dfrac{1}{2 + i} - \dfrac{1}{1 + 5i}$

(c) $5 - 4i + \dfrac{5}{3 - 4i}$

10 Given that $z = -1 + 3i$, express $z + \dfrac{2}{z}$ in the form $a + ib$, where $a, b \in \mathbb{R}$.

11 Given that $T = \dfrac{x - iy}{x + iy}$, where $x, y, T \in \mathbb{R}$, show that

$$\frac{1 + T^2}{2T} = \frac{x^2 - y^2}{x^2 + y^2}$$

12 Show that the complex number $\dfrac{2 + 3i}{5 + i}$ can be expressed in the form $\lambda(1 + i)$, where λ is real.

State the value of λ.

Hence, or otherwise, show that $\left(\dfrac{2 + 3i}{5 + i}\right)^4$ is real and determine its value. [L]

7.3 The Argand diagram

Every pair of coordinates (x, y) can be plotted as a unique point on a pair of cartesian axes (see Book P1, page 63). So $(2, 3)$, $(1, 4)$, $(3, 2)$, $(-5, 7)$ are all distinct points when plotted.

Now the complex numbers $2 + 3i$, $1 + 4i$, $3 + 2i$, $-5 + 7i$ are all distinct. So if you draw a pair of cartesian axes and take the x-axis as the real axis and the y-axis as the imaginary axis, then for each complex number $z = x + iy$ there is a unique point (x, y) that you can plot using the axes. So the complex number $z_1 = 5 + 3i$ can be represented as the point $(5, 3)$, the number $z_2 = 4 - 2i$ can be represented as $(4, -2)$, and so on.

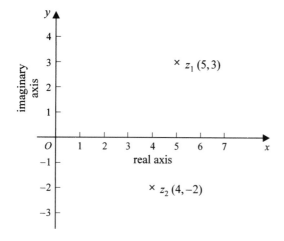

Each complex number besides being represented as a point can also be represented as a vector:

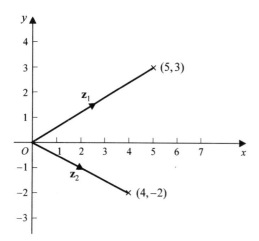

Of course, in this vector method of representation, any vector of the same magnitude as $\mathbf{z_1}$ and in the same direction as $\mathbf{z_1}$ could represent z_1, and the same with z_2, etc. The diagram used to represent complex numbers like this is called an **Argand diagram**.

If the vector method is used to represent complex numbers, then the parallelogram or triangle laws for the addition and subtraction of vectors can be used to find the representation of $z_1 + z_2$ and $z_1 - z_2$ on the Argand diagram:

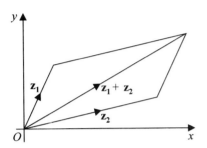
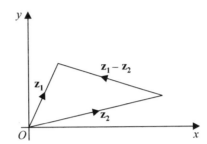

7.4 Modulus and argument of a complex number

The **modulus** of a complex number is defined as the length of the corresponding vector on the Argand diagram. So:

■ **the modulus of $z = x + iy$ is**

$$|z| = \sqrt{(x^2 + y^2)}$$

The **argument** of a complex number is the angle which the vector representing that number makes with the positive x-axis.

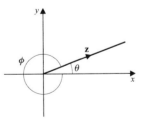

This definition needs a bit of thought though, since as you can see from the diagram the angle could be either θ or ϕ. Moreover, if θ is measured in degrees then $\theta° + 360°$, $\theta° + 720°$, $\theta° + 1080°$, etc. are each an angle which the vector representing z makes with the positive x-axis. Likewise, if θ is measured in radians, $\theta + 2\pi$, $\theta + 4\pi$, $\theta + 6\pi$, etc. could be the angle.

To get over this problem we define the **principal argument** of z to be the angle α which the vector makes with the positive x-axis and such that $-\pi < \alpha \leqslant \pi$ (if α is in radians) or $-180° < \alpha \leqslant 180°$ (if α is in degrees).

It is essential when you are asked to find the argument of a complex number that you draw the relevant vector on an Argand diagram. In this way you will know in which quadrant the vector lies and so you should be able to obtain the correct principal argument. You should be very careful, because a calculator will frequently not give you the *principal* argument.

In this book, and in the examination, you will often be asked for the argument of a complex number. In all cases it is the principal argument that you are being asked to find.

If z is a complex number, then the principal argument is often written as **arg** z.

Example 8
Find the modulus and argument of (a) $1 + i$ (b) $3 - 4i$ (c) $-2 - 3i$ (d) $-5 + 4i$.

(a)

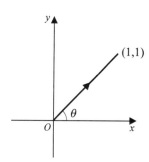

A vector representing $1 + i$ goes from the origin to $(1, 1)$.

$$|1 + i| = \sqrt{(1^2 + 1^2)} = \sqrt{2}$$

$\arg(1 + i)$ is the angle θ marked on the diagram.

Now by trigonometry: $\tan \theta = \frac{1}{1}$ and $\theta = \frac{\pi}{4}$

So: $\qquad |z| = |1 + i| = \sqrt{2}, \arg z = \frac{\pi}{4}$

(b)

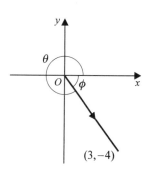

$$|3 - 4i| = \sqrt{[3^2 + (-4)^2]} = \sqrt{25} = 5$$

In this case ϕ is the principal argument, because it is the angle made with the positive x-axis and it is acute. So $\arg(3 - 4i)$ is ϕ as shown on the diagram.

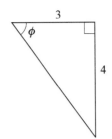

Now in the triangle $\tan\phi = \frac{4}{3}$

So:
$$\phi = 0.9273 \text{ (4 s.f.)}$$

Thus
$$\arg(3 - 4i) = -0.9273 \text{ (4 s.f.)}$$

(c)

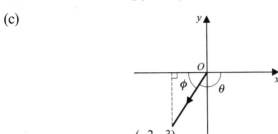

$$|-2 - 3i| = \sqrt{[(-2)^2 + (-3)^2]} = \sqrt{(4 + 9)} = \sqrt{13}$$

Since θ on the diagram is the angle required (because $-\pi < \theta \leqslant \pi$) and since this is obtuse, you need to work in the right-angled triangle containing ϕ:

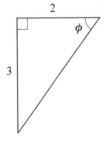

$$\tan\phi = \frac{3}{2}$$
$$\Rightarrow \quad \phi = 0.9828 \text{ (4 s.f.)}$$
$$\pi - 0.9828 = 2.159 \text{ (4 s.f.)}$$

So
$$\arg(-2 - 3i) = -2.159 \text{ (4 s.f.)}$$

(d)

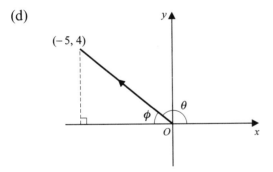

$$|-5 + 4i| = \sqrt{[(-5)^2 + 4^2]} = \sqrt{(25 + 16)} = \sqrt{41}$$

Since θ on the diagram is the angle required and since θ is obtuse, you must work in the right-angled triangle containing ϕ:

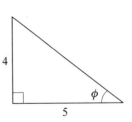

$$\tan\phi = \frac{4}{5}$$
$$\phi = 0.6747 \text{ (4 s.f.)}$$
$$\pi - 0.6747 = 2.467 \text{ (4 s.f.)}$$

So
$$\arg(-5 + 4i) = 2.467 \text{ (4 s.f.)}$$

Example 9

Express $\dfrac{2-i}{3+i}$ in the form $a+ib$ where $a, b \in \mathbb{R}$. Hence find $\left|\dfrac{2-i}{3+i}\right|$ and $\arg\left(\dfrac{2-i}{3+i}\right)$ and show $2-i$, $3+i$ and $\dfrac{2-i}{3+i}$ on an Argand diagram.

$$\frac{2-i}{3+i} = \frac{2-i}{3+i} \times \frac{3-i}{3-i}$$
$$= \frac{6-5i+i^2}{9+1}$$
$$= \frac{5-5i}{10}$$
$$= \tfrac{1}{2} - \tfrac{1}{2}i$$

$$\left|\tfrac{1}{2} - \tfrac{1}{2}i\right| = \sqrt{[(\tfrac{1}{2})^2 + (-\tfrac{1}{2})^2]}$$
$$= \sqrt{(\tfrac{1}{4} + \tfrac{1}{4})} = \tfrac{1}{\sqrt{2}}$$

$\arg(\tfrac{1}{2} - \tfrac{1}{2}i) = \theta$ on the diagram.

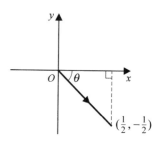

$$\tan\theta = \frac{\tfrac{1}{2}}{\tfrac{1}{2}} = 1$$
$$\theta = \frac{\pi}{4}$$

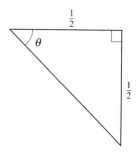

So $\qquad \arg(\tfrac{1}{2} - \tfrac{1}{2}i) = -\dfrac{\pi}{4}$

Finally, the Argand diagram looks like this:

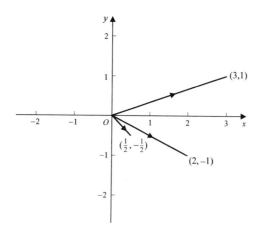

Exercise 7B

1 Represent the following on an Argand diagram:

(a) $2 + 3i$ (b) $-4 + 5i$ (c) $6 + 2i$

(d) $-3 - 2i$ (e) $2 - 4i$ (f) $-7 + 3i$

(g) $2i - 5$ (h) $-5i$ (i) $-3i + 4$

(j) $12i - 5$

2 Find $|z|$ and $\arg z$, in radians to 3 significant figures, where $z =$

(a) $3 - 2i$ (b) $3 + i$ (c) $6i$

(d) -5 (e) $-2 + i$ (f) $1 - 3i$

(g) $i\sqrt{3} + 1$ (h) $-5 + 12i$ (i) $\dfrac{5}{1 - i\sqrt{3}}$

(j) $\dfrac{2}{\sqrt{5} + i}$ (k) $(2 + i)(3 - 2i)$ (l) $\dfrac{1 + i}{2 - i}$

3 $z_1 = 3 + 4i$, $z_2 = 5 - 12i$, $z_3 = -1 - i$, $z_4 = -7 + 24i$. Find:

(a) $|z_1|, |z_2|, |z_3|, |z_4|$

(b) $\arg z_1, \arg z_2, \arg z_3, \arg z_4$

giving your answers in degrees to 1 decimal place.

4 Given that $a, b \in \mathbb{R}$, express each of the following in the form $a + ib$:

(a) $\dfrac{3 + i}{2 - i}$ (b) $3i^3 - 6i^6$ (c) $(1 + i)^4$

Find the modulus and the argument, in radians to 2 decimal places, of each answer.

5 Given that $z = 2 - i$, find z^2 and z^3.

Find $|z|, |z^2|, |z^3|$.

Find also, in radians to 2 decimal places, $\arg z$, $\arg z^2$, $\arg z^3$.

6 Find the modulus and the argument, in radians in terms of π, of

(a) $z_1 = \dfrac{1 + i}{1 - i}$ (b) $z_2 = \dfrac{\sqrt{2}}{1 - i}$ (c) $z_3 = \left(\dfrac{1 + i}{1 - i}\right)^2$

Plot z_1, z_2 and $z_1 + z_2$ on a Argand diagram.

Deduce that $\tan \dfrac{3\pi}{8} = 1 + \sqrt{2}$.

7 Express $(3 + 2i)^2$ and $\dfrac{1}{(3 + 2i)^2}$ in the form $a + ib$, $a, b \in \mathbb{R}$.

Find $|(3 + 2i)^2|$ and $\left|\dfrac{1}{(3 + 2i)^2}\right|$. Find also, in radians to 2

decimal places, $\arg(3 + 2i)^2$ and $\arg \dfrac{1}{(3 + 2i)^2}$.

8 Given that $z = \cos\theta + i\sin\theta$ show that

$$\frac{2}{1 + z} = 1 - i\tan\tfrac{1}{2}\theta$$

9 Given that $z = -1 + 3i$, express $z + \dfrac{2}{z}$ in the form $a + ib$ where $a, b \in \mathbb{R}$.

Find $\left|z + \dfrac{2}{z}\right|$.

10 Find (i) the modulus (ii) the argument, in radians to 2 decimal places, of:

(a) $(-2 + 3i)(1 + i\sqrt{3})$

(b) $\dfrac{-2 + 3i}{1 + i\sqrt{3}}$

(c) $[(-2 + 3i) + (1 + i\sqrt{3})]^2$

11 Given that $z_1 = 3 + 4i$, $z_2 = -1 + 2i$ place z_1, z_2, $z_1 + z_2$, $z_2 - z_1$ on an Argand diagram. Express $\dfrac{z_2 + z_1}{z_2 - z_1}$ in the form $p + iq$ where $p, q \in \mathbb{R}$.

12 Given that $z_1 = 3 - 2i$ and $z_2 = -1 + 7i$ show that

$$|z_1 + z_2| < |z_1 - z_2| < |z_1| + |z_2|$$

13 The complex number z has modulus 4 and argument $\frac{\pi}{3}$. Find in the form $a + ib$, where $a, b \in \mathbb{R}$:

(a) z^2 (b) $\dfrac{1}{z}$ (c) $i^3 z$

14 In an Argand diagram O is the origin, P represents the number $7 - i$ and Q represents the number $12 + 4i$.

(a) Show that $\triangle OPQ$ is isosceles.

(b) Calculate the size of $\angle OPQ$, giving your answer to the nearest degree.

15
$$\frac{1}{w} = 1 - 2z - z^2$$

Given that $z = -1 + 2i$,
(a) express w in the form $a + ib$, where $a, b \in \mathbb{R}$
(b) find $\arg z$ in radians to 2 decimal places.

16
$$z = -10 + 9i$$
(a) Calculate $\arg z$ to the nearest $0.1°$.
(b) Find the complex number w, given that $wz = -11 + 28i$.
(c) Calculate $|w|$, giving your answer to one decimal place.

17 Given that $z = -\dfrac{1}{2} + \dfrac{i\sqrt{3}}{2}$, find z^2.

Show that $1 + z + z^2 = 0$.
Place 1, z and z^2 on an Argand diagram and show that the points representing them, when joined, form an equilateral triangle.

18 $f(x) \equiv x^3 + kx^2 + 9x + 13$, where $k \in \mathbb{R}$.
Given that $f(-1) = 0$, find the value of k and show that the equation $f(x) = 0$ has one real and two complex roots. Display the roots on an Argand diagram.

19 Given that $z = \dfrac{\sqrt{3} + i}{1 + i\sqrt{3}}$, find $|z|$ and $\arg z$, giving $\arg z$ in radians to 2 decimal places. Find z^2 in the form $a + ib$ where $a, b \in \mathbb{R}$. Hence place z and z^2 on the same Argand diagram.

20 Given that $z_1 = 3 - 4i$ and $z_2 = 12 + 5i$,

(a) express $z_1 z_2$ and $\dfrac{z_2}{z_1}$ in the form $a + ib$, where $a, b \in \mathbb{R}$.

(b) place z_1, z_2, $z_1 z_2$ and $\dfrac{z_2}{z_1}$ on the same Argand diagram.

21 Find the modulus and argument of $z_1 = \sqrt{3} - i$ and

$z_2 = -\sqrt{2} + i\sqrt{2}$.

Express $\dfrac{z_2}{z_1}$ in the form $a + ib$ where $a, b \in \mathbb{R}$, and place

$z_1, z_2, z_1 + z_2$ and $\dfrac{z_2}{z_1}$ on an Argand diagram.

22 Given that $z_1 = -1 + i\sqrt{3}$ and $z_2 = \sqrt{3} + i$, find $\arg z_1$ and $\arg z_2$.

Express $\dfrac{z_1}{z_2}$ in the form $a + ib$, where a and b are real, and hence find $\arg \dfrac{z_1}{z_2}$.

Verify that $\arg \dfrac{z_1}{z_2} = \arg z_1 - \arg z_2$.   [L]

23 Given that $z = 2 - i$, show that $z^2 = 3 - 4i$.

Hence, or otherwise, find the roots, z_1 and z_2, of the equation

$$(z + i)^2 = 3 - 4i$$

Display these roots on an Argand diagram.

(a) Deduce that $|z_1 - z_2| = 2\sqrt{5}$.

(b) Find the value of $\arg(z_1 + z_2)$.   [L]

24 Find the modulus and argument of each of the complex numbers z_1 and z_2, where

$$z_1 = 1 + i, \quad z_2 = \sqrt{3} - i$$

Use $\arg \dfrac{z_1}{z_2} = \arg z_1 - \arg z_2$ to show that

$$\arg \dfrac{z_1}{z_2} = \dfrac{5\pi}{12}$$ [L]

25 The complex numbers $z_1 = 2 + 2i$ and $z_2 = 1 + 3i$ are represented on an Argand diagram by the points P and Q respectively.

(a) Display z_1 and z_2 on the same Argand diagram.

(b) Calculate $|z_1|$, $|z_2|$ and the length of PQ.

(c) Hence show that

  (i) $\triangle OPQ$, where O is the origin, is right angled

  (ii) $\arg z_2 - \arg z_1 = \arctan \frac{1}{2}$.

(d) Given that $OPQR$ is a rectangle in the Argand diagram, state the complex number z_3 represented by the point R.   [L]

26 The complex numbers z and w are given by

$$z = \dfrac{5 - 10i}{2 - i} \quad \text{and} \quad w = iz$$

(a) Obtain z and w in the form $p + iq$ where p and q are real numbers.

(b) Show z and w on an Argand diagram.

The origin O and the points representing z and w are the vertices of a triangle.

(c) Show that this triangle is isosceles and state the size of the angle between the equal sides.   [L]

7.5 Condition for two complex numbers to be equal

If you know that

$$a + ib = c + id, \text{where } a, b, c, d \in \mathbb{R}$$

then: $a - c = i(d - b)$

So $(a - c)^2 = i^2(d - b)^2$

that is: $(a - c)^2 = -(d - b)^2$

Now $(a - c)^2 \geqslant 0$ since when you square a real number the answer cannot be negative. Likewise $(d - b)^2 \geqslant 0$

So: $-(d - b)^2 \leqslant 0$

But if $(a - c)^2$ is positive and $-(d - b)^2$ is negative then $(a - c)^2$ cannot equal $-(d - b)^2$. So $(a - c)^2 = 0$ and $-(d - b)^2 = 0$.

Now $(a - c)^2 = 0 \Rightarrow a = c$

and $-(d - b)^2 = 0 \Rightarrow (d - b)^2 = 0 \Rightarrow d = b$

So $a + ib = c + id$

$$\Rightarrow \quad a = c \text{ and } b = d$$

■ **That is, if two complex numbers are equal, their real parts are equal and their imaginary parts are equal.**

Example 10
Find the square roots of $15 + 8i$.

If $a + ib$ is a square root of $15 + 8i$ then

$$(a + ib)^2 = 15 + 8i$$

So:
$$a^2 + 2ab\mathrm{i} - b^2 = 15 + 8\mathrm{i}$$
$$(a^2 - b^2) + 2ab\mathrm{i} = 15 + 8\mathrm{i}$$

If two complex numbers are equal then their real parts are equal and their imaginary parts are equal.

So: $$a^2 - b^2 = 15 \qquad (1)$$
and $$2ab = 8 \qquad (2)$$

From (2) $$a = \frac{4}{b}$$

Substituting in (1) gives:

$$\frac{16}{b^2} - b^2 = 15$$
$$16 - b^4 = 15b^2$$
$$b^4 + 15b^2 - 16 = 0$$
$$(b^2 + 16)(b^2 - 1) = 0$$

$$b^2 = -16 \quad \text{or} \quad b^2 = 1$$

Since $b \in \mathbb{R}$, b^2 cannot be -16.

So: $b^2 = 1 \Rightarrow b = \pm 1$

Thus $a = \pm 4$

So the square roots are $4 + \mathrm{i}$ and $-4 - \mathrm{i}$.

Example 11
Find the real numbers x and y if
$$3x - 2y + 3\mathrm{i} = 4 + (x + y)\mathrm{i}$$

If $3x - 2y + 3\mathrm{i} = 4 + (x + y)\mathrm{i}$ then equating real and imaginary parts gives:

$$3x - 2y = 4 \qquad (1)$$

$$3 = x + y \qquad (2)$$

From (2): $$y = 3 - x$$

Substituting into (1) gives:

$$3x - 2(3 - x) = 4$$
$$3x - 6 + 2x = 4$$
$$5x = 10 \Rightarrow x = 2$$

Then $$y = 3 - 2 = 1$$

Exercise 7C

1 Find the square roots of:
   (a) $5 + 12i$ (b) $7 - 24i$ (c) $3 - 4i$
   (d) $-20i$ (e) $1 - i4\sqrt{3}$

2 Find the real numbers x and y given that:
   (a) $x + 4y + xyi = 12 - 16i$
   (b) $2x + (x - 2y)i = 18 - y - i$
   (c) $3x + 2xi = 7 + 2y + (12 + 5y)i$
   (d) $x - 7y + 8xi = 6y + (6y - 100)i$
   (e) $2x - y + (y - 4)i = 0$

3 Given that $(1 + 5i)A - 2B = 3 + 7i$, find A and B if:
   (a) A and B are real,
   (b) A and B are conjugate complex numbers.

4 Given that $x, y \in \mathbb{R}$ and

$$(x + iy)(2 + i) = 3 - i$$

   find x and y.

5 Given that $p, q \in \mathbb{R}$ find p and q where:
   (a) $p + q + i(p - q) = 4 + 2i$
   (b) $2(p + iq) = q - ip - 2(1 - i)$

6 Solve for real x and real y the equation

$$(x + iy)(3 + 4i) = 3 - 4i \qquad \text{[L]}$$

7 Find the real numbers x and y given that

$$\frac{1}{x + iy} = 2 - 3i \qquad \text{[L]}$$

8 Given that

$$\frac{1}{x + iy} + \frac{1}{1 + 2i} = 1$$

   where x and y are real, find x and y. $\qquad$ [L]

9 Given that $(a - bi)^2 = -4$, where $a, b \in \mathbb{R}$, find the values of a and b.

10 Given that $z = 5 - 12i$ express $\dfrac{1}{z}$ and $z^{\frac{1}{2}}$ in the form $a + ib$ where $a, b \in \mathbb{R}$.

11 Solve for real values of x and y the equation

$$\frac{x}{1+i} - \frac{y}{2-i} = \frac{1-5i}{3-2i}$$

12 $z_1 = 2 - 3i$, $z_2 = 5 + 4i$.

(a) Express $\dfrac{z_1 z_2}{z_1 + z_2}$ in the form $A + iB$ where A and B are real.

(b) Find the real numbers m and n such that
$$mz_1 + nz_2 = 11 + 18i.$$

13 Given that the real and imaginary parts of the complex number $z = x + iy$ satisfy the equation

$$(2-i)x - (1+3i)y - 7 = 0$$

find x and y.

State the values of

(a) $|z|$ (b) $\arg z$. [L]

14 (a) The complex number z and its conjugate z^* are given by
$z = p + iq$ and $z^* = p - iq$ where p and q are real.
Given that $p = 5$ and $q = 8$

(i) display z and z^* on an Argand diagram

(ii) show that $|z + 2z^*| = 17$

(iii) calculate, in radians to 2 decimal places, the argument of $z + 2z^*$.

(b) Given that

$$ww^* = 5$$
$$\frac{w}{w^*} = \tfrac{1}{5}(-3 + 4i)$$

express w in the form $m + ni$, stating the possible values of the real numbers m and n. [L]

15 Find the values of the real numbers A and B given that

$$(5+6i)(3-2i) = A + Bi$$

Deduce that

$$(5-6i)(3+2i) = A - Bi$$

Using your values of A and B deduce that

$$(5^2 + 6^2)(3^2 + 2^2) = 27^2 + 8^2$$

SUMMARY OF KEY POINTS

1 $\sqrt{(-1)} = i$

2 A number of the form bi, where b is real, is called a pure imaginary number.

3 A number of the form $a + b$i, where $a, b \in \mathbb{R}$, is called a complex number.

4 If $z = x + iy$ then the complex conjugate of z is $z^* = x - iy$.

5 Any complex number can be represented by either a point or a vector on an Argand diagram.

6 If $z = x + iy$ then the modulus of z is
$$|z| = \sqrt{(x^2 + y^2)}$$

7 If $z = x + iy$ then $\arg z$ is the principal value of the argument of z.

8 If $a + ib = c + id$, where $a, b, c, d \in \mathbb{R}$, then $a = c$ and $b = d$.

Differential equations

Any relation between the variables x, y, $\dfrac{dy}{dx}$, $\dfrac{d^2y}{dx^2}$, $\dfrac{d^3y}{dx^3}$ ... is called a **differential equation**. If the highest derivative that occurs in the equation is $\dfrac{d^n y}{dx^n}$, then the equation has **order n**. For example, $y\dfrac{dy}{dx} = e^x$ is a **first order differential equation** and $\dfrac{d^2y}{dx^2} + 3\dfrac{dy}{dx} = \sin x$ is a **second order differential equation**.

8.1 The general solution of a first order differential equation in which the variables are separable

Book P2 (page 309) gave the **general solution** of the first order differential equation

$$\frac{dy}{dx} = f(x)\, g(y)$$

as:

$$\int \frac{1}{g(y)}\, dy = \int f(x)\, dx + C$$

provided that $\dfrac{1}{g(y)}$ can be integrated with respect to y and that $f(x)$ can be integrated with respect to x. The constant C is called an **arbitrary constant**. Here are two examples.

Example 1
Find the general solution of the differential equation $2y^2 + xy^2 = x\dfrac{dy}{dx}$.

Rewrite the equation as $\dfrac{dy}{dx} = y^2\left(\dfrac{x+2}{x}\right)$,

that is:
$$\frac{1}{y^2}\frac{dy}{dx} = \left(1 + \frac{2}{x}\right)$$

$$\int \frac{1}{y^2}\,dy = \int \left(1 + \frac{2}{x}\right)dx + C$$

$$-\frac{1}{y} = x + 2\ln|x| + C$$

The general solution of the differential equation is

$$\frac{1}{y} = K - x - 2\ln|x|, \text{ where } K = -C$$

Example 2

Given that $y = 2$ at $x = 0$ and that

$$\frac{dy}{dx} = y^2 + 4$$

find y in terms of x.

Rewrite the equation as $\left(\dfrac{1}{y^2 + 4}\right)\dfrac{dy}{dx} = 1$.

Integrating:
$$\int \frac{1}{y^2 + 4}\,dy = \int 1\,dx + C$$

That is:
$$\tfrac{1}{2}\arctan\frac{y}{2} = x + C$$

Now $y = 2$ at $x = 0$, so you have

$$\tfrac{1}{2}\arctan 1 = C \Rightarrow C = \tfrac{1}{2}\left(\tfrac{\pi}{4}\right) = \tfrac{\pi}{8}$$

That is:
$$\tfrac{1}{2}\arctan\frac{y}{2} = x + \tfrac{\pi}{8}$$

$$\arctan\frac{y}{2} = 2x + \tfrac{\pi}{4} \Rightarrow \frac{y}{2} = \tan(2x + \tfrac{\pi}{4})$$

The solution is $y = 2\tan(2x + \tfrac{\pi}{4})$.

Exercise 8A

Find the general solutions of the differential equations in questions 1–10.

1 $\dfrac{dy}{dx} = \cosh 2x$

2 $\dfrac{dy}{dx} = \operatorname{cosech}\tfrac{1}{3}y$

3 $\tan y \dfrac{dy}{dx} = \cot x$

4 $\dfrac{dy}{dx} = e^{2y}\sec^2 x$

5 $\dfrac{dy}{dx} = \dfrac{y^2 - 1}{x^2 + 1}$, $\quad y > 1$ **6** $(1 + x^2)^{\frac{1}{2}} \dfrac{dy}{dx} = y^2 + 4$

7 $e^{-x^2} \dfrac{dy}{dx} = xy$ **8** $\dfrac{dy}{dx} = e^{x+y}$

9 $\dfrac{dy}{dx} = \dfrac{y}{x^2 - 1}$, $\quad x > 1$ **10** $x^2 \dfrac{dy}{dx} + \sin^2 y = 0$

Obtain the solution that satisfies the given conditions of the differential equations in questions 11–24.

11 $\dfrac{dy}{dx} = 4y^2$, $\quad y = \frac{1}{2}$ at $x = -2$

12 $\dfrac{dy}{dx} = ye^x$, $\quad y = 1$ at $x = 0$

13 $\dfrac{dy}{dx} = \tan^2 x$, $\quad y = 0$ at $x = \frac{\pi}{4}$

14 $\dfrac{dy}{dx} = e^{2y+3x}$, $\quad y = \frac{1}{2}$ at $x = \frac{1}{3}$

15 $\dfrac{dy}{dx} = \dfrac{y}{x}$, $\quad x > 0$ and $y = 4$ at $x = 1$

16 $e^x \dfrac{dy}{dx} = y^{\frac{1}{2}}$, $\quad y = 4$ at $x = 0$

17 $\sin x \dfrac{dy}{dx} = \cosh y$, $\quad 0 < x < \pi$, $\quad y = 0$ at $x = \frac{\pi}{2}$

18 $\sin x \dfrac{dy}{dx} = \tan y (3 \cos x + \sin x)$, $\quad y = \frac{\pi}{6}$ at $x = \frac{\pi}{2}$

19 $(5 - 3 \sin x) \dfrac{dy}{dx} = 40 \cos x$, $\quad y = 0$ at $x = \frac{3\pi}{2}$

20 $(1 + \cos^2 x) \dfrac{dy}{dx} = y(y + 1) \sin 2x$, $\quad y = 2$ at $x = 0$

21 $(1 - x^2) \dfrac{dy}{dx} = xy(1 + y^2)$, $\quad x > 1$, $\quad y = 1$ at $x = 0$

22 $\dfrac{1}{y} \dfrac{dy}{dx} = x + xy$, $\quad y = 1$ at $x = 0$

23 $(1 + \cosh 2x) \dfrac{dy}{dx} = \operatorname{sech} y$, $\quad y = 0$ at $x = 0$

24 $e^{-x^2} \dfrac{dy}{dx} = x(y + 2)^2$, $\quad y = 0$ at $x = 0$

8.2 Family of solution curves

You have seen that the general solution of a first order differential equation always contains an arbitrary constant. If in addition to the differential equation a set of **boundary conditions** such as $y = 1$ at $x = 0$ is given, then you can find the arbitrary constant uniquely by substitution into the general solution. You did this in Exercise 8A, questions 11–24. Notice that different boundary conditions used in the general solution may give rise to *different* values of the arbitrary constant. So a set of specific solutions, all different from each other because the value of the arbitrary constant C is different for each, arises from one differential equation. You can sketch a graph for each of these solutions. The curves do not intersect and they are called **a family of solution curves**.

Two simple examples are used to illustrate such families of curves.

Example 3
Find the general solution of the differential equation $\dfrac{dy}{dx} = 2x$ and sketch the family of solution curves represented by this general solution.

Integrating $\dfrac{dy}{dx} = 2x$ gives:

$$y = x^2 + C$$

which is the general solution.

If $y = 0$ at $x = 0$ then $C = 0$, if $y = 1$ at $x = 0$ then $C = 1$,

If $y = 2$ at $x = 0$ then $C = 2$, if $y = -2$ at $x = 0$ then $C = -2$.

The solution curves corresponding to these different values of C look like this:

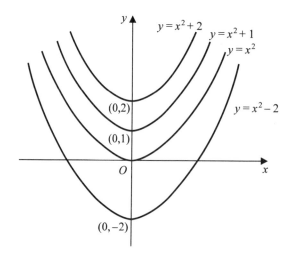

Example 4

Find the general solution of the differential equation $\dfrac{\mathrm{d}y}{\mathrm{d}x} = -\dfrac{x}{y}$ and interpret the solution geometrically.

By separating the variables you obtain

$$\int y\,\mathrm{d}y = -\int x\,\mathrm{d}x$$

That is, $\frac{1}{2}y^2 = -\frac{1}{2}x^2 + C$ is the general solution and this can be written as

$$x^2 + y^2 = a^2, \text{ where } a^2 = 2C$$

The equation $x^2 + y^2 = a^2$ represents a family of circles, all with centre at the origin and radius a, where a is a constant.

Here is the family of solution curves given by the differential equation $\dfrac{\mathrm{d}y}{\mathrm{d}x} = -\dfrac{x}{y}$ for $a = 1, 1\frac{1}{2}, 2$ and 3:

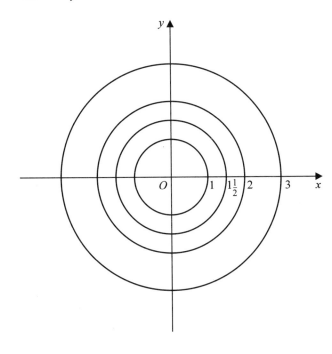

Exercise 8B

In questions 1–8, find the general solution of the differential equation and sketch the family of solution curves represented by this general solution.

1 $\dfrac{dy}{dx} = 4$

2 $\dfrac{dy}{dx} = \dfrac{4}{y}$

3 $\dfrac{dy}{dx} = \dfrac{y}{x}$

4 $\dfrac{dy}{dx} = e^{2x}$

5 $\dfrac{dy}{dx} = \cos x$

6 $\dfrac{dy}{dx} = \dfrac{1-x}{y}$

7 $\dfrac{dy}{dx} = \dfrac{x}{2y}$

8 $\dfrac{dy}{dx} = -\dfrac{y}{x}$, $x > 0$ and $y > 0$

9 Given that A is an arbitrary constant, show that $y = Ae^x$ is the general solution of the differential equation $\dfrac{dy}{dx} = y$. Sketch the family of solution curves for different values of A.

10 Given that $x > 0$ show that the general solution of the differential equation $\dfrac{dy}{dx} = \dfrac{y}{x \ln x}$ is $y = A \ln x$, where A is an arbitrary constant. Sketch the family of solution curves for different values of A.

8.3 First order exact differential equations

The differential equation $y + x\dfrac{dy}{dx} = x^3$ is first order but the variables cannot be separated. However, you should notice that the left-hand side can be written as $\dfrac{d}{dx}(xy)$. That, is $\dfrac{d}{dx}(xy) = x^3$ is another form of the equation and this form can be integrated at once to give

$$xy = \tfrac{1}{4}x^4 + C$$

as the general solution.

■ **Equations of this form, where one side is the *exact* derivative of a product and the other side can be integrated with respect to x, are called *exact differential equations of the first order*.**

8.4 First order linear differential equations

A **first order linear differential equation** is of the form

$$\frac{dy}{dx} + Py = Q$$

where P and Q are either functions of x or constants.

This type of first order differential equation may be exact, but more often it can be *made* exact by multiplying through the equation by a function of x. This function of x is called an **integrating factor**.

As a simple illustration consider the differential equation

$$\frac{dy}{dx} + \frac{y}{x} = x^2$$

Multiplication by x gives

$$x\frac{dy}{dx} + y = x^3 \quad \text{or} \quad y + x\frac{dy}{dx} = x^3$$

and makes the equation exact. The solution follows, as you have already seen. In this case the integrating factor is x.

Suppose now that the linear equation

$$\frac{dy}{dx} + Py = Q$$

where P and Q are functions of x, is made exact by multiplying throughout by the integrating factor $f(x)$. That is, $f(x)\dfrac{dy}{dx} + Pf(x)y$ is an exact derivative of a product. It follows that

$$f(x)\frac{dy}{dx} + Pf(x)y \equiv \frac{d}{dx}[yf(x)] \tag{1}$$

But $$\frac{d}{dx}[yf(x)] = f(x)\frac{dy}{dx} + yf'(x) \tag{2}$$

by using the product rule of differentiation.

Therefore, comparing (1) and (2): $Pf(x) = f'(x)$

Dividing by $f(x)$ and integrating with respect to x:

$$\int P\,dx = \int \frac{f'(x)}{f(x)}\,dx = \ln[f(x)]$$

That is, the integrating factor $f(x)$ is given by

$$f(x) = e^{\int P\,dx}$$

The linear equation $\dfrac{dy}{dx} + Py = Q$ can be solved by multiplying by

the integrating factor $e^{\int P\,dx}$, provided that $e^{\int P\,dx}$ can be found and

that the function $Qe^{\int P\,dx}$ can be integrated with respect to x.

So if $\dfrac{dy}{dx} + Py = Q$ then:

$$e^{\int P\,dx}\frac{dy}{dx} + Pe^{\int P\,dx}y = Qe^{\int P\,dx}$$

That is:

$$\frac{d}{dx}\left[ye^{\int P\,dx}\right] = Qe^{\int P\,dx}$$

Integrating gives the solution

$$ye^{\int P\,dx} = \int Qe^{\int P\,dx}\,dx + C$$

Notice that you do not have to spend a lot of time trying to integrate the left-hand side. It is always of the form ($y \times$ integrating factor).

Example 5
Find the general solution of the differential equation

$$\frac{dy}{dx} + \left(\frac{1}{x}\right)y = x^2$$

If you compare the equation with the general linear form $\dfrac{dy}{dx} + Py = Q$ you can see that the integrating factor is

$$e^{\int P\,dx} = e^{\int \frac{1}{x}dx} = e^{\ln x} = x$$

Multiplying by x gives

$$x\frac{dy}{dx} + y = x^3$$
$$\frac{d}{dx}(xy) = x^3$$

Integrating: $\qquad xy = \tfrac{1}{4}x^4 + C$

as you saw on page 188. The general solution is $xy = \tfrac{1}{4}x^4 + C$.

Example 6
Find the general solution of the differential equation

$$\cos x \, \frac{dy}{dx} + y \sin x = \sin x \cos^3 x$$

First write the equation in linear form by dividing by $\cos x$ to obtain

$$\frac{dy}{dx} + (\tan x)y = \sin x \cos^2 x \qquad (1)$$

The integrating factor is then

$$e^{\int \tan x \, dx} = e^{\ln \sec x} = \sec x$$

Multiply equation (1) by $\sec x$ to make it exact:

$$\sec x \, \frac{dy}{dx} + (\sec x \tan x)y = \sin x \cos^2 x \sec x$$

$$\frac{d}{dx}(y \sec x) = \sin x \cos x = \tfrac{1}{2} \sin 2x$$

Integrating with respect to x you obtain the general solution as

$$y \sec x = C - \tfrac{1}{4} \cos 2x$$

Example 7
Find y in terms of x given that

$$\frac{dy}{dx} - \frac{2}{x} y = x^2 \ln x, \quad x > 0$$

and that $y = 2$ at $x = 1$.

The equation $\dfrac{dy}{dx} - \dfrac{2}{x} y = x^2 \ln x$ is linear and the integrating factor is given by

$$e^{\int -\frac{2}{x} dx} = e^{-2 \ln x} = e^{\ln x^{-2}} = x^{-2}$$

Multiplying the equation by x^{-2} to make it exact gives you

$$x^{-2} \frac{dy}{dx} - 2x^{-3}y = \ln x$$

That is:
$$\frac{d}{dx}(x^{-2}y) = \ln x \qquad (1)$$

Remember that $\int \ln x \, dx = x(\ln x - 1)$. This result can be obtained by integration by parts. So by integrating equation (1) you have

$$x^{-2}y = x(\ln x - 1) + C$$

which is the general solution of the differential equation.

You know also that $y = 2$ at $x = 1$ and you can find the value of C by substituting $y = 2$ and $x = 1$ in the general solution. Hence

$$2 = -1 + C \Rightarrow C = 3$$

That is: $\qquad\qquad x^{-2}y = x(\ln x - 1) + 3$

Multiply by x^2 to obtain

$$y = x^3(\ln x - 1) + 3x^2$$

which is the form of the solution required.

Exercise 8C

In questions 1–5 the differential equations are exact. Find the general solution of each.

1 $\quad y + x\dfrac{dy}{dx} = x^2$
$\qquad\qquad$ **2** $\quad 2xy\dfrac{dy}{dx} + y^2 = x^3$

3 $\quad \dfrac{dy}{dx}\sin x + y\cos x = \tan x$
$\qquad$ **4** $\quad e^{2x}\dfrac{dy}{dx} + 2e^{2x}y = x\sin x$

5 $\quad \dfrac{y - x\dfrac{dy}{dx}}{y^2} = \cos 2x$

In questions 6–12 find the general solution of each linear differential equation.

6 $\quad \dfrac{dy}{dx} + \dfrac{y}{x} = \cos x$
$\qquad\qquad$ **7** $\quad \dfrac{dy}{dx} + \left(\dfrac{2}{x}\right)y = 4x + 3$

8 $\quad \dfrac{dy}{dx} - \dfrac{y}{x} = \ln x$
$\qquad\qquad$ **9** $\quad \dfrac{dy}{dx} + \dfrac{y}{2x} = -x^{\frac{1}{2}}$

10 $\quad \dfrac{dy}{dx} + y\cot x = \cos 3x$
$\qquad$ **11** $\quad \dfrac{dy}{dx} + 2y\tan x = \sin x$

12 $\quad \dfrac{dy}{dx} - \dfrac{y}{x+1} = x$

13 Given that $x \dfrac{dy}{dx} - 2y = x^3 \ln x$, find y in terms of x such that $y = 2$ at $x = 1$.

14 Find y in terms of x given that

$$\frac{dy}{dx} + 2y = \sin x$$

and that the solution curve passes through the origin O.

15 Find the general solution of the differential equation

$$\frac{dy}{dx} - 2y \operatorname{cosec} x = \tan \frac{x}{2}, \quad 0 < x < \pi$$

16 Find the general solution of the differential equation

$$\frac{dy}{dx} + 2y = e^{-2x}(x^3 + x^{-1}), \quad x > 0$$

If you also know that $y = 0$ at $x = 1$, find y in terms of x.

17 Find y in terms of x given that $x \dfrac{dy}{dx} + 3y = e^x$ and that $y = 1$ at $x = 1$.

18 Solve the differential equation, giving y in terms of x, where $x^2 \dfrac{dy}{dx} - xy = 1$ and $y = 2$ at $x = 1$.

8.5 The second order differential equation $a\dfrac{d^2y}{dx^2} + b\dfrac{dy}{dx} + cy = 0$

Here you have a second order linear equation with constant coefficients a, b and c. The equation is called second order because its highest derivative of y with respect to x is $\dfrac{d^2y}{dx^2}$. The equation is called linear because only first degree terms in y and its derivatives occur. For example, the second order differential equation $\dfrac{d^2y}{dx^2} + \left(\dfrac{dy}{dx}\right)^3 = 0$ is *non*-linear because of the term $\left(\dfrac{dy}{dx}\right)^3$.

Suppose that $y = u$ and $y = v$ are either constants or functions of x and that they are particular distinct solutions of the differential equation

$$a\frac{d^2y}{dx^2} + b\frac{dy}{dx} + cy = 0$$

where $u \neq v$. This means that u and v both satisfy the differential equation.

That is:

$$a\frac{d^2u}{dx^2} + b\frac{du}{dx} + cu = 0$$

and

$$a\frac{d^2v}{dx^2} + b\frac{dv}{dx} + cv = 0$$

When you are solving a second order differential equation, the general solution will have *two* arbitrary constants. So let's consider as a general solution:

$$y = Au + Bv,$$

where A and B are non-zero constants. Then:

$$\frac{dy}{dx} = A\frac{du}{dx} + B\frac{dv}{dx}$$

and

$$\frac{d^2y}{dx^2} = A\frac{d^2u}{dx^2} + B\frac{d^2v}{dx^2}$$

The left-hand side of the original equation now becomes

$$a\frac{d^2y}{dx^2} + b\frac{dy}{dx} + cy$$

$$= a\left(A\frac{d^2u}{dx^2} + B\frac{d^2v}{dx^2}\right) + b\left(A\frac{du}{dx} + B\frac{dv}{dx}\right) + c(Au + Bv)$$

$$= A\left(a\frac{d^2u}{dx^2} + b\frac{du}{dx} + cu\right) + B\left(a\frac{d^2v}{dx^2} + b\frac{dv}{dx} + cv\right)$$

$$= A(0) + B(0) = 0$$

Since A and B are arbitrary constants, this proves that $y = Au + Bv$ is indeed a general solution of the differential equation.

■ **The general solution of the second order differential equation**

$$a\frac{d^2y}{dx^2} + b\frac{dy}{dx} + cy = 0$$

is $\qquad\qquad$ **$y = Au + Bv$**
where $y = u$ and $y = v$ are particular, distinct solutions of the differential equation.

Now you need to find the functions u and v in specific cases. This is how you do it. In the differential equation

$$a \frac{d^2 y}{dx^2} + b \frac{dy}{dx} + cy = 0$$

you try as a solution $y = e^{mx}$, where m is a constant to be found.

Hence $\frac{dy}{dx} = me^{mx}$ and $\frac{d^2 y}{dx^2} = m^2 e^{mx}$.

If $y = e^{mx}$ is a solution of the differential equation, then

$$am^2 e^{mx} + bm e^{mx} + c e^{mx} = 0$$

$$\Rightarrow \quad e^{mx}(am^2 + bm + c) = 0$$

So either $e^{mx} = 0$ or $am^2 + bm + c = 0$.

But $e^{mx} > 0$ for all m, so the two values of m which you require are the roots of the quadratic equation $am^2 + bm + c = 0$. This equation in m is often called the **auxiliary quadratic equation** and it may have real, identical or complex roots. You now need to consider the different types of roots which can occur in the auxiliary quadratic equation.

The equation $am^2 + bm + c = 0$ has **real distinct roots** if $b^2 - 4ac > 0$; it has **coincident real roots** if $b^2 - 4ac = 0$; it has **complex roots** if $b^2 - 4ac < 0$. The following examples show what happens in each case.

Example 8

Find the general solution of the differential equation

$$\frac{d^2 y}{dx^2} + \frac{dy}{dx} - 6y = 0$$

Take $y = e^{mx}$ as a particular solution, then $\frac{dy}{dx} = me^{mx}$ and $\frac{d^2 y}{dx^2} = m^2 e^{mx}$. When you substitute these into the given equation, you get:

$$m^2 e^{mx} + me^{mx} - 6e^{mx} = 0$$
$$e^{mx}(m^2 + m - 6) = 0$$

$e^{mx} > 0$, so:

$$m^2 + m - 6 = 0$$
$$(m + 3)(m - 2) = 0$$

$$\Rightarrow \quad m = -3 \text{ or } m = 2$$

So two particular solutions are $y = e^{-3x}$ and $y = e^{2x}$. The general solution of the differential equation is then

$$y = Ae^{-3x} + Be^{2x}$$

where A and B are constants.

- **Generalising this result, you can say that for the differential equation $a\dfrac{d^2y}{dx^2} + b\dfrac{dy}{dx} + cy = 0$, whose auxiliary quadratic equation $am^2 + bm + c = 0$ has real, distinct roots α and β, the general solution is**

$$y = Ae^{\alpha x} + Be^{\beta x}$$

where A and B are arbitrary constants.

Exercise 8D

Find the general solution of each of the following differential equations:

1 $\dfrac{d^2y}{dx^2} - 3\dfrac{dy}{dx} + 2y = 0$ **2** $\dfrac{d^2y}{dx^2} + 4\dfrac{dy}{dx} + 3y = 0$

3 $\dfrac{d^2y}{dx^2} - 5\dfrac{dy}{dx} + 4y = 0$ **4** $\dfrac{d^2y}{dx^2} + 7\dfrac{dy}{dx} - 18y = 0$

5 $\dfrac{d^2y}{dx^2} - 2\dfrac{dy}{dx} - 8y = 0$ **6** $\dfrac{d^2y}{dx^2} + \dfrac{dy}{dx} - 6y = 0$

7 $3\dfrac{d^2y}{dx^2} - 4\dfrac{dy}{dx} - 4y = 0$ **8** $\dfrac{d^2y}{dx^2} - 2\dfrac{dy}{dx} - 2y = 0$

9 $6\dfrac{d^2y}{dx^2} + 5\dfrac{dy}{dx} - 6y = 0$ **10** $3\dfrac{d^2y}{dx^2} - 2\dfrac{dy}{dx} - 21y = 0$

Auxiliary quadratic equation with real coincident roots

Example 9

Find the general solution of the differential equation

$$\frac{d^2y}{dx^2} - 4\frac{dy}{dx} + 4y = 0$$

Take $y = e^{mx}$, then $\dfrac{dy}{dx} = me^{mx}$ and $\dfrac{d^2y}{dx^2} = m^2e^{mx}$. When you substitute these into the given equation you get:

$$m^2 e^{mx} - 4m e^{mx} + 4 e^{mx} = 0$$

$$e^{mx}(m^2 - 4m + 4) = 0$$

$$e^{mx} > 0 \Rightarrow m^2 - 4m + 4 = 0$$

$$(m - 2)^2 = 0$$

$$m = 2 \text{ only}$$

The general solution of the differential equation in this case is $y = Ae^{2x} + Bxe^{2x}$ and you can verify this by differentiation:

$$y = Ae^{2x} + Bxe^{2x}$$

$$\frac{dy}{dx} = 2Ae^{2x} + Be^{2x} + 2Bxe^{2x}$$

$$\frac{d^2y}{dx^2} = 4Ae^{2x} + 2Be^{2x} + 2Be^{2x} + 4Bxe^{2x}$$

$$= 4Ae^{2x} + 4Be^{2x} + 4Bxe^{2x}$$

So:

$$\frac{d^2y}{dx^2} - 4\frac{dy}{dx} + 4y = 4Ae^{2x} + 4Be^{2x} + 4Bxe^{2x} - 8Ae^{2x} - 4Be^{2x} - 8Bxe^{2x} + 4Ae^{2x} + 4Bxe^{2x}$$

$$= 0$$

which shows that the differential equation $\dfrac{d^2y}{dx^2} - 4\dfrac{dy}{dx} + 4y = 0$ is satisfied by the general solution $y = (A + Bx)e^{2x}$.

- **Generalising this result, you can say that for the differential equation $a\dfrac{d^2y}{dx^2} + b\dfrac{dy}{dx} + cy = 0$, whose auxiliary quadratic equation $am^2 + bm + c = 0$ has equal roots α, the general solution is $y = (A + Bx)e^{\alpha x}$, where A and B are arbitrary constants.**

Exercise 8E

Find the general solution of each of the following differential equations:

1 $\dfrac{d^2y}{dx^2} - 2\dfrac{dy}{dx} + y = 0$

2 $\dfrac{d^2y}{dx^2} + 4\dfrac{dy}{dx} + 4y = 0$

3 $\dfrac{d^2y}{dx^2} - 6\dfrac{dy}{dx} + 9y = 0$

4 $\dfrac{d^2y}{dx^2} + 8\dfrac{dy}{dx} + 16y = 0$

5 $4\dfrac{d^2y}{dx^2} + 4\dfrac{dy}{dx} + y = 0$

6 $9\dfrac{d^2y}{dx^2} - 6\dfrac{dy}{dx} + y = 0$

7 $4\dfrac{d^2y}{dx^2} - 12\dfrac{dy}{dx} + 9y = 0$ **8** $9\dfrac{d^2y}{dx^2} + 30\dfrac{dy}{dx} + 25y = 0$

9 $\dfrac{d^2y}{dx^2} - \sqrt{8}\dfrac{dy}{dx} + 2y = 0$ **10** $2\dfrac{d^2y}{dx^2} + \sqrt{40}\dfrac{dy}{dx} + 5y = 0$

Auxiliary quadratic equation with pure imaginary roots

Example 10

Find the general solution of the differential equation

$$\frac{d^2y}{dx^2} + 4y = 0$$

Take $y = e^{mx}$, $\dfrac{dy}{dx} = me^{mx}$ and $\dfrac{d^2y}{dx^2} = m^2e^{mx}$ and you have on substituting into the given equation:

$$m^2e^{mx} + 4e^{mx} = 0 \Rightarrow (m^2 + 4)e^{mx} = 0$$

Since $e^{mx} > 0$ then $m^2 = -4$ or $m = \pm 2i$. The general solution is therefore

$$y = Pe^{2ix} + Qe^{-2ix}$$

where P and Q are constants.

Now it will be shown in Book P4 that

$$e^{ni\theta} = \cos n\theta + i\sin n\theta \quad \text{and} \quad e^{-ni\theta} = \cos n\theta - i\sin n\theta$$

So the general solution can be written

$$\begin{aligned} y &= P(\cos 2x + i\sin 2x) + Q(\cos 2x - i\sin 2x) \\ &= (P + Q)\cos 2x + i(P - Q)\sin 2x \end{aligned}$$

or $$y = A\cos 2x + B\sin 2x$$

where A and B are constants and $A = P + Q$ and $B = i(P - Q)$.

■ **Generalising the result, you can say that for the differential equation** $\dfrac{d^2y}{dx^2} + n^2y = 0$**, the general solution is**

$y = A\cos nx + B\sin nx$**, where A and B are arbitrary constants.**

Auxiliary quadratic equation with complex conjugate roots

Example 11

Find the general solution of the differential equation

$$\frac{d^2y}{dx^2} - 4\frac{dy}{dx} + 13y = 0$$

Take $y = e^{mx}$, $\dfrac{dy}{dx} = me^{mx}$, $\dfrac{d^2y}{dx^2} = m^2e^{mx}$ and you have on substituting into the given equation:

$$m^2e^{mx} - 4me^{mx} + 13e^{mx} = 0$$
$$e^{mx}(m^2 - 4m + 13) = 0$$

$$e^{mx} > 0 \Rightarrow m = \frac{4 \pm \sqrt{(16 - 52)}}{2}$$
$$= \frac{4 \pm \sqrt{(-36)}}{2} = 2 \pm 3i$$

So the general solution is

$$y = Pe^{(2+3i)x} + Qe^{(2-3i)x}$$

where P and Q are constants,

or $$y = e^{2x}(Pe^{3ix} + Qe^{-3ix})$$

So $y = e^{2x}(A\cos 3x + B\sin 3x)$ where $A = P + Q$ and $B = i(P - Q)$.

- **Generalising this result, you can say that for the differential equation $a\dfrac{d^2y}{dx^2} + b\dfrac{dy}{dx} + cy = 0$, where the auxiliary quadratic equation has complex conjugate roots $p + iq$ and $p - iq$, and $p, q \in \mathbb{R}$, the general solution is**

$$y = e^{px}(A\cos qx + B\sin qx)$$

where A and B are arbitrary constants.

Exercise 8F

Find the general solution of each of the following differential equations:

1 $\dfrac{d^2y}{dx^2} + y = 0$

2 $\dfrac{d^2y}{dx^2} + 25y = 0$

3 $4\dfrac{d^2y}{dx^2} + 9y = 0$

4 $16\dfrac{d^2y}{dx^2} + 49y = 0$

5 $\dfrac{d^2y}{dx^2} - 2\dfrac{dy}{dx} + 5y = 0$

6 $\dfrac{d^2y}{dx^2} + 4\dfrac{dy}{dx} + 5y = 0$

7 $\dfrac{d^2y}{dx^2} - 6\dfrac{dy}{dx} + 10y = 0$

8 $\dfrac{d^2y}{dx^2} + 8\dfrac{dy}{dx} + 25y = 0$

9 $4\dfrac{d^2y}{dx^2} - 4\dfrac{dy}{dx} + 5y = 0$

10 $25\dfrac{d^2y}{dx^2} - 20\dfrac{dy}{dx} + 13y = 0$

8.6 The second order differential equation $a\dfrac{d^2y}{dx^2} + b\dfrac{dy}{dx} + cy = f(x)$

The method of finding a general solution to this differential equation is an extension of the work learned in section 8.5. First of all, you need to solve the differential equation

$$a\dfrac{d^2y}{dx^2} + b\dfrac{dy}{dx} + cy = 0$$

just as you did previously, and this solution is called the **complementary function**.

Next you need to find a solution of the equation $a\dfrac{d^2y}{dx^2} + b\dfrac{dy}{dx} + cy = f(x)$, where $f(x)$ could be any one of these forms:

(i)   a constant, k
(ii) a linear function, $px + q$
(iii) an exponential function, ke^{px}
(iv) a trigonometric function, e.g. $p\sin x$, $q\cos 2x$ or $p\sin 3x + q\cos 3x$.

A solution of the differential equation for any of the forms of $f(x)$ given in (i)–(iv) can be found by inspection. This solution, when found, is called a **particular integral** of the equation. The following examples are typical.

Example 12

$$\frac{d^2y}{dx^2} + 3\frac{dy}{dx} + 2y = f(x)$$

Find a particular integral of this differential equation in the cases where $f(x) =$

(a) 12   (b) $3x + 5$ (c) $3e^{2x}$ (d) $\cos 2x$.

(a) Try $y = k$ as the particular integral; then:

$$\frac{dy}{dx} = 0, \quad \frac{d^2y}{dx^2} = 0$$

and by substituting in the equation you get:

$$0 + 0 + 2k = 12 \Rightarrow k = 6$$

So $y = 6$ is the particular integral.

(b) Try $y = ax + b$ as the particular integral, then

$$\frac{dy}{dx} = a, \quad \frac{d^2y}{dx^2} = 0$$

and by substituting in the equation you get:

$$0 + 3a + 2(ax + b) \equiv 3x + 5$$

Equating x coefficients: $2a = 3 \Rightarrow a = \frac{3}{2}$

Equating constant terms: $3a + 2b = 5 \Rightarrow \frac{9}{2} + 2b = 5$

$$\Rightarrow b = \frac{1}{4}$$

So $y = \frac{3}{2}x + \frac{1}{4}$ is the particular integral.

(c) Try $y = ke^{2x}$ as the particular integral, then

$$\frac{dy}{dx} = 2ke^{2x} \text{ and } \frac{d^2y}{dx^2} = 4ke^{2x}$$

By substituting in the equation you get

$$4ke^{2x} + 6ke^{2x} + 2ke^{2x} \equiv 3e^{2x}$$

That is, $12k = 3 \Rightarrow k = \frac{1}{4}$

The particular integral is $y = \frac{1}{4}e^{2x}$.

(d) Try $y = a\cos 2x + b\sin 2x$, then

$$\frac{dy}{dx} = -2a\sin 2x + 2b\cos 2x$$

$$\frac{d^2y}{dx^2} = -4a\cos 2x - 4b\sin 2x$$

Substituting in the equation:

$-4a\cos 2x - 4b\sin 2x + 3(-2a\sin 2x + 2b\cos 2x) + 2(a\cos 2x + b\sin 2x) \equiv \cos 2x$

Equating terms in $\cos 2x$: $-4a + 6b + 2a = 1$ (1)

Equating terms in $\sin 2x$: $-4b - 6a + 2b = 0$ (2)

Solving equations (1) and (2) simultaneously gives

$$a = -\tfrac{1}{20} \quad \text{and} \quad b = \tfrac{3}{20}$$

The particular integral is

$$y = -\tfrac{1}{20}\cos 2x + \tfrac{3}{20}\sin 2x$$

■ **The general solution of the differential equation**

$$a\frac{d^2y}{dx^2} + b\frac{dy}{dx} + cy = f(x)$$

is: $y = \textbf{complementary function} + \textbf{particular integral}$

For each differential equation you need to find the complementary function and the particular integral. Then, in general, the solution is the sum of these two.

Example 13

Find the general solution of the differential equation

$$\frac{d^2y}{dx^2} + 3\frac{dy}{dx} + 2y = f(x)$$

in the cases where $f(x) =$

(a) 12   (b) $3x + 5$ (c) $3e^{2x}$ (d) $\cos 2x$.

You can find the complementary function by solving

$$\frac{d^2y}{dx^2} + 3\frac{dy}{dx} + 2y = 0$$

Take $y = e^{mx}$, $\dfrac{dy}{dx} = me^{mx}$ and $\dfrac{d^2y}{dx^2} = m^2 e^{mx}$, so by substituting in the equation you have:

$$e^{mx}(m^2 + 3m + 2) = 0$$

$e^{mx} \neq 0 \Rightarrow m = -2$ or $m = -1$

The complementary function is $Ae^{-2x} + Be^{-x}$, where A and B are arbitrary constants.

The particular integrals for parts (a), (b), (c) and (d) have been found already in example 12, and you are now able to write down the general solutions as:

(a) $y = Ae^{-2x} + Be^{-x} + 6$

(b) $y = Ae^{-2x} + Be^{-x} + \tfrac{3}{2}x + \tfrac{1}{4}$

(c) $y = Ae^{-2x} + Be^{-x} + \frac{1}{4}e^{2x}$

(d) $y = Ae^{-2x} + Be^{-x} - \frac{1}{20}\cos 2x + \frac{3}{20}\sin 2x$

Finally, in an examination question, you may be given two conditions from which the values of the arbitrary constants A and B in the general solution can be determined. Here is an example using one of the general solutions found already.

Example 14

Find y in terms of x for the differential equation

$$\frac{d^2y}{dx^2} + 3\frac{dy}{dx} + 2y = \cos 2x$$

given that $\frac{dy}{dx} = 0$ at $x = 0$ and $y = 0$ at $x = 0$.

First you find the complementary function and the particular integral, as in example 13(d), so that you can give the general solution of the differential equation as

$$y = Ae^{-2x} + Be^{-x} - \frac{1}{20}\cos 2x + \frac{3}{20}\sin 2x$$

Since $y = 0$ at $x = 0$ you have by substitution

$$0 = A + B - \frac{1}{20} \qquad (1)$$

Differentiating the general solution with respect to x gives

$$\frac{dy}{dx} = -2Ae^{-2x} - Be^{-x} + \frac{1}{10}\sin 2x + \frac{3}{10}\cos 2x$$

and since $\frac{dy}{dx} = 0$ at $x = 0$ you have

$$0 = -2A - B + \frac{3}{10} \qquad (2)$$

You can now solve equations (1) and (2) to obtain

$$A = \frac{1}{4}, \quad B = -\frac{1}{5}$$

The solution of the differential equation subject to the conditions $\frac{dy}{dx} = 0$ and $y = 0$ at $x = 0$ is

$$y = \frac{1}{4}e^{-2x} - \frac{1}{5}e^{-x} - \frac{1}{20}\cos 2x + \frac{3}{20}\sin 2x$$

Note: If the complementary function already contains a term of the type which also needs to be in the particular integral, then you must amend your trial function for the particular integral by a factor of x or x^2, as the following example illustrates.

Example 15

Find the general solution of the differential equation

$$\frac{d^2y}{dx^2} - 3\frac{dy}{dx} = 6$$

Let's deal first with the equation $\frac{d^2y}{dx^2} - 3\frac{dy}{dx} = 0$. Using $y = e^{mx}$, you have $e^{mx}(m^2 - 3m) = 0$, from which $m = 0$ or 3 and the complementary function is $A + Be^{3x}$, where A and B are constants. If you were to take the particular integral as $y = k$, then you have the left-hand side of the equation equal to zero, which does not make sense. This occurs because the function $y = A$ is already part of the solution contained in the complementary function. So you try $y = kx$ as the possible particular integral. Then $\frac{dy}{dx} = k$ and $\frac{d^2y}{dx^2} = 0$, so you have in the equation

$$0 - 3k = 6 \Rightarrow k = -2$$

The particular integral is taken as $y = -2x$ and the general solution of the differential equation is

$$y = A + Be^{3x} - 2x$$

Example 16

Find y in terms of x given that

$$\frac{d^2y}{dx^2} - 4\frac{dy}{dx} + 4y = e^{2x}$$

and that $\frac{dy}{dx} = 1$ and $y = 0$ at $x = 0$.

Complementary function: $y = e^{mx}$, $\frac{dy}{dx} = me^{mx}$, $\frac{d^2y}{dx^2} = m^2e^{mx}$

Hence $e^{mx}(m^2 - 4m + 4) = 0 \Rightarrow m = 2$ (double root).

The complementary function is $(A + Bx)e^{2x}$.

Particular integral: As both Ae^{2x} and Bxe^{2x} are included in the complementary function, try $y = kx^2e^{2x}$ as the particular integral.

Then: $\quad \frac{dy}{dx} = 2kxe^{2x} + 2kx^2e^{2x} = e^{2x}(2kx + 2kx^2)$

$$\frac{d^2y}{dx^2} = 2ke^{2x} + 4kxe^{2x} + 4kxe^{2x} + 4kx^2e^{2x}$$

$$= e^{2x}(2k + 8kx + 4kx^2)$$

In the original equation, you have

$$\frac{d^2y}{dx^2} - 4\frac{dy}{dx} + 4y = e^{2x}$$

So: $e^{2x}(2k + 8kx + 4kx^2) - 4e^{2x}(2kx + 2kx^2) + 4e^{2x}kx^2 \equiv e^{2x}$

that is: $2ke^{2x} \equiv e^{2x}$

But $e^{2x} \neq 0 \Rightarrow 2k = 1$ and hence $k = \frac{1}{2}$.

The general solution of the differential equation is

$$y = (A + Bx)e^{2x} + \frac{1}{2}x^2e^{2x}$$

Since $y = 0$ at $x = 0$: $\quad 0 = (A + 0)e^0 + 0(e^0)$

$$\Rightarrow A = 0$$

So the general solution reduces to

$$y = Bxe^{2x} + \frac{1}{2}x^2e^{2x}$$

Differentiating $y = Bxe^{2x} + \frac{1}{2}x^2e^{2x}$ with respect to x:

$$\frac{dy}{dx} = Be^{2x} + 2Bxe^{2x} + xe^{2x} + x^2e^{2x}$$

and $\frac{dy}{dx} = 1$ at $x = 0$.

So: $\quad 1 = B + 0 + 0 + 0 \Rightarrow B = 1$

The solution subject to $\frac{dy}{dx} = 1$ and $y = 0$ at $x = 0$ is:

$$y = xe^{2x} + \frac{1}{2}x^2e^{2x}$$

Exercise 8G

Solve each of the differential equations in questions 1–15, giving the general solution.

1 $\dfrac{d^2y}{dx^2} - 4\dfrac{dy}{dx} + 3y = 12$
2 $\dfrac{d^2y}{dx^2} + 3\dfrac{dy}{dx} + 2y = 4x$

3 $\dfrac{d^2y}{dx^2} - 2\dfrac{dy}{dx} + y = e^{2x}$
4 $\dfrac{d^2y}{dx^2} + 4\dfrac{dy}{dx} + 4y = 2x - 1$

5 $\dfrac{d^2y}{dx^2} + y = \cos 2x$
6 $\dfrac{d^2y}{dx^2} + 9y = e^{\frac{1}{2}x}$

7 $\dfrac{d^2y}{dx^2} + 4\dfrac{dy}{dx} + 5y = 10x - 12$
8 $\dfrac{d^2y}{dx^2} - 2\dfrac{dy}{dx} + 2y = \cos x$

9 $\dfrac{d^2y}{dx^2} - 4\dfrac{dy}{dx} + 3y = 6 - 3x$ **10** $\dfrac{d^2y}{dx^2} + \dfrac{dy}{dx} = e^{-x}$

11 $\dfrac{d^2y}{dx^2} - 3\dfrac{dy}{dx} = 5$ **12** $3\dfrac{d^2y}{dx^2} - 2\dfrac{dy}{dx} - y = x$

13 $\dfrac{d^2y}{dx^2} + 4\dfrac{dy}{dx} + 5y = \sin 2x$ **14** $\dfrac{d^2y}{dx^2} + 16y = 24$

15 $4\dfrac{d^2y}{dx^2} + 4\dfrac{dy}{dx} + 2y = \sin x + \cos x$

In questions 16–25 find the solution subject to the given boundary conditions for each of the following differential equations:

16 $\dfrac{d^2y}{dx^2} - 4\dfrac{dy}{dx} + 3y = 12;\ \dfrac{dy}{dx} = 1$ and $y = 0$ at $x = 0$

17 $\dfrac{d^2y}{dx^2} + y = e^x;\ \dfrac{dy}{dx} = y = 0$ at $x = 0$

18 $\dfrac{d^2y}{dx^2} - 2\dfrac{dy}{dx} + y = \cos x;\ \dfrac{dy}{dx} = 0$ and $y = 1$ at $x = 0$

19 $\dfrac{d^2y}{dx^2} - 6\dfrac{dy}{dx} + 5y = e^{2x};\ \dfrac{dy}{dx} = y = 2$ at $x = 0$

20 $\dfrac{d^2y}{dx^2} + 2\dfrac{dy}{dx} + 2y = 4x;\ \dfrac{dy}{dx} = y = 0$ at $x = 0$

21 $\dfrac{d^2y}{dx^2} + 4\dfrac{dy}{dx} + 4y = 2x + 4;\ y = 1,\ \dfrac{dy}{dx} = 0$ at $x = 0$

22 $\dfrac{d^2y}{dx^2} + 2\dfrac{dy}{dx} + 10y = 20x - 6;\ y = 0,\ \dfrac{dy}{dx} = 6$ at $x = 0$

23 $\dfrac{d^2y}{dx^2} + 6\dfrac{dy}{dx} + 25y = 6\sin x;\ \dfrac{dy}{dx} = y = 0$ at $x = 0$

24 $\dfrac{d^2y}{dx^2} + 9y = 8\sin x;\ \dfrac{dy}{dx} = y = 0$ at $x = \frac{\pi}{2}$

25 $\dfrac{d^2y}{dx^2} - 7\dfrac{dy}{dx} + 6y = 36x;\ \dfrac{dy}{dx} = 4$ and $y = 0$ at $x = 0$

26 Show that $\frac{1}{2}x\sin x$ is a particular integral of the differential equation

$$\frac{d^2y}{dx^2} + y = \cos x.$$

Hence find the general solution.

27 Find the value of the constant k so that kxe^{2x} is a particular integral of the differential equation

$$\frac{d^2y}{dx^2} - 14\frac{dy}{dx} + 24y = 4e^{2x}$$

Hence find y in terms of x, given that $y = 0$ and $\frac{dy}{dx} = 0$ at $x = 0$.

28 Find y in terms of x given that

$$\frac{d^2y}{dx^2} + 2\frac{dy}{dx} + 5y = 20e^{-x}$$

and that $\frac{dy}{dx} = 3$ and $y = 1$ at $x = 0$.

29 Find the general solution of the differential equation

$$4\frac{d^2y}{dx^2} - 5\frac{dy}{dx} + y = 17(\cos x - \sin x)$$

30 For the differential equation $\frac{d^2y}{dx^2} + 4y = 10e^{-x}$ find the solution for which $\frac{dy}{dx} = -1$ and $y = \frac{1}{2}$ at $x = 0$.

8.7 Solving differential equations using a change of variable

Some first order and second order differential equations can be transformed by a substitution that changes one of the variables in the equation into a new variable. You can often use substitutions to move from an equation that cannot be easily integrated to a transformed equation which you know how to solve from work already covered in this chapter. Examination questions give you the substitution needed. The following examples are typical.

Example 17

Use the substitution $y = vx$, where v is a function of x, to transform the differential equation

$$\frac{dy}{dx} = 1 + \frac{y}{x} + \left(\frac{y}{x}\right)^2, \quad x > 0$$

into a differential equation in v and x. By first solving this equation, find y in terms of x, given that $y = 1$ at $x = 1$.

Since $y = vx$, using the product rule of differentiation gives you

$$\frac{dy}{dx} = v + x\frac{dv}{dx}$$

Using this result and writing $y = vx$ in the differential equation

$$\frac{dy}{dx} = 1 + \frac{y}{x} + \left(\frac{y}{x}\right)^2$$

you have: $\qquad\qquad v + x\dfrac{dv}{dx} = 1 + v + v^2$

that is: $\qquad\qquad x\dfrac{dv}{dx} = 1 + v^2$

This is a first order differential equation in which the variables can be separated to give on integration

$$\int \frac{1}{1 + v^2}\,dv = \int \frac{1}{x}\,dx + C$$

where C is an arbitrary constant.

So: $\qquad\qquad\qquad \arctan v = \ln x + C$

But $v = \dfrac{y}{x} \Rightarrow \arctan \dfrac{y}{x} = \ln x + C$ is the general solution of the original differential equation. Now $y = 1$ at $x = 1$. So if you substitute this in the general solution you get

$$\arctan 1 = \ln 1 + C \Rightarrow C = \frac{\pi}{4}$$

That is: $\qquad\qquad \arctan \dfrac{y}{x} = \ln x + \dfrac{\pi}{4}$

$$\Rightarrow \quad \frac{y}{x} = \tan\left(\frac{\pi}{4} + \ln x\right)$$

$$y = x\tan\left(\frac{\pi}{4} + \ln x\right)$$

which gives y in terms of x, as required.

Example 18

Given that $x = e^u$, where u is a function of x, show that

(a) $x \dfrac{dy}{dx} = \dfrac{dy}{du}$ (b) $x^2 \dfrac{d^2y}{dx^2} = \dfrac{d^2y}{du^2} - \dfrac{dy}{du}$.

Hence find the general solution of the differential equation

$$x^2 \frac{d^2y}{dx^2} - 5x \frac{dy}{dx} + 9y = 0$$

(a) $x = e^u \Rightarrow \dfrac{dx}{du} = e^u$

Using the chain rule:

$\dfrac{dy}{du} = \dfrac{dy}{dx} \cdot \dfrac{dx}{du} = e^u \dfrac{dy}{dx} = x \dfrac{dy}{dx}$, as required.

(b) $\dfrac{d^2y}{du^2} = \dfrac{d}{du}\left(\dfrac{dy}{du}\right)$

$= \dfrac{d}{du}\left(e^u \dfrac{dy}{dx}\right)$

$= e^u \dfrac{dy}{dx} + e^u \dfrac{d^2y}{dx^2} \cdot \dfrac{dx}{du}$

$= \dfrac{dy}{du} + x^2 \dfrac{d^2y}{dx^2}$, since $\dfrac{dx}{du} = e^u$ and $e^u = x$

So: $x^2 \dfrac{d^2y}{dx^2} = \dfrac{d^2y}{du^2} - \dfrac{dy}{du}$, as required.

Put these results (a) and (b) into the differential equation

$$x^2 \frac{d^2y}{dx^2} - 5x \frac{dy}{dx} + 9y = 0$$

to obtain: $\dfrac{d^2y}{du^2} - \dfrac{dy}{du} - 5\dfrac{dy}{du} + 9y = 0$

which is a second order differential equation with constant coefficients: you know how to solve it.

Put $y = e^{mu}$, $\dfrac{dy}{du} = me^{mu}$ and $\dfrac{d^2y}{du^2} = m^2 e^{mu}$. Substituting these gives the auxiliary quadratic equation as

$$m^2 - 6m + 9 = 0$$

$$\Rightarrow \text{double root } m = 3$$

The general solution of the differential equation

$$\frac{d^2y}{du^2} - 6\frac{dy}{du} + 9y = 0$$

is

$$y = (A + Bu)e^{3u}$$

where A and B are arbitrary constants.

$x = e^u \Rightarrow u = \ln x$ and the general solution of the differential equation

$$x^2\frac{d^2y}{dx^2} - 5x\frac{dy}{dx} + 9y = 0$$

is

$$y = (A + B\ln x)e^{3\ln x}$$

that is:

$$y = (A + B\ln x)x^3$$

Exercise 8H

In questions 1–8 find the general solution of each differential equation using the substitution given, where v is a function of x.

1 $\dfrac{dy}{dx} = \dfrac{x}{y} + \dfrac{y}{x}$, $x > 0$, $y > 0$; $y = vx$

2 $x\dfrac{dy}{dx} = x + y$, $x > 0$; $y = vx$

3 $\dfrac{dy}{dx} = -(x - y)^2$; $y = x + v$

4 $\dfrac{dy}{dx} = \dfrac{y(x + 2y)}{x(y + 2x)}$, $x \neq 0$; $y = vx$

5 $(x + y)\dfrac{dy}{dx} = x^2 + xy + x + 1$; $y = v - x$

6 $x^2\dfrac{d^2y}{dx^2} + x\dfrac{dy}{dx} + y = 0$; $x = e^v$

7 $x^2\dfrac{d^2y}{dx^2} - 4x\dfrac{dy}{dx} + 6y = 0$; $x = e^v$

8 $x\dfrac{d^2y}{dx^2} - 2\dfrac{dy}{dx} + x = 0$; $\dfrac{dy}{dx} = v$

9 Given that $y = 1$ at $x = 2$, use the substitution $v = 3x - y - 3$ to solve the differential equation

$$(3x - y - 1)\frac{dy}{dx} = (3x - y + 3)$$

10 Use the substitution $v = y^{-2}$ to find the general solution of the differential equation

$$\frac{dy}{dx} + \frac{y}{x} = x^2 y^3$$

Find also y in terms of x, given that $y = 1$ at $x = 1$.

SUMMARY OF KEY POINTS

1 The general solution of the differential equation
$\frac{dy}{dx} = f(x)g(y)$ is

$$\int \frac{1}{g(y)}\, dy = \int f(x)\, dx + C$$

provided that $\frac{1}{g(y)}$ can be integrated with respect to y and $f(x)$ can be integrated with respect to x. C is an arbitrary constant.

2 In the general solution of a differential equation, different values of the arbitrary constant C, arising from different initial conditions, give rise to a series of equations whose graphs when sketched are called a family of solution curves for the differential equation.

3 An exact first order differential equation is one that can be integrated directly as it stands without any processing.

4 The first order linear differential equation

$$\frac{dy}{dx} + Py = Q$$

where P and Q are functions of x, is made into an exact first order differential equation by multiplying the equation by the integrating factor $e^{\int P\,dx}$, provided that $e^{\int P\,dx}$ and the integral of $e^{\int P\,dx}Q(x)$ exist.

The general solution is then

$$ye^{\int P\,dx} = \int Qe^{\int P\,dx}\,dx + C$$

where C is an arbitrary constant.

5 For the second order differential equation

$$a\frac{d^2y}{dx^2} + b\frac{dy}{dx} + cy = 0$$

the auxiliary quadratic equation is

$$am^2 + bm + c = 0$$

(i) If the auxiliary quadratic equation has real distinct roots α and β (condition $b^2 > 4ac$), then the general solution is

$$y = Ae^{\alpha x} + Be^{\beta x}$$

where A and B are constants.

(ii) If the auxiliary quadratic equation has real coincident roots α (condition $b^2 = 4ac$), then the general solution is

$$y = (A + Bx)e^{\alpha x}$$

where A and B are constants.

(iii) If the auxiliary quadratic equation has pure imaginary roots $\pm ni$, arising from $m^2 + n^2 = 0$, the general solution is

$$y = A\cos nx + B\sin nx$$

where A and B are constants and $n \in \mathbb{R}$.

(iv) If the auxiliary quadratic equation has complex conjugate roots $p \pm iq$, $p, q \in \mathbb{R}$ (condition $b^2 < 4ac$), the general solution is

$$y = e^{px}[A\cos qx + B\sin qx]$$

where A and B are constants.

6 For the differential equation

$$a\frac{d^2y}{dx^2} + b\frac{dy}{dx} + cy = f(x)$$

where a, b and c are constants, the *complementary function* is the general solution of the differential equation $a\dfrac{d^2y}{dx^2} + b\dfrac{dy}{dx} + cy = 0$ and a *particular integral* is any solution (i.e. function of x) that satisfies the differential equation

$$a\frac{d^2y}{dx^2} + b\frac{dy}{dx} + cy = f(x)$$

The general solution of the differential equation is

$$y = \text{complementary function} + \text{particular integral}$$

7   A change of variable given by a substitution can transform a differential equation from one in say (x, y) which is not immediately integrable into a differential equation in say (x, v) which *is* immediately integrable or a recognised equation for which a method of solution has already been learned.

Numerical methods

9

Chapter 10 of Book P1 described how you can detect an interval in which a root of the equation $f(x) = 0$ lies. You can do this by using the fact that a root lies in the interval $[a, b]$ if $f(a) < 0$ and $f(b) > 0$ or vice versa.

Chapter 12 of Book P2 introduced iterative procedures for finding the root of an equation to whatever degree of accuracy you require. In this chapter you will learn three other procedures for finding approximations to the roots of equations:

(a) linear interpolation
(b) interval bisection
(c) the Newton–Raphson process.

9.1 Review of iterative procedures

The technique of iteration gives a sequence of approximations. Usually this sequence converges to a root of the equation. However, sometimes the sequence diverges and takes you further and further away from the root. The conditions under which such a sequence will diverge are given in Book P2 (page 372).

In the P3 examination any iterative procedure (other than the Newton–Raphson process which you will be shown later in this chapter) will be given on the examination paper. So you need only the same knowledge of iterative procedures in P3 as you learned in P2 – but the questions may be a little more tricky and involved.

Example 1
Show that the equation $f(x) = 0$, where $f(x) \equiv 4x - \sec^2 x$, has a root in the interval $[0.2, 0.3]$.

Use the iterative procedure

$$x_{n+1} = \tfrac{1}{4}\sec^2 x_n \text{ with } x_1 = 0.2$$

to find this root correct to 4 decimal places.

$f(0.2) = -0.241\,09\ldots$, $f(0.3) = 0.104\,311\ldots$ so a root lies in the interval $[0.2, 0.3]$.

$$x_{n+1} = \tfrac{1}{4}\sec^2 x_n; \quad x_1 = 0.2$$

So, using a calculator you obtain:

$$x_2 = 0.260\,272\,8\ldots$$
$$x_3 = 0.267\,730\,7\ldots$$
$$x_4 = 0.268\,812\,3\ldots$$
$$x_5 = 0.268\,972\,3\ldots$$
$$x_6 = 0.268\,996\,0\ldots$$

Since both x_5 and x_6 give the root as 0.2690 to 4 decimal places it is now necessary to test this to see if the root is 0.2690 to this degree of accuracy.

To do this you need to go either side of 0.2690. So you consider the interval $[0.268\,95, 0.269\,05]$:

$$f(0.268\,95) = -0.000\,170\,8\ldots$$
$$f(0.269\,05) \doteq 0.000\,169\,85\ldots$$

Since there is a sign change, the root does indeed lie in the interval $[0.268\,95, 0.269\,05]$ and so the root is 0.2690 (4 d.p.).

9.2 Linear interpolation

If you want to find a root of $f(x) = 0$, another method of finding the approximate value of the root is to first consider the graph of $y = f(x)$.

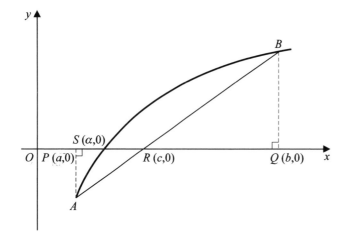

From the graph you can see that since the curve cuts the x-axis at $S(\alpha, 0)$, a root of the equation $f(x) = 0$ is α, and it lies in the interval $[a, b]$. To find an approximation to α you join A and B with a straight line and use the point where this straight line crosses the x-axis as a first approximation to the root. So in this case you try to find c and use this as an approximation to α.

To find c, use the fact that triangles PAR and QBR are similar ($\angle APR = \angle BQR = 90°$ and $\angle ARP = \angle BRQ$ since they are vertically opposite). You can then see that

$$\frac{PR}{AP} = \frac{QR}{BQ}$$

From this you can work out the value of c.

You can repeat this process to get a closer approximation to α, and go on repeating it until you have a value for the root to the desired degree of accuracy, as the next example shows.

Example 2

Show that the equation $x^3 + 5x - 10 = 0$ has a root in the interval $[1, 2]$. Using linear interpolation, find this root to 1 decimal place.

Let $f(x) \equiv x^3 + 5x - 10$. Then:

$$f(1) = 1 + 5 - 10 = -4$$
$$f(2) = 8 + 10 - 10 = 8$$

Since there is a sign change, the equation $x^3 + 5x - 10 = 0$ has a root in $[1, 2]$.

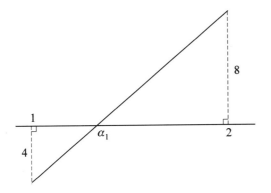

Using similar triangles:

$$\frac{2 - \alpha_1}{\alpha_1 - 1} = \frac{8}{4}$$

So:

$$2 - \alpha_1 = 2\alpha_1 - 2$$

$$4 = 3\alpha_1$$

$$\alpha_1 = \frac{4}{3} = 1.333\ldots$$

$f(1.333\ldots) = -0.962\,96\ldots$. Since $f(2) > 0$ and $f(1.333\ldots) < 0$, the root lies in the interval $[1.333\ldots, 2]$.

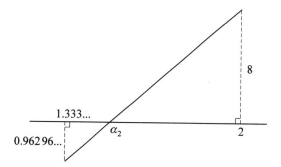

By similar triangles:

$$\frac{2 - \alpha_2}{\alpha_2 - 1.333\ldots} = \frac{8}{0.962\,96\ldots}$$

$$\alpha_2 = 1.404\,95\ldots$$

$$f(1.404\,95\ldots) = -0.2019\ldots$$

So the root lies in the interval $[1.404\,95\ldots, 2]$.

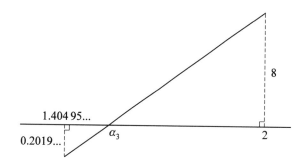

$$\frac{2 - \alpha_3}{\alpha_3 - 1.404\,95\ldots} = \frac{8}{0.2019\ldots}$$

$$\alpha_3 = 1.4196\ldots$$

Two successive approximations give the root as 1.4 to 1 decimal place, so you can now test either side of 1.4 by considering the interval $[1.35, 1.45]$:

$$f(1.35) = -0.789\,625$$
$$f(1.45) = 0.298\,62\ldots$$

Since $f(1.35) < 0$ and $f(1.45) > 0$, the root lies in $[1.35, 1.45]$ and so $\alpha = 1.4$ (1 d.p.).

9.3 Interval bisection

Another method of finding an approximation to a root of the equation $f(x) = 0$ is to find an interval $[a, b]$ in which the root lies and then take the mid-point $\dfrac{a+b}{2}$ of this interval as a first approximation to the root.

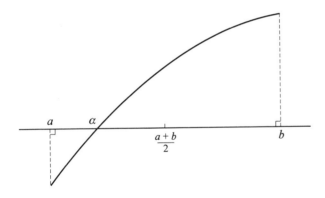

When you have done this it is obvious that the root will then lie either in the left-hand interval $\left[a, \dfrac{a+b}{2}\right]$ or in the right-hand interval $\left[\dfrac{a+b}{2}, b\right]$.

You decide which one it is (in the diagram it is the left-hand interval), and then choose the mid-point of this interval as a second approximation to the root. You then repeat the process until you obtain the root to the accuracy required.

Example 3

Use interval bisection to obtain a sequence of approximations to the positive root of the equation $x^2 - 7 = 0$. Hence find $\sqrt{7}$ to 2 decimal places.

Let $f(x) \equiv x^2 - 7$

Since $f(2) = -3 < 0$ and $f(3) = 2 > 0$ the positive root lies in $[2, 3]$. Take $x_0 = 2$ and $x_1 = 3$. Then:

$$x_2 = \frac{2+3}{2} = 2.5 \text{ and } f(2.5) = -0.75$$

$f(2.5) < 0$ and $f(3) > 0$ so the root lies in $[2.5, 3]$.

So: $\qquad x_3 = \frac{2.5+3}{2} = 2.75 \text{ and } f(2.75) = 0.5625$

$f(2.75) > 0$ and $f(2.5) < 0$ so the root lies in $[2.5, 2.75]$.

Thus: $\qquad x_4 = \frac{2.5+2.75}{2} = 2.625 \text{ and } f(2.625) = -0.1093\ldots$

$f(2.625) < 0$ and $f(2.75) > 0$ so the root lies in $[2.625, 2.75]$.

Thus: $\quad x_5 = \frac{2.625+2.75}{2} = 2.6875 \text{ and } f(2.6875) = 0.222\,656\,25$

$f(2.6875) > 0$ and $f(2.625) < 0$ so the root lies in $[2.625, 2.6875]$.

Thus: $\qquad x_6 = \frac{2.625+2.6875}{2} = 2.656\,25$

and $\qquad f(2.656\,25) = 0.055\,664\ldots$

$f(2.656\,25) > 0$ and $f(2.625) < 0$ so the root lies in $[2.625, 2.656\,25]$.

Thus: $\qquad x_7 = \frac{2.625+2.656\,25}{2} = 2.640\,625$

and $\qquad f(2.640\,625) = -0.027\,09\ldots$

$f(2.640\,625) < 0$ and $f(2.656\,25) > 0$
so the root lies in $[2.640\,625, 2.656\,25]$.

Thus: $\qquad x_8 = \frac{2.640\,625+2.656\,25}{2} = 2.648\,437\,5$

and $\qquad f(2.648\,437\,5) = 0.014\,22\ldots$

$f(2.648\,437\,5) > 0$ and $f(2.640\,625) < 0$
so the root lies in $[2.640\,625, 2.648\,437\,5]$.

So: $x_9 = \dfrac{2.640\,625 + 2.648\,437\,5}{2} = 2.644\,531\,25$

and $f(2.644\,531\,25) = -0.006\,45\ldots$

$f(2.644\,531\,25) < 0$ and $f(2.648\,437\,5) > 0$
so the root lies in $[2.644\,531\,25, 2.648\,437\,5]$

So: $x_{10} = \dfrac{2.644\,531\,25 + 2.648\,437\,5}{2} = 2.646\,484\,375$

and $f(2.646\,484\,375) = 0.003\,87\ldots$

$f(2.646\,484\,375) > 0$ and $f(2.644\,531\,25) < 0$
so the root lies in $[2.644\,531\,25, 2.646\,484\,375]$.

So: $x_{11} = \dfrac{2.644\,531\,25 + 2.646\,484\,375}{2} = 2.645\,507\,813$

and: $f(2.645\,507\,813) = -0.001\,28\ldots$

The root lies in $[2.645\,507\,813, 2.646\,484\,375]$. Since both ends of the interval when corrected to 2 decimal places are 2.65, the root is 2.65 to 2 decimal places.

If you put these calculations in a table, the working becomes more concise and less prone to errors:

a	b	$\dfrac{a+b}{2}$
2	3	2.5
2.5	3	2.75
2.5	2.75	2.625
2.625	2.75	2.6875
2.625	2.6875	2.656\,25
2.625	2.656\,25	2.640\,625
2.640\,625	2.656\,25	2.648\,437\,5
2.640\,625	2.648\,437\,5	2.644\,531\,25
2.644\,531\,25	2.648\,437\,5	2.646\,484\,375
2.644\,531\,25	2.646\,484\,375	2.645\,507\,813

The root is 2.65 to 2 decimal places.

As you can see, while this method is very easy to apply, it sometimes takes a long time to get the root to the accuracy that you require.

9.4 The Newton–Raphson process

You can derive another method of finding an approximation to a root of the equation $f(x) = 0$ by considering the graph of $y = f(x)$:

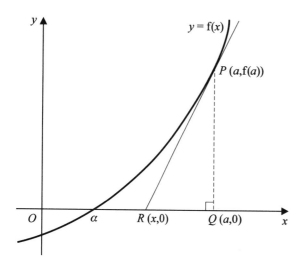

As you can see from the diagram α is a root of $f(x) = 0$. Take a as a first approximation to α. Since the point P on the curve has a as its x-coordinate, draw the tangent to the curve at P. This cuts the x-axis at $R(x, 0)$.

The gradient of the curve $y = f(x)$ is given by $\dfrac{dy}{dx} = f'(x)$. So the gradient of the curve at P is $f'(a)$. Using the fact that at P, $x = a$, $y = f(a)$ and $\dfrac{dy}{dx} = f'(a)$, the equation of the tangent at P is

$$y - f(a) = f'(a)(x - a)$$

The tangent cuts the x-axis where $y = 0$, so at R:

$$-f(a) = f'(a)(x - a)$$

That is:
$$x - a = \frac{-f(a)}{f'(a)}$$

or:
$$x = a - \frac{f(a)}{f'(a)}$$

So the x-coordinate of R is $a - \dfrac{f(a)}{f'(a)}$.

■ **That is, if a is a first approximation to a root of $f(x) = 0$, a better
approximation is, in general,**

$$a - \frac{f(a)}{f'(a)}$$

You can now use this value, repeat the process, and obtain a third
approximation, which will, in general, be a better approximation
than the second, and so on.

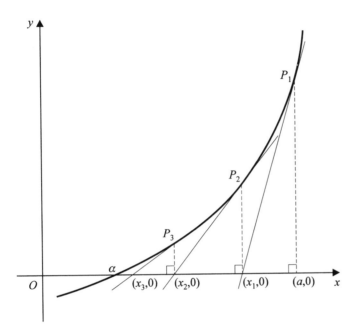

As you can see from the diagram each successive tangent cuts the
x-axis closer and closer to the point where the curve cuts the x-axis.
Consequently, the sequence of approximations $a, x_1, x_2, x_3, \ldots$ is
getting closer and closer to the root α of the equation $f(x) = 0$.

Although the Newton–Raphson process works well in general, there
are occasions on which the sequence of approximations takes you
further and further from a root.

For example, you can see in the diagram on the next page that the
tangent at $(a, f(a))$ cuts the x-axis at a point which is further from
$(\alpha, 0)$ than is $(a, 0)$. Under these circumstances the Newton–
Raphson process fails.

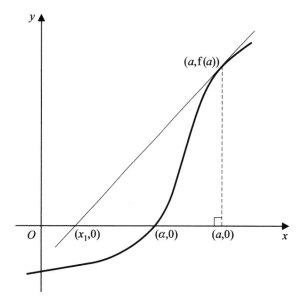

Example 4

Show that a root of the equation $\ln x = 4 - x$ lies between 2.9 and 3.

By taking 2.9 as a first approximation and applying the Newton–Raphson process once to the equation $\ln x - 4 + x = 0$, find a second approximation, giving your answer to 3 significant figures.

Let $f(x) \equiv \ln x - 4 + x$

then: $\qquad\qquad\qquad f(2.9) = -0.0352\ldots$

and $\qquad\qquad\qquad\quad f(3) = 0.0986\ldots$

Since there is a change of sign a root lies between 2.9 and 3.

$$f(x) \equiv \ln x - 4 + x$$

so: $\qquad\qquad\qquad f'(x) \equiv \dfrac{1}{x} + 1$

$$x_0 = 2.9$$

Using $x_0 - \dfrac{f(x_0)}{f'(x_0)}$ as a better approximation you get

$$x_1 = 2.9 - \frac{\ln 2.9 - 4 + 2.9}{\dfrac{1}{2.9} + 1}$$
$$= 2.9262\ldots$$
$$= 2.93 \text{ (3 s.f.)}$$

Example 5

Show that the equation $4x^2 - 1 - 2\tan x = 0$ has a root α in the interval $[-0.4, -0.3]$. Use the Newton–Raphson procedure once, starting with -0.3, to find a second approximation to α, giving your answer to 3 decimal places. Show further that this approximation to α is correct to 3 decimal places.

Let $f(x) \equiv 4x^2 - 1 - 2\tan x$

$$f(-0.4) = 0.4855\ldots$$
$$f(-0.3) = -0.0213\ldots$$

Since there is a sign change, a root lies in the interval $[-0.4, -0.3]$.

$$f(x) \equiv 4x^2 - 1 - 2\tan x$$
$$f'(x) \equiv 8x - 2\sec^2 x$$

$$x_0 = -0.3$$
$$x_1 = -0.3 - \frac{4(-0.3)^2 - 1 - 2\tan(-0.3)}{8(-0.3) - 2\sec^2(-0.3)}$$
$$= -0.3046\ldots$$

So the root is -0.305 (3 d.p.).

Consider the interval $[-0.3055, -0.3045]$ to check that the root is correct to 3 decimal places:

$$f(-0.3055) = 0.004\,066\ldots$$
$$f(-0.3045) = -0.000\,571\ldots$$

The sign change indicates that the root is -0.305 correct to 3 decimal places.

Exercise 9A

1 Show that a root of the equation $x^3 - 5x - 3 = 0$ lies in the interval $[2, 3]$. Use linear interpolation to find this root correct to 2 decimal places.

2 Show that a root of the equation $4 = xe^{2x}$ lies in the interval $[0, 1]$. Use linear interpolation to find this root correct to 2 decimal places.

3 Show that a root of the equation $4x^3 - 9x^2 + 3 = 0$ lies in the interval $[0, 1]$. Use linear interpolation to find this root correct to 2 decimal places.

4 Show that a root of the equation $x + 2 = \dfrac{4}{x}$ lies in the interval $[1, 2]$. Use linear interpolation to find this root correct to 2 decimal places.

5 Show that the equation $xe^x - 1 = x$ has a root in the interval $[0, 1]$. Use linear interpolation to find this root correct to 2 decimal places.

6 Show that the equation $4x - 3 - e^{-x}(x^2 + 1) = 0$ has a root α in the interval $[0.9, 1]$. By using linear interpolation find an approximation x_0 to α. Taking x_0 as a first approximation to α, use the Newton–Raphson process once to find a second approximation to α, giving your answer to 3 decimal places.

7 Verify that the equation $x^3 - x^2 + 8x - 4 = 0$ has a root α in the interval $[0.5, 0.6]$. Use a sequence of linear interpolations to find α correct to 2 decimal places.

8 Show that the equation $4x^2 - \tan x - 1 = 0$ has a root α in the interval $[0.6, 0.7]$. Use the iterative procedure

$$x_{n+1} = \tfrac{1}{2}\sqrt{(1 + \tan x_n)}$$

with $x_0 = 0.7$ to find α correct to 3 decimal places.

9 Show that $x^5 + 5x - 1 = 0$ has a root α in the interval $[0.1, 0.3]$. Taking $x_0 = 0.3$, use the iterative procedure

$$x_{n+1} = \tfrac{1}{5}(1 - x_n^5)$$

to find α correct to 6 decimal places.

10 Show that the largest positive root of the equation $x^3 - 3x^2 - 2 = 0$ lies between 3 and 4. Use a sequence of linear interpolations to estimate this root correct to 2 decimal places.

11 Use interval bisection to find, correct to 2 decimal places, the root of the equation $x^4 + 3x^2 - x - 8 = 0$ that lies in the interval $[1, 2]$.

12 Use interval bisection to find the positive root of the equation $x^2 - 5 = 0$, correct to 2 decimal places.

13 Show that a root of the equation $x^3 - 5x - 3 = 0$ lies in the interval $[-2, -1]$. Use interval bisection to find this root correct to 2 decimal places.

14 Show that a root of the equation $e^{2x} + 3x = 5$ lies in the interval $[0, 1]$. Use interval bisection to find this root correct to 3 decimal places.

15 Show that the equation

$$\frac{15}{2+x} = 3 + \sqrt{x}$$

has a root lying in the interval $[1, 2]$. Use interval bisection to find this root correct to 2 decimal places.

16 Show that the equation $f(x) = 0$ has a root in the given interval. Use the Newton–Raphson process once, starting with x_0, to find a second approximation and give your answer to 2 decimal places:

(a) $f(x) \equiv x^3 - x^2 + 6x - 1$; $[0.15, 0.20]$; $x_0 = 0.2$

(b) $f(x) \equiv x^3 + 2x^2 + 5x - 27$; $[2, 2.2]$; $x_0 = 2.1$

(c) $f(x) \equiv x^3 - 30$; $[3, 3.2]$; $x_0 = 3.2$

(d) $f(x) \equiv \tan x - e^x$; $[0, \frac{5\pi}{12}]$; $x_0 = 1.3$

(e) $f(x) \equiv x^3 + x^2 - 100$; $[4, 5]$; $x_0 = 4.4$

(f) $f(x) \equiv x + \sin x - 1$; $[0.4, 0.6]$; $x_0 = 0.54$

(g) $f(x) \equiv \ln x - 1 - \dfrac{1}{x}$; $[3, 4]$; $x_0 = 3.6$

17 Show that the equation $x^3 - 12x - 7.2 = 0$ has one positive and two negative roots. Obtain the positive root to 3 significant figures using the Newton–Raphson process. [L]

18 Find, correct to 1 decimal place, the real root of $x^3 + 2x - 1 = 0$ by using the Newton–Raphson process. [L]

19 Using the same axes draw accurate graphs of $y = \ln x$ and $y = 3 - x$ in the interval $1 \leqslant x \leqslant 4$. Deduce that the equation $x + \ln x - 3 = 0$ has a root near 2.2. Clearly showing your method, obtain alternative approximations to the root of the equation

(a) by linear interpolation between $x = 2.2$ and $x = 2.3$

(b) by one application of the Newton–Raphson process using $x = 2.2$ as the initial value. [L]

20 Use the Newton–Raphson process to find the real root of the equation $x^3 + 2x^2 + 4x - 6 = 0$, taking $x = 0.9$ as the first approximation and carrying out one iteration. **[L]**

21 Show that the equation $x^3 + 3x - 3 = 0$ has only one real root and that it lies between 0.8 and 1. Obtain approximations to the root

(a) by performing one application of the Newton–Raphson process using $x = 0.8$ as the first approximation

(b) by performing two iterations using the procedure defined by

$$x_{n+1} = \frac{(3 - x_n^3)}{3}$$

and starting with $x = 0.8$. **[L]**

22 Given that $f(x) \equiv 4x - e^x$, show that the equation $f(x) = 0$ has a root α in the interval $[0.3, 0.4]$. Taking 0.35 as an initial approximation to α, use the Newton–Raphson process twice to obtain two further approximations to α, giving your final answer to 3 decimal places.

23
$$f(x) \equiv x^3 + 3x + 3$$

(a) Show that the equation $f(x) = 0$ has a root α in the interval $[-1, 0]$.

(b) Use linear interpolation once on the interval $[-1, 0]$ to obtain an approximation x_0 to α.

(c) Using your value x_0, use the Newton–Raphson procedure once to find a second approximation x_1 to α, giving your answer to 2 decimal places.

(d) Show that x_1 is correct to 2 decimal places.

24 It is given that

$$f(x) \equiv x - (\sin x + \cos x)^{\frac{1}{2}}, \ 0 \leqslant x \leqslant \tfrac{3}{4}\pi.$$

(a) Show that the equation $f(x) = 0$ has a root lying between 1.1 and 1.2.

(b) Using 1.2 as a first approximation to this root, apply the Newton–Raphson procedure once to obtain a second approximation, giving your answer to 2 decimal places.

(c) When x is small enough for terms in x^2 and higher powers of x to be neglected, use the approximations $\sin x \approx x$ and $\cos x \approx 1$ with the binomial expansion to show that

$$f(x) = A + Bx$$

and find the values of the constants A and B. [L]

SUMMARY OF KEY POINTS

1 In order to find a root of the equation $f(x) = 0$ by iteration, the equation must first be rearranged in the form $x = g(x)$. An iteration formula is then

$$x_{n+1} = g(x_n)$$

2 To find a root of an equation $f(x) = 0$ by linear interpolation, use a straight line to join two points with x-coordinates a and b on the graph of $y = f(x)$ that lie on opposite sides of the x-axis. Take the point where the line cuts the x-axis as a first approximation α_1 to the root α and work out its value by similar triangles. Work out $f(\alpha_1)$ to find out whether the root lies in the interval $[a, \alpha_1]$ or $[\alpha_1, b]$ and repeat the process on the appropriate interval to find a closer approximation to α, etc.

3 Interval bisection: If a root α of the equation $f(x) = 0$ lies in the interval $[a, b]$, the mid-point $\dfrac{a+b}{2}$ is a first approximation to α. Calculate $f(a), f(b)$ and $f\left(\dfrac{a+b}{2}\right)$ to find out whether the root lies in the interval $\left[a, \dfrac{a+b}{2}\right]$ or $\left[\dfrac{a+b}{2}, b\right]$ and then find the mid-point of the appropriate interval to find a closer approximation to α, etc.

4 The Newton–Raphson process:
If a is a first approximation to a root of $f(x) = 0$, then

$$a - \frac{f(a)}{f'(a)}$$

is in general a better approximation.

Review exercise 3

1 Given that the complex numbers w_1 and w_2 are the roots of the equation

$$z^2 - 5 - 12i = 0$$

express w_1 and w_2 in the form $a + ib$, where a and b are real.

[L]

2 Find z in the form $x + iy$, where x and y are real, when

$$(z + 1)(2 - i) = 3 - 4i$$

and show the position of z on an Argand diagram. [L]

3 Given that $x > 1$ and $y > 0$, find the general solution of the differential equation

$$\frac{dy}{dx} = \frac{xy}{x - 1}$$

Given further that $y = 1$ at $x = \frac{5}{3}$, find the value of y at $x = 2$, giving your answer in the form $y = ke^c$, where k and c are numbers to be found. [L]

4 In the figure, O is the centre of a circle, radius $10\,\text{cm}$, and the points A and B are situated on the circumference so that $\angle AOB = 2\theta$ radians. The area of the shaded segment is $44\,\text{cm}^2$. Show that

$$2\theta - \sin 2\theta - 0.88 = 0.$$

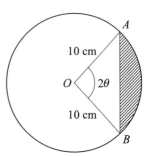

Show further that a root of this equation lies between 0.9 and 1. By taking 0.9 as a first approximation to this root, use the Newton–Raphson procedure once to determine a second approximation, giving your answer to 2 decimal places. [L]

5 The complex numbers z_1 and z_2 are given by

$$z_1 = 24 + 7i, \quad z_2 = 4 - 3i$$

(a) Given that $z_1 + \alpha z_2$ is real, where α is real, find the value of α.

(b) Given that $z_1 + (p + iq)z_2 = 0$, where p and q are real numbers, find p and q. [L]

6 Find the general solution of the differential equation

$$\frac{1}{x}\frac{dy}{dx} + 2y = 8, \quad x > 0$$

Express your answer in the form $y = f(x)$. [L]

7 (a) The complex numbers z_1 and z_2 are given by

$$z_1 = 57 - 17i, \quad z_2 = 5 + 6i$$

(i) Express $\dfrac{z_1}{z_2}$ in the form $p + qi$, where p and q are real integers.

(ii) Find $\arg z_1$, giving your answer in degrees to 1 decimal place.

(b) Given the two complex numbers w and $2wi$, state precisely

(i) the relation between their moduli

(ii) the relation between their arguments. [L]

8 The diagram shows a semicircle with O the mid-point of the diameter AB. The point P on the semicircle is such that the area of sector POB is equal to the area of the shaded segment. Angle POB is x radians.

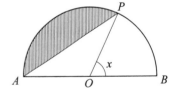

(a) Show that $x = \frac{1}{2}(\pi - \sin x)$.

The iterative method based on the relation $x_{n+1} = \frac{1}{2}(\pi - \sin x_n)$ can be used to evaluate x.

(b) Starting with $x_1 = 1$ perform two iterations to find the values of x_2 and x_3, giving your answers to 2 decimal places. [L]

9 Given that $z_1 = 1 + 2i$ and $z_2 = \frac{3}{5} + \frac{4}{5}i$, write $z_1 z_2$ and $\dfrac{z_1}{z_2}$ in the form $p + iq$, where p and $q \in \mathbb{R}$. In an Argand diagram, the origin O and the points representing $z_1 z_2$, $\dfrac{z_1}{z_2}$, z_3 are the vertices of a rhombus. Find z_3 and sketch the rhombus on this Argand diagram.

Show that $|z_3| = \dfrac{6\sqrt{5}}{5}$. [L]

10 Solve the equation

$$z^3 + 1 = 0$$

giving your solutions in the form $a + ib$, where a and b are real, and showing them on an Argand diagram. [L]

11 Find y in terms of k and x, given that

$$\frac{d^2y}{dx^2} + k^2y = 0$$

where k is a constant, and $y = 1$ and $\dfrac{dy}{dx} = 1$ at $x = 0$. [L]

12 Show that the equation $x^3 - 12x + 7 = 0$ has one negative real root and two positive real roots.

Show that one root α lies in the interval $[3, 3.2]$.

Use linear interpolation once on this interval to estimate α, giving your answer to 2 decimal places. Show further that your estimate is correct to 2 decimal places. [L]

13 A particular solution of the differential equation

$$\frac{d^2y}{dx^2} + 4\frac{dy}{dx} + 4y = 8\sin 2x$$

is $y = p\cos 2x + q\sin 2x$, where p and q are constants.

Find the values of p and q. Given that $y = 1$ and $\dfrac{dy}{dx} = 0$ at $x = 0$ find the solution of the differential equation. [L]

14 The tangent at $P(x_n, x_n^2 - 2)$, where $x_n > 0$, to the curve with equation $y = x^2 - 2$ meets the x-axis at the point $Q(x_{n+1}, 0)$. Show that

$$x_{n+1} = \frac{x_n^2 + 2}{2x_n}$$

This relationship between x_{n+1} and x_n is used, starting with $x_1 = 2$, to find successive approximations for the positive root of the equation $x^2 - 2 = 0$. Find x_2 and x_3 as fractions and show that $x_4 = \frac{577}{408}$.

Find the error, to 1 significant figure, in using $\frac{577}{408}$ as an approximation to $\sqrt{2}$. [L]

15 Find the general solution of the differential equation

$$\frac{d^2y}{dx^2} + \frac{dy}{dx} + y = 0 \qquad\qquad \text{[L]}$$

16 The complex numbers z_1 and z_2 are given by

$$z_1 = 4 + 2i \text{ and } z_2 = -3 + i$$

(a) Display z_1 and z_2 on the same Argand diagram.

(b) Calculate $|z_1 - z_2|$.

(c) Given that $w = \dfrac{z_1}{z_2}$,

   (i) express w in the form $a + bi$, where $a, b \in \mathbb{R}$

   (ii) calculate $\arg w$, giving your answer in radians.　　[L]

17 Show that the substitution $y = z \cos x$, where z is a function of x, reduces the differential equation

$$\cos^2 x \frac{d^2y}{dx^2} + 2 \cos x \sin x \frac{dy}{dx} + 2y = x \cos^3 x$$

to the differential equation

$$\frac{d^2z}{dx^2} + z = x$$

Hence find y given that $y = 0$ and $\dfrac{dy}{dx} = 1$ at $x = 0$.　　[L]

18 (a) Given that $z_1 = 5 + i$ and $z_2 = -2 + 3i$,

   (i) show that $|z_1|^2 = 2|z_2|^2$

   (ii) find $\arg(z_1 z_2)$.

(b) Calculate, in the form $a + ib$, where $a, b \in \mathbb{R}$, the square roots of $16 - 30i$.　　[L]

19 Given that $f(x) \equiv 3 + 4x - x^4$, show that the equation $f(x) = 0$ has a root $x = a$, where a is in the interval $1 \leqslant a \leqslant 2$. It may be assumed that if x_n is an approximation to a, then a better approximation is given by x_{n+1}, where

$$x_{n+1} = (3 + 4x_n)^{\frac{1}{4}}$$

Starting with $x_0 = 1.75$, use this result twice to obtain the value of a to 2 decimal places.　　[L]

20
$$f(x) \equiv \ln x + x^2 - 4x$$

Show that the equation $f(x) = 0$ has a root α in the interval $[3, 4]$. Use the method of interval bisection to find α, giving your answer correct to 2 decimal places.   [L]

21 A chord divides a circle, centre O, into two regions whose areas are in the ratio $2 : 1$. Prove that the angle θ, subtended by this chord at O, satisfies the equation $f(\theta) = 0$, where

$$f(\theta) \equiv \theta - \sin\theta - \frac{2\pi}{3}$$

Using the same axes, sketch for $0 \leqslant \theta \leqslant \pi$, the graphs of $y = \theta - \dfrac{2\pi}{3}$ and $y = \sin\theta$.

By taking $\dfrac{5\pi}{6}$ as a first approximation to the positive root of the equation $f(\theta) = 0$, apply the Newton–Raphson procedure once to obtain a second approximation, giving your answer to three decimal places.   [L]

22 Obtain the values of the constants a and b, given that $y = a\cos 2x + b\sin 2x$ is a particular solution of

$$3\frac{d^2y}{dx^2} - 4\frac{dy}{dx} - 4y = 10\cos 2x$$

Hence obtain the general solution of the differential equation.
                    [L]

23 Use the substitution $z = y^{-2}$ to transform the differential equation

$$xy - \frac{dy}{dx} = y^3 e^{-x^2}$$

into the differential equation

$$\frac{dz}{dx} + 2xz = 2e^{-x^2}$$

Hence obtain the general solution of the first differential equation.   [L]

24 Show, graphically or otherwise, that the equation $x = 2 \sin x$ has a root near $x = 1.9$. Use one iteration of the Newton–Raphson method to find a more accurate approximation to this root. [L]

25 Find the solution of

$$\frac{dy}{dx} + \frac{y}{x} = \tfrac{1}{2}\sin(\tfrac{1}{2}x), \quad x > 0$$

such that $y = 1$ at $x = 2\pi$.

Given that as $x \to 0$, $y \to k$, determine the value of k. [L]

26 Find the values of the constants a and b in order that $y = a\cos 3x + b\sin 3x$ shall satisfy the differential equation

$$\frac{d^2y}{dx^2} + 2\frac{dy}{dx} = 5\sin 3x$$

Hence find the general solution of the differential equation.

[L]

27 A curve which passes through the point $(1, 1)$ has equation $y = f(x)$, where

$$\frac{dy}{dx} + \frac{2(x-1)}{x^2 - 2x + 2}y = \frac{2(x+1)}{x^2 - 2x + 2}$$

(a) Solve this differential equation, to show that

$$f(x) \equiv \frac{x^2 + 2x - 2}{x^2 - 2x + 2}$$

(b) Show that $-1 \leqslant f(x) \leqslant 3$. [L]

28 Show that, if $y = xz$, where z is a function of x, then

$$\frac{dy}{dx} = z + x\frac{dz}{dx}$$

Using the substitution $y = xz$, or otherwise, find the general solution of the differential equation

$$x\frac{dy}{dx} = y + 2x(x + y)$$ [L]

29 Verify that the equation

$$x^3 + x - 11 = 0$$

has a root in the interval $2 \leqslant x \leqslant 3$.
By writing $x = 2 + h$, and neglecting h^2 and h^3, find an approximate value for this root, giving your answer to 2 decimal places. [L]

30 Given that the differential equation

$$\frac{d^2 y}{dx^2} - 4 \frac{dy}{dx} + 13y = e^{2x}$$

has a particular integral of the form ke^{2x}, determine the value of the constant k. Find the general solution of the equation. [L]

31 Taking 1.55 as a first approximation to a root of the equation $x - 2 + \ln x = 0$, use one application of the Newton–Raphson method to obtain a second approximation. [L]

32 Find the values of the constants p and q if $y = p \cos x + q \sin x$ satisfies the differential equation

$$\frac{d^2 y}{dx^2} + 8 \frac{dy}{dx} + 25y = 48 \cos x - 16 \sin x$$

and hence find the general solution of this differential equation. Find the solution of this differential equation for which $y = 8$ and $\frac{dy}{dx} = 3$ at $x = 0$. [L]

33 Find the general solution of the differential equation

$$\cos x \frac{dy}{dx} + 2y \sin x = \sin^2 x \cos x, \quad 0 < x < \frac{\pi}{2} \qquad \text{[L]}$$

34 Express in the form $a + bi$, where a and b are real, each of the complex numbers

$$z_1 = \frac{-2 + i}{1 - 3i} \quad \text{and} \quad z_2 = \frac{-3 + i}{2 + i}$$

Represent z_1, z_2 and $z_1 z_2$ on the Argand diagram. [L]

35 (a) Show that the substitution $v = xy$ transforms the differential equation

$$x\frac{d^2y}{dx^2} + 2(1 + 2x)\frac{dy}{dx} + 4(1 + x)y = 32e^{2x}, \quad x \neq 0$$

into the differential equation

$$\frac{d^2v}{dx^2} + 4\frac{dv}{dx} + 4v = 32e^{2x}$$

(b) Given that $v = ae^{2x}$, where a is a constant, is a particular integral of this transformed equation, find a.

(c) Find the solution of the differential equation

$$x\frac{d^2y}{dx^2} + 2(1 + 2x)\frac{dy}{dx} + 4(1 + x)y = 32e^{2x}$$

for which $y = 2e^2$ and $\frac{dy}{dx} = 0$ at $x = 1$.

(d) Determine whether or not this solution remains finite as $x \to \infty$. [L]

36 Show, graphically, that the equation

$$\cosh x - 4 + 2x = 0$$

has two real roots, one of which lies between 0 and 2.
If the root which lies between 0 and 2 is called α, verify that $\alpha \approx 1.14$ and by using the Newton–Raphson process once, and giving your answer to 3 decimal places, obtain a better approximation. [L]

37 Given that $z = \dfrac{\sqrt{3} + i}{1 - i}$, find $z^2 + \dfrac{1}{z^2}$, giving your answer in the form $a + ib$, where a and b are real. [L]

38 Find the solution of the differential equation

$$\frac{dy}{dx} + y\cot x = \sin 2x, \quad 0 < x < \pi$$

for which $y = 1$ at $x = \frac{\pi}{4}$. [L]

39 Find the general solution of the differential equation

$$\frac{d^2y}{dx^2} - 5\frac{dy}{dx} + 6y = 5\sin x \qquad [L]$$

40 Show that the equation $e^x \cos 2x - 1 = 0$ has a root between 0.4 and 0.45.

Taking 0.45 as a first approximation to this root, apply the Newton–Raphson procedure once to obtain a second approximation, giving your answer to 3 significant figures.   [L]

41 The complex number z is given by

$$z = -\sqrt{3} + i$$

Find the value of

(a) $|z|$

(b) $\arg z$, giving your answer in degrees

(c) $\arg\left(\dfrac{i}{z}\right)$, giving your answer in degrees.   [L]

42 Find the general solution of the differential equation

$$\frac{d^2y}{dx^2} + 2\frac{dy}{dx} + 5y = 0$$ [L]

43 Find the general solution of the differential equation

$$\frac{d^2y}{dx^2} + 2\frac{dy}{dx} + 10y = 0$$

(a) Find the constants k and p such that ke^{px} is a particular integral of the differential equation

$$\frac{d^2y}{dx^2} + 2\frac{dy}{dx} + 10y = 54e^{2x}$$

and hence find the solution of this differential equation for which $y = 0$ and $\dfrac{dy}{dx} = 3$ at $x = 0$.

(b)   (i) Find the solution of

$$\frac{d^2y}{dx^2} + 2\frac{dy}{dx} + 10y = 0$$

for which $y = 0$ and $\dfrac{dy}{dx} = 3$ at $x = 0$.

(ii) Find the stationary values of y.

(iii) Hence show that the moduli of consecutive stationary values of y form a geometric progression.   [L]

44 Solve the differential equation

$$\frac{\mathrm{d}y}{\mathrm{d}x} - \frac{y}{x} = x^2, \quad x > 0$$

giving your answer for y in terms of x.   [L]

45 The complex number z is given by

$$z = \frac{3 + \mathrm{i}}{2 - \mathrm{i}}$$

(a) Show that $\arg z = 45°$ and find $|z|$.

The complex number z is represented by the point P in an Argand diagram, origin O. The complex number $-5 + k\mathrm{i}$ is represented by the point Q and $\angle POQ$ is $90°$.

(b) Find the value of k.

(c) Find the complex number w, represented by the mid-point M of PQ.

(d) Calculate $\arg w$, giving your answer in degrees to 1 decimal place.   [L]

46 (a) Show that there is a root of the equation $8 \sin x - x = 0$ lying between 2.7 and 2.8.

(b) Taking 2.8 as a first approximation to this root, apply the Newton–Raphson procedure once to $\mathrm{f}(x) \equiv 8 \sin x - x$ to obtain a second approximation, giving your answer to 2 decimal places.

(c) Explain, with justification, whether or not this second approximation is correct to 2 decimal places.

(d) Evaluate $\mathrm{f}\left(\dfrac{5\pi}{2}\right)$, and hence, by sketching suitable graphs, determine the number of roots of the equation $8 \sin x = x$ in the range $x > 0$.   [L]

47 Use the substitution $y = vx$, where v is a function of x, to transform the differential equation

$$x^2 \frac{\mathrm{d}y}{\mathrm{d}x} = x^2 + xy + y^2, \quad x > 0$$

into the differential equation

$$x \frac{\mathrm{d}v}{\mathrm{d}x} = 1 + v^2, \quad x > 0$$

Hence, given that $y = \sqrt{3}$ at $x = 1$, find y in terms of x.   [L]

48 Given that $x = e^t$, show that

$$\frac{d^2y}{dx^2} = e^{-2t}\left(\frac{d^2y}{dt^2} - \frac{dy}{dt}\right)$$

Hence show that the substitution $x = e^t$ transforms the differential equation

$$x^2\frac{d^2y}{dx^2} - 4x\frac{dy}{dx} + 6y = 3 \tag{1}$$

into

$$\frac{d^2y}{dt^2} - 5\frac{dy}{dt} + 6y = 3 \tag{2}$$

Hence find the general solution of the differential equation (1).

[L]

49 The complex number z is given by

$$z = (1 + 3i)(p + qi)$$

where p and q are real and $p > 0$.

Given that $\arg z = \dfrac{\pi}{4}$,

(a) show that $p + 2q = 0$.
Given also that $|z| = 10\sqrt{2}$,
(b) find the values of p and q.
(c) Write down the value of $\arg z^*$. [L]

50 Obtain the solution of

$$\frac{dy}{dx} + y\tan x = e^{2x}\cos x \quad \left(0 \leqslant x < \frac{\pi}{2}\right)$$

for which $y = 2$ at $x = 0$, giving your answer in the form $y = f(x)$. [L]

51 Given that $z = 3 + 4i$, express in the form $p + qi$, where p and $q \in \mathbb{R}$,

(a) $\dfrac{1}{z}$ (b) $\dfrac{1}{z^2}$

Find the argument of $\dfrac{1}{z^2}$, giving your answer in degrees to 1 decimal place. [L]

52 (a) Using the same axes, sketch the graphs of $y = e^x$ and $y = \dfrac{1}{x}$.

(b) Deduce the number of real solutions of the equation

$$e^x = \frac{1}{x}$$

and show that this equation may be written in the form

$$x - e^{-x} = 0$$

(c) Show that the equation $x - e^{-x} = 0$ has a root in the interval $0.5 < x < 0.6$.

(d) Taking $x = 0.6$ as a first approximation to this root, use the Newton–Raphson procedure once to find a second approximation, giving your answer to 3 decimal places.

[L]

53 (a) Sketch, for $0 < x < \dfrac{\pi}{2}$, the curve $y = \tan x$. By using your sketch show that the equation $\tan x = \dfrac{1}{x}$ has one and only one root in $0 < x < \dfrac{\pi}{2}$.

(b) Show further that this root lies between 0.85 and 0.87.

(c) Taking 0.85 as a first approximation to this root, use the Newton–Raphson procedure once to determine a second approximation, giving your answer to 4 decimal places.

[L]

54 Obtain the general solution of the differential equation

$$\frac{d^2 y}{dx^2} + 4\frac{dy}{dx} + 13y = e^{-3x} \qquad \text{[L]}$$

55 Show that the substitution $z = \dfrac{1}{y^2}$ transforms the differential equation

$$\frac{dy}{dx} - y = 2xy^3, \quad y > 0 \qquad (1)$$

into the differential equation

$$\frac{dz}{dx} + 2z = -4x$$

Hence find the general solution of the differential equation (1).

[L]

56 Find the general solution of the differential equation

$$\frac{dy}{dx} - y \tan x = \sec^2 x, \quad 0 < x < \frac{\pi}{2}$$

giving your answer for y in terms of x. [L]

57 Solve the differential equation

$$\frac{d^2y}{dx^2} - 4\frac{dy}{dx} + 4y = 4x$$

given that $y = 3$ and $\frac{dy}{dx} = 8$ at $x = 0$.

Show that $y = 2 + 5e^2$ at $x = 1$. [L]

58 Starting with $x = 1.5$, apply the Newton–Raphson procedure once to $f(x) \equiv x^3 - 3$ to obtain a better approximation to the cube root of 3, giving your answer to 3 decimal places. [L]

59 The complex number z satisfies the equation

$$\frac{z-2}{z+3i} = \lambda i, \quad \lambda \in \mathbb{R}$$

(a) Show that $z = \dfrac{(2-3\lambda)(1+\lambda i)}{1+\lambda^2}$

(b) In the case when $\lambda = 1$ find $|z|$ and $\arg z$. [L]

60 (a) Show the equation $x^3 - 3x + 1 = 0$ has a root α lying between 1.5 and 1.6.

Given that x_0 is an approximate solution to this equation, a better approximation x_1 is sought using the iterative formula

$$x_1 = \sqrt{\left(\frac{3x_0 - 1}{x_0}\right)}$$

(b) Take 1.51 as a first approximation to α, and apply this iterative formula twice to obtain two further approximations to α. Hence state the value of α as accurately as your working justifies. [L]

Examination style paper P3

1. Evaluate $\displaystyle\sum_{r=11}^{30} r(3r-1)$.

(7 marks)

2. Find the set of values of x for which

$$\frac{2}{x+2} > \frac{1}{x-3}.$$

(7 marks)

3. (a) Find $\displaystyle\int \frac{1}{(x^2-6x+13)^{\frac{1}{2}}}\,dx$.

   (b) Hence evaluate $\displaystyle\int_{\frac{23}{6}}^{\frac{9}{2}} \frac{1}{(x^2-6x+13)^{\frac{1}{2}}}\,dx$, giving your answer
   in the form $\ln \dfrac{p}{q}$, where p and q are integers.

(10 marks)

4. Express $E \equiv 24\cos\theta - 7\sin\theta$ in the form $R\cos(\theta+\alpha)$, where
   $R > 0$ and $0 < \alpha < \frac{\pi}{2}$. Hence find
   (a) the greatest value of E and the smallest positive value of θ
   for which it occurs,
   (b) the values of θ, to 2 decimal places, for which

$$E = 10, \quad 0 \leqslant \theta < 2\pi.$$

(11 marks)

5. $f(x) \equiv x^3 + x^2 - 6$

   (a) Show that the real root α of the equation $f(x) = 0$ lies in the
   interval $[1,2]$.
   (b) Use linear interpolation on the interval $[1,2]$ to find a first
   approximation to α.
   (c) Use the Newton–Raphson procedure on $f(x)$ once, starting
   with your answer to (b), to find another approximation to
   α, giving your answer to 2 decimal places.

(11 marks)

6. (a) Find, in radians to 2 decimal places, the argument of the complex number $-6 + 5i$.

   (b) Given that $(-6 + 5i)(p + qi) = -13 + 21i$, $p, q \in \mathbb{R}$, find the value of p and the value of q.

   (c) Using your values of p and q, show that $p + qi$ is a root of the equation $z^2 - 6z + 10 = 0$ and find the other root of this equation.

   (12 marks)

7. (a) Find the angle between the vectors $\mathbf{i} - 2\mathbf{j} + 2\mathbf{k}$ and $-\mathbf{i} + 4\mathbf{j} + 8\mathbf{k}$.

   Referred to an origin O, the points A and B are given by $\overrightarrow{OA} = \mathbf{i} - 2\mathbf{j} + 2\mathbf{k}$ and $\overrightarrow{OB} = -\mathbf{i} + 4\mathbf{j} + 8\mathbf{k}$.

   (b) Find, in the form $\mathbf{r} = \mathbf{p} + \mathbf{q}t$ an equation of the line L passing through A and B.

   (c) The points P and Q lie on L. The point P has x-coordinate zero and the point Q has y-coordinate zero. Find PQ^2 to 1 decimal place.

   (13 marks)

8. Starting from the definitions of $\sinh x$ and $\cosh x$ in terms of e^x, prove that

   (a) $\cosh^2 x + \sinh^2 x \equiv \cosh 2x$,

   (b) $\cosh x + \cosh 3x \equiv 2 \cosh x \cosh 2x$.

   The function $\cosh x \cosh 2x$ is expanded in ascending powers of x.

   (c) Find the terms of the expansion up to and including the term in x^4.

   (14 marks)

9. (a) Given that $ye^{2x} = A\cos 3x + B\sin 3x$, where A and B are constants, show that

   $$\frac{d^2 y}{dx^2} + 4\frac{dy}{dx} + 13y = 0.$$

   For the differential equation

   $$\frac{d^2 y}{dx^2} + 4\frac{dy}{dx} + 13y = 63e^{4x},$$

   find

   (b) the general solution,

   (c) the specific solution for which $\dfrac{dy}{dx} = y = 0$ at $x = 0$.

   (15 marks)

Answers

The University of London Examination and Assessment Council accepts no responsibility whatsoever for the accuracy or method of working in the answers given for examination questions.

Exercise 1A

1. $x > 5\frac{1}{2}$
2. $x \geqslant 24$
3. $x < 1$ or $x > 5$
4. $-3\frac{1}{2} \leqslant x \leqslant -3$
5. $-1 < x < 4$
6. $1 < x < 4$
7. $0 < x < 1$
8. $x < 1$ or $x > 2$
9. $-3 < x < -1$
10. $-\frac{2}{3} < x < 1$
11. $x \geqslant 3$ or $-2 \leqslant x \leqslant 0$
12. $x > 5$ or $0 < x < 2$
13. $x > -1$
14. $0 < x < 1, x < -1$
15. $x > 1$ or $x < -11$
16. $x \geqslant 3$ or $-2 \leqslant x \leqslant -1$
17. $2 < x < 8$ or $x < -1$
19. $x < -3$ or $-1 < x < 1$
20. $x \geqslant 0$

Exercise 1B

1. $-3 < x < 3$
2. $x > 2$ or $x < -2$
3. $x < -1$ or $0 < x < 5$
4. $x < -2$ or $x > \frac{2}{3}$
5. $1 < x < 3 - \sqrt{2}$ or $3 + \sqrt{2} < x < 5$
6. $x < -3$ or $-\frac{1}{2} < x < \frac{1}{2}$
7. $x < -1$ or $0 < x < 1$
8. $0 < x < \frac{1}{2}$ or $x > \frac{5}{8}$
9. $-2 < x < 0$ or $x > 1$
10. $x < -3$ or $-1 < x < 1$

Exercise 1C

1. $x < -2$ or $x > 6$
2. $-5 < x < 2$
3. $x < \frac{2}{5}$
4. $x \geqslant -\frac{1}{2}$ or $x \leqslant -2$
5. $1 \leqslant x \leqslant \sqrt{7}$ or $-\sqrt{7} \leqslant x < -1$
6. $-2 \leqslant x \leqslant 3$
7. $-2 < x < \frac{2}{3}$
8. $1 < x < 3$
9. $-1 - \sqrt{17} < x < -2$
   or $0 < x < -1 + \sqrt{17}$
10. $x < 2$
12. $-4 \leqslant x \leqslant 0$ or $x \geqslant \frac{1}{4}$

Exercise 2A

1. $1 - \dfrac{1}{n+1}$
2. $n^2 + 2n$
3. $\dfrac{n}{2n+1}$
4. $n^2(n+1)$
5. $\dfrac{n}{n+1}$
6. $\frac{1}{4}n(n+1)(n+2)(n+3)$
7. $\dfrac{n(n+3)}{4(n+1)(n+2)}$
8. $\dfrac{n(n+2)}{(n+1)^2}$
9. $\frac{1}{3}n(n+1)(n+2)$
10. $1 - \dfrac{1}{(n+1)!}$

Exercise 2B

1 819 **2** 4320 **3** 4760

4 3230 **5** $\frac{20}{21}$ **6** 29 141

7 2.95 (3 s.f.) **8** 0.1655 (4 d.p.)

9 130 663 **10** 89 670 **13** $\frac{20}{41}$

14 $\frac{n}{6}(n+1)(14n+1)$ **15** $\frac{28}{1755}$

17 6734 **18** $-2\,010\,000$

19 $-n(2n+1)$

20 $\frac{n}{6}(n+1)(4n+5) + 2^{n+3} - 8$

Exercise 2C

1 $1 - 2x + 3x^2 - 4x^3 + \ldots,$ $|x| < 1$

2 $1 + 3x + 6x^2 + 10x^3 + \ldots,$ $|x| < 1$

3 $1 + 5x + 15x^2 + 35x^3 + \ldots,$ $|x| < 1$

4 $1 - \frac{1}{2}x + \frac{3}{8}x^2 - \frac{5}{16}x^3 + \ldots,$ $|x| < 1$

5 $1 + \frac{3}{2}x + \frac{3}{8}x^2 - \frac{1}{16}x^3 \ldots,$ $|x| < 1$

6 $1 - \frac{3}{4}x - \frac{3}{32}x^2 - \frac{5}{128}x^3 \ldots$ $|x| < 1$

7 $1 - x - x^2 - \frac{5}{3}x^3 - \ldots$ $|x| < \frac{1}{3}$

8 $1 - x + 2x^2 - \frac{14}{3}x^3 + \ldots$ $|x| < \frac{1}{3}$

9 $1 + x + \frac{3}{4}x^2 + \frac{1}{2}x^3 + \ldots$ $|x| < 2$

10 $1 - 6x + 36x^2 - 216x^3 + \ldots$ $|x| < \frac{1}{6}$

11 $\frac{1}{3} - \frac{x}{9} + \frac{x^2}{27} - \frac{x^3}{81} + \ldots$ $|x| < 3$

12 $\frac{1}{4} + \frac{1}{4}x + \frac{3}{16}x^2 + \frac{1}{8}x^3 + \ldots$ $|x| < 2$

13 $2 + \frac{3}{4}x - \frac{9}{64}x^2 + \frac{27}{512}x^3 - \ldots$ $|x| < \frac{4}{3}$

14 $2 - \frac{5}{12}x - \frac{25}{288}x^2 - \frac{625}{20736}x^3 - \ldots$ $|x| < \frac{8}{5}$

15 $\frac{1}{10} - \frac{1}{2000}x + \frac{3}{800\,000}x^2 - \frac{1}{32\,000\,000}x^3 + \ldots$ $|x| < 100$

16 $2 + 3x + 5x^2 + 9x^3 + \ldots$ $|x| < \frac{1}{2}$

17 $3 - 3x + 9x^2 - 15x^3 + \ldots$ $|x| < \frac{1}{2}$

18 $-\frac{1}{4} - \frac{x}{16} - \frac{3}{64}x^2 - \frac{5}{256}x^3 - \ldots$ $|x| < 2$

19 $\frac{1}{2} - \frac{3}{4}x + \frac{7}{8}x^2 - \frac{15}{16}x^3 + \ldots$ $|x| < 1$

20 $-\frac{4}{3} + \frac{7}{18}x - \frac{31}{108}x^2 + \frac{73}{648}x^3 - \ldots$ $|x| < 2$

21 $1 + 3x + \frac{9}{2}x^2 + \frac{13}{2}x^3 + \ldots$

22 $1 - x^{-1} - \frac{1}{2}x^{-2} - \frac{1}{2}x^{-3},\ 9.949\,874\,4;$
10.049 875 6

23 (a) $p = 5,\ q = -2$ (b) $-500,\ 3125$
(c) $|x| < \frac{1}{5}$

24 $1 + \frac{2}{3}x + \frac{2}{9}x^2$

25 $p = -2,\ q = -1$

26 (a) $p = -4,\ q = \frac{3}{2}$ (b) $4x^3,\ 6x^4$
(c) $|x| < \frac{1}{4}$

Exercise 2D

6 $x + \frac{1}{3}x^3 + \frac{2}{15}x^5 \ldots$

7 $x^2 - \frac{1}{3}x^4 + \frac{2}{45}x^6 \ldots$

8 $2x + \frac{2}{3}x^3 + \frac{2}{5}x^5 \ldots$

9 $1 - x^2 - \frac{1}{2}x^4 \ldots$

10 $1 + x - \frac{1}{3}x^3 \ldots$

Exercise 2E

1 $A = 2,\ B = -\frac{7}{6}$ **2** $C = 1,\ D = \frac{1}{3}$

3 $\frac{1}{4}\sqrt{3}$ **7** 1.43 **8** $A = 0$

9 (a) $-\frac{1}{2}$ (b) $-\frac{1}{2}$

Exercise 3A

1 17, 61.9° **2** 13, 67.4°

3 $\sqrt{10}$, 18.4° **4** 10, 53.1°

5 $\sqrt{2}$, 45°

6 17, 298.1°; -17, 118.1°

7 13, 22.6°; -13, 202.6°

8 $\sqrt{10}$, 108.4°; $-\sqrt{10}$, 288.4°

9 10, 53.1°; -10, 233.1°

10 $\sqrt{2}$, 315°; $-\sqrt{2}$, 135°

11 66.9° or 186.9° **12** 4.9° or 129.9°

13 114.3° or 335.7°

14 39.0°, 162.8°, 219.0°, 342.8°

15 110.6°, 230.6°, 350.6°

16 0, 4.71, 6.28 **17** 1.57, 6.00

18 3.36, 5.09

19 0.34, 1.40, 3.48, 4.54

20 2.67

21 226.3°, 346.3°; -25, 106.3°

22 $\sqrt{10}$, 18.4°; 57.7°, 159.2°, 417.7°, 519.2°

23 $-336.9°, -276.9°, 23.1°, 83.1°$

24 (a) $-\dfrac{1}{\sqrt{13}}, 0.2457$

(b) $0, 0.49, 2.06, 3.63, 5.20, 1.57, 3.14,$
$4.71, 6.28$

25 (a) $\frac{1}{7}, \frac{1}{17}$ (b) $2.36, 2.64, 5.50, 5.78$

Exercise 3B

1 $180°n + 45°, n\pi + \frac{\pi}{4}$

2 $360°n \pm 60°, 2n\pi \pm \frac{\pi}{3}$

3 $180°n + (-1)^n 60°, n\pi + (-1)^n \frac{\pi}{3}$

4 $180°n - 60°, n\pi - \frac{\pi}{3}$

5 $360°n \pm 150°, 2n\pi \pm \frac{5\pi}{6}$

6 $180°n - (-1)^n 30°, n\pi - (-1)^n \frac{\pi}{6}$

7 $180°n \pm 45°, n\pi \pm \frac{\pi}{4}$

8 $60°n - 15°, \frac{1}{3}n\pi - \frac{\pi}{12}$

9 $360°n + (-1)^n 100°, 2n\pi + (-1)^n (\frac{5\pi}{9})$

10 $120°n, \frac{2}{3}n\pi$

11 $90°n, \frac{1}{2}n\pi$

12 $120°n + 30°, \frac{2}{3}n\pi + \frac{\pi}{6}$

13 $n180° + 22.62° + (-1)^n 30°;$
$n\pi + (-1)^n \frac{\pi}{6} + 0.395$

14 $360°n \pm 120°, 360°n; 2n\pi, 2n\pi \pm \frac{2\pi}{3}$

15 $180°n \pm 45°, 180°n \pm 60°; n\pi \pm \frac{\pi}{4}, n\pi \pm \frac{\pi}{3}$

17 (a) $\frac{1}{3}n\pi, n\pi + \frac{\pi}{2}$ (b) $n\pi, \frac{2}{3}n\pi \pm \frac{\pi}{9}$

20 (a) $2n\pi \pm \frac{\pi}{2}, \frac{2}{3}n\pi \pm \frac{\pi}{6}$

(b) $2n\pi \pm \frac{\pi}{2}, \frac{2}{3}n\pi \pm \frac{\pi}{9}$

(c) $n\pi \pm \frac{\pi}{3}, \frac{2}{3}n\pi \pm \frac{\pi}{6}$

21 $\frac{1}{4}n\pi$ **22** $2n\pi - \frac{\pi}{3} \pm \frac{\pi}{4}$

23 $180° n + 56.3°, 180°n + 45°$

24 $\frac{n\pi}{2} \pm \frac{\pi}{8}$

25 $360°n - 100°, 120°n - \frac{40°}{3}$

Exercise 3C

1 (a) $\frac{\pi}{2}$ (b) $-\frac{\pi}{3}$ (c) $\frac{\pi}{6}$

   (d) $\frac{\pi}{2}$ (e) $-\frac{\pi}{3}$ (f) $\frac{5\pi}{12}$

2 (a) 0.85 (b) 1.43 (c) 2.40

   (d) -1.45 (e) 1.68 (f) -0.34

6 (a) $\frac{\pi}{6}$ (b) $\frac{\pi}{12} + \frac{3}{2}$ (c) $\frac{\pi}{4}$

7 (a) $\dfrac{3}{\sqrt{(1 - 9x^2)}}$ (b) $\dfrac{2\arcsin x}{\sqrt{(1 - x^2)}}$

(c) $\dfrac{-1}{x\sqrt{(x^2 - 1)}}$

8 (a) $\dfrac{-1}{\sqrt{(4 - x^2)}}$ (b) $\dfrac{-6x}{\sqrt{(1 - 9x^4)}}$

(c) $\dfrac{-1}{(x + 2)\sqrt{(x^2 + 4x + 3)}}$

9 (a) $\dfrac{2}{1 + 4x^2}$ (b) $\dfrac{e^{\arctan x}}{1 + x^2}$

(c) $\dfrac{1}{x[1 + (\ln x)^2]}$

10 (a) $\arcsin x + \dfrac{x}{\sqrt{(1 - x^2)}}$

(b) $e^x \arccos x - \dfrac{e^x}{\sqrt{(1 - x^2)}}$

(c) $\dfrac{e^x \arctan x - \frac{e^x}{1 + x^2}}{(\arctan x)^2}$

(d) $\dfrac{-1}{2(1 + x)\sqrt{x}}$ (e) $\dfrac{2}{x\sqrt{(x^4 - 1)}}$

13 (a) $\dfrac{1}{x\sqrt{(x^2 - 1)}}$ (b) $\dfrac{-1}{1 + x^2}$

14 $y - \dfrac{\pi}{3} = -\dfrac{3}{2}\left(x - \dfrac{2}{\sqrt{3}}\right)$

15 (a) $\dfrac{-1}{\sqrt{(k^2 - x^2)}}$ (b) $\dfrac{-k}{x\sqrt{(x^2 - k^2)}}$

(c) $\dfrac{-k}{x^2 + k^2}$

Review exercise 1

1 (b) $x < \frac{8}{9}$

2 $1 + x - 4x^2 - \frac{13}{3}x^3 + \ldots$

3 (a) $\dfrac{-2}{\sqrt{(1 - 4x^2)}}$ (b) $-\dfrac{1}{1 + x^2}$

4 $\alpha = 60°; 255°, 345°$

5 $x < 40$ or $1 < x < 4$

7 $1 - \frac{1}{2}x - \frac{3}{8}x^2 - \frac{7}{16}x^3$

8 $2n\pi + \frac{\pi}{6}$, $2n\pi + \frac{5\pi}{6}$, $2n\pi \pm \frac{\pi}{2}$

9 $\frac{n}{6}(n+1)(2n+7)\ln 2$

10 $\frac{2}{9}n\pi$, $n\pi$

11 $\dfrac{1}{2x-1} - \dfrac{1}{2x+1}$

13 $1 - 4x - 8x^2 - 32x^3 \ldots$ $|x| < \frac{1}{8}$

14 $-\frac{1}{2}x^2 - \frac{1}{12}x^4 + \ldots$; $\frac{1}{2}x^2 + \frac{1}{12}x^4$

15 (b) $\dfrac{1}{x+1} - \dfrac{1}{x+2}$

16 $n\pi + \frac{\pi}{4}$ or $\frac{n\pi}{2} + \frac{\pi}{24}$

17 $x < -2$ or $0 < x < 1$

18 (b) $1 - x + \dfrac{x^2}{2} - \dfrac{x^3}{2}$ (c) $1 + \dfrac{x^2}{2}$

19 -1, 11, 3

20 (a) $n\pi$, $\left(\dfrac{4n+1}{4}\right)\pi$ or $\left(\dfrac{4n+1}{8}\right)\pi$

  (b) $180°n + 12.7°$ or $180°n - 65.8°$

21 $-2 < x < -1$ or $0 < x < 2$

22 (a) $1 + \frac{3}{2}x + \frac{11}{8}x^2$; 1.51% increase

23 $\dfrac{n(n+2)}{(n+1)^2}$

24 (a) $90.0°$, $323.1°$

  (b) $-6 < x < 0$ or $x > \frac{1}{2}$

25 $2\left[x + \dfrac{x^3}{3} + \dfrac{x^5}{5} + \ldots + \dfrac{x^{2n-1}}{2n-1}\right]$, $|x| < 1$;

  $a = \dfrac{2\sqrt{3}}{3}$, $b = \sqrt{3}$

26 $-3 < x < 1$

27 $\frac{2}{5}n\pi$

28 169, 0

29 $-3x^2 - 2x^3$

30 $\dfrac{2}{r-1} - \dfrac{1}{r} - \dfrac{1}{r+1}$

31 (b) $x < a$ or $x > a + \frac{1}{2}$

32 $1 + 4x - 6x^2 - 32x^3$; $a = 6$, $b = 4$;
  $|x| < \frac{1}{4}$

33 (a) $\dfrac{2n\pi}{3}$, $n\pi$ (b) $26.6°$ or $-153.4°$

35 (a) $135°$, $315°$, $22.5°$, $292.5°$, $112.5°$
    $202.5°$

  (b) $74.0°$, $353.4°$

36 $7x + \frac{1}{2}x^2 + \frac{43}{3}x^3 + \ldots$

37 $x < -3$ or $-1 < x < 1$

38 $x + \frac{1}{2}x^2 - \frac{1}{6}x^3$

39 (a) $p = \frac{1}{12}$, $q = -\frac{1}{288}$

  (b) 2.41

  (c) 2.15%

40 (a) $1 + \frac{1}{2}x^2 + \frac{3}{8}x^4 + \frac{5}{16}x^6$

  (c) 1.414 15

41 (a) $90°$, $270°$, $26.6°$, $206.6°$

  (b) $n\pi \pm \frac{\pi}{6}$

42 (b) $2x - \frac{4}{3}x^3 + \ldots$ (c) $k = 2$

43 $a = b = 3$

45 $\dfrac{n\pi}{3}$ or $\dfrac{n\pi}{5} + \dfrac{\pi}{10}$

46 $A = 2$, $B = -3$; $\frac{11}{2} - \frac{11}{4}x + \frac{13}{8}x^2$

47 $R = 5\sqrt{2}$, $\alpha = 0.14$; 1.23, 4.77

48 $360°n - 13°$ or $360°n + 120°$

49 $2(1+x)\ln(1+x) + (1+x)$;

  $2\ln(1+x) + 3$; $\dfrac{2}{1+x}$; $x + \frac{3}{2}x^2 + \frac{1}{3}x^3 + \ldots$

51 (a) $-\frac{\pi}{6}$ (b) $y = x\sqrt{2} + \frac{\pi}{4} - 1$

53 $1 + \frac{1}{2}x^2 + \frac{5}{24}x^4$

54 $1 + x + x^2 + \frac{2}{3}x^3$

55 $x - \frac{1}{2}x^2 + \frac{1}{6}x^3 - \frac{1}{12}x^4$; 0.116

56 0.035%

57 (a) $0 < x < 2$, $x > 3$

  (b) $x < 0$, $2 < x < 3$

  (c) $x > 3$

58 (b) $1 + \frac{1}{2}x - \frac{1}{8}x^2 + \frac{1}{16}x^3 - \ldots$;
    $a = -\frac{1}{2}$, $b = -\frac{1}{8}$

59 (b) 5.76   (c) 0.40, 4.84

60 (b) $1 - x + \frac{1}{2}x^2$ (c) $-\frac{1}{15}$

Exercise 4A

1 (a) $\frac{1}{2}(e^2 - e^{-2})$ (b) $\frac{1}{2}(e^{\frac{1}{2}} + e^{-\frac{1}{2}})$

  (c) $-\dfrac{e^3 - e^{-3}}{e^3 + e^{-3}}$ (d) $\frac{1}{2}(e^{\sqrt{2}} + e^{-\sqrt{2}})$

  (e) $\frac{1}{2}(e^\pi - e^{-\pi})$ (f) $2\left(\dfrac{e - e^{-1}}{e + e^{-1}}\right)$

2 (a) 1.818   (b) -1.818 (c) ± 0.962

  (d) ± 1.444 (e) 0.973   (f) -0.805

3 (a) 27.31   (b) 0.7172   (c) -0.9640

  (d) -0.5211 (e) 11.59   (f) 0.9287

4 $e^x = 3$ or $\frac{1}{3}$, $x = \pm \ln 3$

5 (a) $x = 0$, $y = 0$ (b) $y = \pm 1$, $x = 0$

6 0.72, 0.48

21 $\sec\theta$, $\sin\theta$ **22** $\dfrac{x^2 + 1}{2x}$

23 2.37

24 2, $\frac{1}{2}\ln 2$

25 $\sinh x = x + \dfrac{x^3}{3!} + \dfrac{x^5}{5!} + \cdots$

     $\cosh x = 1 + \dfrac{x^2}{2!} + \dfrac{x^4}{4!} + \dfrac{x^6}{6!} + \cdots$

27 $0, -\ln 3$ **28** $-\ln \frac{5}{2}, -\ln 10$

29 $\sqrt{(a^2 - b^2)}$ **30** $x + \frac{1}{3}x^3 + \frac{1}{5}x^5 + \cdots$

31 $-\frac{1}{2}\ln 5$ **32** $\pm\frac{1}{2}\ln(3 + 2\sqrt{2})$

33 $\ln \frac{5}{3}$ **35** 0.481, 0.881

36 $\frac{1}{3}$; $\frac{3}{4}, \frac{5}{4}, \frac{3}{5}$

38 (a) $x^2 \operatorname{cosec}^2\theta - y^2 \sec^2\theta = 1$

  (b) $x^2 \operatorname{sech}^2 t + y^2 \operatorname{cosech}^2 t = 1$

Exercise 4B

1 $2\sinh 2x$ **2** $\frac{1}{2}\cosh \dfrac{x}{2}$

3 $3\operatorname{sech}^2 3x$ **4** $-2\operatorname{sech} 2x \tanh 2x$

5 $-\frac{1}{3}\operatorname{cosech} \dfrac{x}{3}\coth \dfrac{x}{3}$

6 $e^x(\cosh x + \sinh x)$

7 $6\sinh 3x \cosh 3x$ **8** $3\tanh^2 x \operatorname{sech}^2 x$

9 $-\dfrac{1}{x}\operatorname{cosech}^2(\ln x)$

10 $\coth x$

11 $\sinh 2x + 2x\cosh 2x$

12 $3(x^2 \cosh 3x + x^3 \sinh 3x)$

13 $\dfrac{1}{\sinh x \cosh x}$ **14** $(\cosh x)e^{\sinh x}$

15 $\dfrac{\cosh x - x\sinh x}{\cosh^2 x}$ **16** $\dfrac{x\sinh x - \cosh x}{x^2}$

17 $3\cosh^2 x \sinh x\, e^{\cosh^3 x}$

18 $-\dfrac{2x\operatorname{cosech}^2 2x + 3\coth 2x}{x^4}$

19 $\dfrac{-\operatorname{cosech}(x^2)(2x^2 \coth x^2 + 1)}{x^2}$

20 $\dfrac{\operatorname{sech} x(\operatorname{sech} x + \tanh x)}{\tanh x - \operatorname{sech} x}$ **21** $\dfrac{1}{\sqrt{2}}$

22 $y - \frac{9}{2} = -\frac{2}{7}(x - \ln 2)$

23 $(\ln 3, 0)$, $y = 3(x - \ln 3)$

24 $y = 5$ at $x = -\ln 5$

25 $\dfrac{c}{2}(3e^{-2} - e^2)$

26 max. $(-0.962, 11.18)$,

    min. $(0.962, -11.18)$

29 $\dfrac{dy}{dx} = 3\sinh 3x \sin x + \cosh 3x \cos x$

     $\dfrac{d^2 y}{dx^2} = 8\cosh 3x \sin x + 6\sinh 3x \cos x$

30 $x - \dfrac{x^3}{3} + \cdots$

31 $y - 0.905 = 0.181(x - 1.5)$

    $y - 0.905 = -5.534(x - 1.5)$

32 $\dfrac{1}{\sqrt{(1 + x^2)}}$ **33** $\dfrac{1}{\sqrt{(x^2 - 4)}}$ **34** $\dfrac{2x}{1 - 4x^2}$

35 $\dfrac{-1}{x\sqrt{(1 - x^2)}}$ **36** $\dfrac{-1}{x\sqrt{(1 + x^2)}}$ **37** $\dfrac{2}{1 - 4x^2}$

38 $\dfrac{-1}{2x\sqrt{(1 - x)}}$ **39** $\operatorname{arcosh} x + \dfrac{x}{\sqrt{(x^2 - 1)}}$

40 $\dfrac{\operatorname{arsinh} x - \frac{x}{\sqrt{(1+x^2)}}}{(\operatorname{arsinh} x)^2}$

41 $\dfrac{2\,\text{artanh}\,x}{1 - x^2}$

42 $\dfrac{-1}{2x\sqrt{(1 - x^2)}\sqrt{(\text{arsech}\,x)}}$

43 $2x\,e^{x^2}\,\text{arsinh}\,x + \dfrac{e^{x^2}}{\sqrt{(1 + x^2)}}$

44 $\dfrac{\frac{1}{x}\,\text{arcosh}\,x - \frac{\ln x}{\sqrt{(x^2 - 1)}}}{(\text{arcosh}\,x)^2}$

45 $\dfrac{\cos x}{1 - \sin^2 x} = \sec x$ **46** $\dfrac{\cosh x}{1 - \sinh^2 x}$

47 $\dfrac{\text{arsinh}\,x\sqrt{(1 + x^2)} - \arcsin x\sqrt{(1 - x^2)}}{(\text{arsinh}\,x)^2\sqrt{(1 - x^4)}}$

48 $y - x = 0$, $\; y - \text{arsinh}\,1 = \dfrac{1}{\sqrt{2}}(x - 1)$

50 $y - \frac{1}{2}\ln 7 = -\frac{7}{16}\left(x - \frac{3}{4}\right)$

52 $(0, 3)$ **55** ± 0.31 **56** $(\ln 2, 4)$

57 $-\frac{1}{2}\,\text{sech}\,x\tanh x$

60 (a) $(-1, 0)$ (b) $y + x + 1 = 0$

19 $\arcsin \dfrac{x}{5}$ **20** $\frac{1}{3}\arctan \dfrac{3x}{5}$

21 $\frac{1}{4}\,\text{arcosh}\dfrac{4x}{3}$ **22** $\frac{1}{3}\,\text{arsinh}\dfrac{3x}{8}$

23 $\frac{1}{24}\arctan \dfrac{3x}{8}$ **24** $\frac{1}{4}\,\text{arcosh}\,4x$

25 $\frac{1}{4}\,\text{arsinh}\,4x$ **26** $\arctan e^{2x}$

27 $\frac{1}{2}\ln\cosh 2x$ **28** $\dfrac{x}{2} + \frac{1}{6}\sinh 3x$

29 $\frac{5}{8}\sinh\dfrac{4x}{5} - \dfrac{x}{2}$ **30** $x - \frac{1}{5}\tanh 5x$

31 1.81 **32** 0.255 **33** 1.33 **34** 1.57

35 0.881 **36** 0.446 **37** 0.161 **38** 1.10

39 64.0 **40** 1.05 **41** 44.1 **42** 16.6

43 0.67

44 $\ln\left|\dfrac{e^x - 1}{e^x + 1}\right|$

45 2.02 **46** (a) 1.25 (b) 1.23

47 2.80 **49** 0.632 **50** 2π

Exercise 5A
(Constant omitted in indefinite integration questions)

1 $\frac{1}{2}\sinh 2x$ **2** $\frac{1}{3}\cosh 3x$

3 $-2\cosh\dfrac{x}{2}$ **4** $\frac{1}{4}e^{2x} + \frac{1}{2}x$

5 $\frac{1}{6}e^{3x} - \frac{1}{2}e^x$

6 $\frac{1}{2}\sinh^2 x$ (or $\frac{1}{4}\cosh 2x$)

7 $\dfrac{x}{2} + \frac{1}{4}\sinh 2x$ **8** $\frac{1}{4}\sinh 2x - \dfrac{x}{2}$

9 $\frac{1}{2}\tanh 2x$ **10** $x - \frac{1}{2}\tanh 2x$

11 $x - 2\coth\dfrac{x}{2}$ **12** $-\frac{1}{2}\,\text{cosech}\,2x$

13 $-\frac{1}{3}\,\text{sech}\,3x$ **14** $\arcsin\dfrac{x}{2}$

15 $\text{arsinh}\dfrac{x}{2}$ **16** $\text{arcosh}\dfrac{x}{2}$

17 $\frac{1}{2}\arctan\dfrac{x}{2}$ **18** $\frac{1}{4}\ln\left|\dfrac{x - 2}{x + 2}\right|$

Exercise 5B
(Constant omitted in indefinite integration questions)

1 $\frac{1}{2}\ln\left|\dfrac{x - 2}{x}\right|$ **2** $\text{arcosh}\,(x - 1)$

3 $\arcsin(x - 1)$

4 $\dfrac{2}{\sqrt{3}}\arctan\left(\dfrac{2x + 1}{\sqrt{3}}\right)$

5 $\text{arsinh}\left(\dfrac{2x + 1}{\sqrt{3}}\right)$ **6** $\frac{1}{2}\ln\left(\dfrac{x^2}{x^2 + 1}\right)$

7 $\ln|1 + \sinh x|$ **8** $\ln(\cosh x - 1)$

9 $\frac{1}{4}\sinh^4 x$ **10** $\ln|x^2 + 6x + 1|$

11 $\frac{1}{2}\ln|x^2 - 4x - 2|$ **12** $(x^2 + 1)^{\frac{1}{2}}$

13 $\ln|ax + bx^2|$ **14** $\frac{1}{2}(\text{arsinh}\,x)^2$

15 $\frac{1}{2}(\arcsin x)^2$ **16** $2\sqrt{(2x^2 + 7x + 3)}$

17 $\frac{1}{5}\ln\left|\dfrac{2x + 1}{x + 3}\right|$ **18** $\arctan(x + 4)$

19 $2\sqrt{(x^2 - 9)} - 3\,\text{arcosh}\dfrac{x}{3}$

20 $4\sqrt{(x^2+16)} - \operatorname{arsinh} \dfrac{x}{4}$

21 $\frac{1}{2}\arctan(2x+1)$ **22** $\arcsin\left(\dfrac{2x+1}{\sqrt{5}}\right)$

23 $\frac{1}{3}\arctan\left(\dfrac{x-2}{3}\right)$ **24** $\arcsin\left(\dfrac{x+2}{3}\right)$

31 (a) $2\arctan e^x$

    (b) $\ln\left|\dfrac{e^x-1}{e^x+1}\right|$

33 $-\frac{1}{12}\arctan\left(\dfrac{3\cos x}{4}\right)$

34 $\frac{1}{3}\arctan(3\tan x)$ **35** $\frac{2}{3}\arctan(3e^x)$

36 0.0358   **37** 0.326   **38** 0.256

39 0.458   **40** 0.202   **41** 0.220

42 0.933   **43** 0.768   **44** 4.93

45 0.902   **46** 0.128   **47** 0.682

48 17.2   **49** 0.470   **50** 0.524

Exercise 5C

(Constant omitted in indefinite integration questions)

1 $\frac{1}{7}\arctan\dfrac{x}{7}$ **2** $\frac{1}{2}\ln(4+x^2)$

3 $-\dfrac{1}{x+3}$ **4** $\frac{1}{\sqrt{2}}\arcsin\left(x\sqrt{\tfrac{2}{5}}\right)$

5 $\frac{1}{4}\ln\left|\dfrac{1+2x}{1-2x}\right|$ **6** $\frac{1}{\sqrt{2}}\operatorname{arcosh}\left(x\sqrt{\tfrac{2}{5}}\right)$

7 $\frac{1}{\sqrt{10}}\arctan\left(x\sqrt{\tfrac{2}{5}}\right)$

8 $\frac{1}{30}(5x+3)(x-3)^5$

9 $-\frac{1}{2}\cos 2x + \frac{1}{6}\cos^3 2x$

10 $\frac{2}{3}\sqrt{(x-2)(x+4)}$

11 $\frac{1}{2}\tan 2x - x$ **12** $\frac{1}{5}e^x(\cos 2x + 2\sin 2x)$

13 $(2x - 4\sqrt{x} + 4)e^{\sqrt{x}}$

14 $2e^{\sqrt{x}}$

15 $-2\ln|x-3| + 3(x-3)^{-1}$

16 $\frac{1}{17}\ln\left|\dfrac{5x-2}{x+3}\right|$ **17** $\frac{1}{2\sqrt{2}}\arcsin 2x$

18 $\frac{1}{\sqrt{5}}\arctan x\sqrt{5}$ **19** $\frac{1}{\sqrt{5}}\operatorname{arsinh} x\sqrt{5}$

20 $\frac{1}{2}\operatorname{arcosh}\left(\dfrac{2x}{\sqrt{3}}\right)$ **21** $\frac{1}{2}\arctan\left(\dfrac{x+2}{2}\right)$

22 $\frac{1}{2}\arcsin\left(\dfrac{2x-1}{6}\right)$ **23** $\frac{1}{5}\ln(\cosh 5x)$

24 $x - \frac{1}{5}\tanh 5x$ **25** $\dfrac{x^3}{9}(3\ln|x|-1)$

26 $\frac{3}{2}x + 2\sin x + \frac{1}{4}\sin 2x$

27 $\dfrac{1}{1+\cos x}$ **28** $x + 8\ln|x-4|$

29 $\ln\left(\dfrac{e^x}{e^x+1}\right)$ **30** $e^{\sin x}$

31 $\tan x(\ln\tan|x|-1)$

32 $\frac{2}{3}(x+1)^{\frac{1}{2}}(x-2)$

33 $\ln|x^2-9| + \frac{1}{6}\ln\left|\dfrac{x-3}{x+3}\right|$

34 $\frac{1}{9}x - \frac{1}{27}\arctan 3x$

35 $\frac{1}{5}x\sin 5x + \frac{1}{25}\cos 5x$

36 $-\frac{2}{9}(1-x^3)^{\frac{3}{2}}$

37 $x\operatorname{arsinh}\frac{x}{2} - \sqrt{(4+x^2)}$

38 $x\arctan 3x - \frac{1}{6}\ln(1+9x^2)$

39 $\frac{1}{2}e^x(\cos x + \sin x)$

40 $\sinh x + \frac{1}{3}\sinh^3 x$

41 $\frac{1}{32}\sin 4x + \frac{1}{4}\sin 2x + \frac{3}{8}x$

42 $\frac{1}{12}\arctan\left(\dfrac{3x+2}{4}\right)$

43 $\frac{1}{3}\operatorname{arcosh}\left(\dfrac{3x+2}{2}\right)$

44 $\frac{2}{3}\cos^3\dfrac{x}{2} - 2\cos\dfrac{x}{2}$ **45** $x\sinh x - \cosh x$

46 $-\frac{1}{8}(2x^2+5)^{-2}$ **47** $\frac{2}{3}\ln\left(\sinh\dfrac{3x}{2}\right)$

48 $3\ln\left|\tanh\dfrac{x}{6}\right|$

49 $\frac{1}{3}\tan^3 x - \tan x + x$

50 $-\frac{1}{6}\cot^3 2x - \frac{1}{2}\cot 2x$

51 $\frac{\pi}{18}$ **52** $\frac{1}{8}e^2 + \frac{1}{2} - \frac{1}{8}e^{-2}$ **53** $\dfrac{5\pi-3}{24}$

54 $\frac{\pi}{4} - \frac{1}{2}\ln 2$ **55** $\ln(7+5\sqrt{2})$

56 $\frac{\pi}{6}$ **57** $\dfrac{\pi+2}{4}$ **58** $\frac{26}{3}$ **59** $\frac{1}{2}\ln\frac{9}{8}$

60 0.530 **61** $\frac{\pi}{6}$ **62** $2(\sqrt{3}-1)$

63 $\frac{\pi}{12}+\frac{1}{2}\ln 2$ **64** $\frac{\pi^2}{16}+\frac{1}{4}$

65 $\frac{1}{15}(1+x^2)^{\frac{3}{2}}(3x^2-2)$ **67** $\frac{1}{4}\ln 3$

68 (a) $\operatorname{arsinh} x$ (b) $\sqrt{(x^2+1)}$
    (c) $\frac{1}{2}x\sqrt{(x^2+1)}-\frac{1}{2}\operatorname{arsinh} x$

78 (a) $\frac{1}{4}\ln\left|\dfrac{2+\tan\frac{x}{2}}{2-\tan\frac{x}{2}}\right|$ (b) $\frac{1}{2}\arctan(2\tan\frac{x}{2})$

Exercise 6A

1 (a) $\overrightarrow{AF}$ (b) $\overrightarrow{PU}$ (c) $\overrightarrow{LP}+\overrightarrow{QR}$
  (d) $\overrightarrow{AH}$ (e) $\overrightarrow{PS}$

2 (a) $\mathbf{r}-\mathbf{q}$ (b) $\mathbf{q}-\mathbf{p}$ (c) $\mathbf{p}+\mathbf{r}-\mathbf{q}$

3 (a) $\mathbf{a}-\mathbf{d}$ (b) $-(\mathbf{b}+\mathbf{c}+\mathbf{d})$
  (c) $-(\mathbf{a}+\mathbf{b})$ (d) $\mathbf{b}+\mathbf{d}$

Exercise 6B

1 (a) $3\mathbf{a}$ (b) $2\mathbf{a}$ (c) $3\mathbf{b}$
  (d) $-2\mathbf{b}$ (e) $-4\mathbf{b}$ (f) $2\mathbf{a}+\mathbf{b}$
  (g) $3\mathbf{a}+2\mathbf{b}$ (h) $\mathbf{a}-\mathbf{b}$ (i) $-(\mathbf{a}+2\mathbf{b})$
  (j) $4(\mathbf{a}+\mathbf{b})$ (k) $2(\mathbf{b}-\mathbf{a})$ (l) $3(\mathbf{b}-\mathbf{a})$
  (m) $-5\mathbf{a}+4\mathbf{b}$

2 (a), (b), (e)

3 $\overrightarrow{AE}=3\mathbf{b}$, $\overrightarrow{AC}=\mathbf{a}+\mathbf{b}$, $\overrightarrow{EC}=\mathbf{a}-2\mathbf{b}$

4 (a) $\mathbf{a}-\mathbf{b}$ (b) $\frac{4}{5}(\mathbf{b}-\mathbf{a})$
  (c) $\frac{1}{5}\mathbf{a}+\frac{4}{5}\mathbf{b}$

5 (a) $2\mathbf{b}-\mathbf{a}$ (b) $\mathbf{a}+\frac{1}{2}\mathbf{b}$
  (c) $\mathbf{a}-3\mathbf{b}$ (d) $\mathbf{a}-2\frac{1}{2}\mathbf{b}$

7 $\overrightarrow{OD}=\frac{1}{2}(\mathbf{b}+\mathbf{c})$, $\overrightarrow{OG}=\frac{1}{3}(\mathbf{a}+\mathbf{b}+\mathbf{c})$

8 (a) $\mathbf{a}+\mathbf{b}$ (b) $\mathbf{b}-\mathbf{a}$
  (c) $\mathbf{b}-2\mathbf{a}$ (d) $-(\mathbf{a}+\mathbf{b})$

10 (a) $\overrightarrow{AB}=6(\mathbf{b}-\mathbf{a})$, $\overrightarrow{OP}=2(\mathbf{a}+2\mathbf{b})$,
    $\overrightarrow{MN}=2(\mathbf{b}-\mathbf{a})$
  (c) 2.4

11 (a) $\lambda=7,\ \mu=1$ (b) $\lambda=-8,\ \mu=2$
  (c) $\lambda=6,\ \mu=5$ (d) $\lambda=2\frac{2}{3},\ \mu=-5$
  (e) $\lambda=\frac{1}{2},\ \mu=\frac{1}{2}$ (f) $\lambda=2,\ \mu=-3$
  (g) $\lambda=-3,\ \mu=-9$

    (h) $\lambda=3,\ \mu=-1$

12 (a) $\overrightarrow{AB}=\mathbf{b}-\mathbf{a}$, $\overrightarrow{AC}=\frac{5}{6}(\mathbf{b}-\mathbf{a})$,
    $\overrightarrow{OC}=\frac{1}{6}\mathbf{a}+\frac{5}{6}\mathbf{b}$
  (b) $\overrightarrow{CE}=-\frac{1}{6}\mathbf{a}+(\lambda-\frac{5}{6})\mathbf{b}$
  (c) $\overrightarrow{ED}=-\mu\mathbf{a}+(\mu-\lambda)\mathbf{b}$
  (d) $\lambda=\frac{1}{2},\ \mu=\frac{1}{6}$

13 (a) $\frac{2}{3}\mathbf{b}$ (b) $\frac{5}{6}\mathbf{b}$ (c) $\frac{1}{2}\mathbf{a}+\frac{1}{3}\mathbf{b}$
  (d) $(1-t)\mathbf{a}+\frac{5}{6}t\mathbf{b}$ (e) $\frac{1}{2}s\mathbf{a}+(1-\frac{2}{3}s)\mathbf{b}$
  (f) $\frac{1}{3}\mathbf{a}+\frac{5}{9}\mathbf{b}$ (g) $CP:CQ=2:3$

14 (a)(i) $2\mathbf{a}-\mathbf{b}$ (ii) $\mathbf{a}-3\mathbf{b}$
   (iii) $2\mathbf{a}-3\mathbf{b}$
  (b) $2\lambda\mathbf{a}+(1-\lambda)\mathbf{b}$
  (f) $\frac{4}{3}\mathbf{a}+\mathbf{b}$

15 (a)(i) $(\mathbf{b}-\mathbf{a})$ (ii) $\frac{2}{3}\mathbf{a}-\frac{7}{4}\mathbf{b}$
  (b) $\mu(\mathbf{b}-\mathbf{a})+\frac{3}{4}\mathbf{b}=\lambda(-\frac{2}{3}\mathbf{a}+\frac{7}{4}\mathbf{b})$
  (d) $\frac{6}{13}$ (e) $\frac{6}{13}\mathbf{a}+\frac{7}{13}\mathbf{b}$ (f) $\frac{13}{10}$

16 (a) $\mathbf{b}-\mathbf{a}$ (b) $\frac{1}{2}(\mathbf{a}+\mathbf{b})$ (c) $\frac{3}{8}(\mathbf{a}+\mathbf{b})$
  (d) $-\frac{5}{8}\mathbf{a}+\frac{3}{8}\mathbf{b}$ (e) $-\mathbf{a}+k\mathbf{b}$
  (f) $5:3;\ k=\frac{3}{5}$

17 (a) $\overrightarrow{OM}=\frac{1}{2}\mathbf{a}$, $\overrightarrow{OX}=\frac{3}{4}\mathbf{b}$, $\overrightarrow{OY}=\frac{1}{5}\mathbf{a}+\frac{3}{5}\mathbf{b}$
  (d) $2:3$

18 (a) $\frac{1}{3}\mathbf{a}$ (b) $\frac{1}{4}\mathbf{a}+\frac{3}{4}\mathbf{b}$
  (c) $-\frac{1}{12}\mathbf{a}+\frac{3}{4}\mathbf{b}$ (d) $2\mathbf{b}$
  (e) $\frac{1}{4}(\mathbf{b}-\mathbf{a})$ (f) $2\frac{1}{4}\mathbf{b}-\frac{1}{4}\mathbf{a}$
  (g) $1:3$
  (h) $\overrightarrow{EB}=-\frac{1}{3}\mathbf{a}+\mathbf{b}$, $\overrightarrow{AG}=3\mathbf{b}-\mathbf{a}$

19 (a) $\overrightarrow{OB}=5\mathbf{a}+3\mathbf{b}$, $\overrightarrow{OC}=\frac{3}{2}(5\mathbf{a}+3\mathbf{b})$
    $\overrightarrow{DC}=4\frac{1}{2}\mathbf{a}+4\frac{1}{2}\mathbf{b}$
  (b) $\mu\mathbf{b}=-2\mathbf{a}+\lambda(\mathbf{a}+\mathbf{b})$
  (c) $\lambda=\mu=2$ (d)(i) $2:1$ (ii) $4:5$
  (e) $\frac{10}{3}\mathbf{a}=2\mathbf{b}$

20 (a)(i) $\frac{2}{3}\mathbf{a}$ (ii) $\frac{1}{3}\mathbf{b}$ (iii) $\frac{1}{3}\mathbf{b}-\frac{2}{3}\mathbf{a}$
  (b) $\mathbf{b}-2\mathbf{a}$ (c) $3:1$
  (d) $\overrightarrow{PS}=\frac{2}{3}\mathbf{a}-\frac{1}{3}\mathbf{b}$, $\overrightarrow{AS}=\frac{1}{3}(\mathbf{a}-\mathbf{b})$

Exercise 6C

1 (a) 13   (b) 25   (c) $\sqrt{26}$ (d) 7
  (e) 3   (f) $\sqrt{54}$

2 (a) $\frac{1}{13}(-5\mathbf{i} + 12\mathbf{j})$ (b) $\frac{1}{\sqrt{26}}(-\mathbf{i} - 5\mathbf{j})$

    (c) $\frac{1}{\sqrt{65}}(4\mathbf{i} - 7\mathbf{j})$ (d) $\frac{1}{7}(3\mathbf{i} - 2\mathbf{j} + 6\mathbf{k})$

    (e) $\frac{1}{9}(8\mathbf{i} - \mathbf{j} - 4\mathbf{k})$ (f) $\frac{1}{5\sqrt{3}}(7\mathbf{i} - 5\mathbf{j} + \mathbf{k})$

3 $\frac{27}{5}(3\mathbf{i} + 4\mathbf{j})$

4 $\frac{3}{\sqrt{14}}(\mathbf{i} - 3\mathbf{j} + 2\mathbf{k})$

5 (a) $3\mathbf{i} - 2\mathbf{j} - 8\mathbf{k}$ (b) $-\mathbf{i} + 6\mathbf{j} + 2\mathbf{k}$

    (c) $\sqrt{41}$ (d) $\sqrt{158}$

6 (a) $\sqrt{242}$ (b) $\sqrt{163}$

    (c) $\frac{1}{\sqrt{507}}(5\mathbf{i} - 19\mathbf{j} + 11\mathbf{k})$

7 $5\mathbf{i} + 2\mathbf{j} - 7\mathbf{k}$ **8** $\pm\frac{4}{\sqrt{5}}$

9 $\pm\sqrt{2}$ **10** $\pm\sqrt{2}$

Exercise 6D

1 (a) -46 (b) -8 (c) 12

    (d) -21 (e) -133

2 (a) $32.3°$ (b) $79.4°$ (c) $112.5°$

    (d) $124.9°$ (e) $95.2°$ (f) $105.7°$

    (g) $138.7°$ (h) $40.4°$ (i) $83.7°$

    (j) $77.0°$

3 12

4 (a) -3 (b) $\frac{4}{3}$ (c) 10

5 $\pm\sqrt{2}$

6 (a)(i) $41.8°$ (ii) $72.7°$ (iii) $53.4°$

    (b)(i) $27.3°$ (ii) $83.6°$ (iii) $116.4°$

    (c)(i) $68.2°$ (ii) $123.9°$ (iii) $42.0°$

    (d)(i) $107.5°$ (ii) $107.5°$ (iii) $154.8°$

    (e)(i) $29.2°$ (ii) $115.9°$ (iii) $102.6°$

7 (a) $2\mathbf{i} + \mathbf{j} + 5\mathbf{k}$ (b) $\mathbf{i} - \mathbf{j} + \mathbf{k}$

    (c) $-2\mathbf{i} + \mathbf{j} - 2\mathbf{k}$ (d) $-\mathbf{i} + 6\mathbf{j} - 9\mathbf{k}$

    (e) $-5\mathbf{i} - 6\mathbf{j} + 2\mathbf{k}$

8 $-1, 2$

9 (a) $\frac{19}{9}$ (b) $\frac{8}{3}$ (c) $\frac{3}{\sqrt{14}}$ (d) $\frac{11\sqrt{5}}{5}$

    (e) $\frac{3}{\sqrt{42}}$

10 $\frac{26}{17}$

15 $2\mathbf{b} \cdot \mathbf{c}$

16 $\angle AOB = 96.0°$, $\angle BAO = 49.9°$,

    $\angle ABO = 34.1°$

17 $\frac{14}{\sqrt{255}}$

18 $\cos B\hat{C}A = \frac{13}{\sqrt{806}}$, area $= 12.6$

19 $\frac{2}{\sqrt{17}}$, $\sqrt{\frac{3276}{17}}$

20 $120°$

Exercise 6E

1 (a) $\mathbf{r} = -\mathbf{i} + \mathbf{j} + \mathbf{k} + \lambda(2\mathbf{i} - 3\mathbf{j} + \mathbf{k})$

    (b) $\mathbf{r} = 2\mathbf{i} - 7\mathbf{j} - 11\mathbf{k} + \lambda(-3\mathbf{i} + 9\mathbf{j} + 17\mathbf{k})$

    (c) $\mathbf{r} = -3\mathbf{i} + 9\mathbf{j} - 15\mathbf{k} + \lambda(2\mathbf{i} + \mathbf{j})$

    (d) $\mathbf{r} = 3\mathbf{i} - \mathbf{k} + \lambda(-\mathbf{i} - 5\mathbf{j} + 2\mathbf{k})$

    (e) $\mathbf{r} = 5\mathbf{i} - \mathbf{j} + 4\mathbf{k} + \lambda(\mathbf{i} - 2\mathbf{j} + \mathbf{k})$

2 $\mathbf{r} = -\mathbf{i} + 7\mathbf{j} + 4\mathbf{k} + \lambda\mathbf{j}$

3 $\mathbf{r} = 2\mathbf{i} - \mathbf{j} + 6\mathbf{k} + \lambda\mathbf{i}$

4 (a) $\mathbf{r} = \mathbf{i} - \mathbf{j} + 2\mathbf{k} + \lambda(6\mathbf{i} - 3\mathbf{j})$

    (b) $\mathbf{r} = 2\mathbf{i} - \mathbf{j} + 7\mathbf{k} + \lambda(5\mathbf{i} + \mathbf{j} - 10\mathbf{k})$

    (c) $\mathbf{r} = -3\mathbf{i} - \mathbf{j} + 2\mathbf{k} + \lambda(11\mathbf{i} + 2\mathbf{j} - 5\mathbf{k})$

    (d) $\mathbf{r} = 2\mathbf{i} - 6\mathbf{j} + 4\mathbf{k} + \lambda(3\mathbf{i} - 4\mathbf{j} + 7\mathbf{k})$

    (e) $\mathbf{r} = 3\mathbf{i} + \mathbf{j} + 4\mathbf{k} + \lambda(4\mathbf{i} - \mathbf{j} - \mathbf{k})$

5 $-3\frac{1}{2}$

6 (a) $\dfrac{x+3}{2} = \dfrac{2-y}{4} = \dfrac{z+5}{1}$

    (b) $\dfrac{1-x}{1} = \dfrac{y+3}{1} = \dfrac{2-z}{2}$

    (c) $\dfrac{-1-x}{6} = \dfrac{y-3}{4} = \dfrac{4-z}{9}$

    (d) $\dfrac{2-x}{2} = \dfrac{y+3}{6} = \dfrac{4-z}{1}$

    (e) $\dfrac{x+3}{2} = \dfrac{4-y}{3} = \dfrac{-1-z}{1}$

7 (a) $\mathbf{r} = \mathbf{i} - \mathbf{j} + \mathbf{k} + \lambda(2\mathbf{i} + 4\mathbf{j} + 3\mathbf{k})$

    (b) $\mathbf{r} = \mathbf{i} - \mathbf{j} + 3\mathbf{k} + \lambda(3\mathbf{i} - 4\mathbf{j} - \mathbf{k})$

    (c) $\mathbf{r} = \mathbf{i} - 2\mathbf{j} - 3\mathbf{k} + \lambda(-2\mathbf{i} + 4\mathbf{j} + 5\mathbf{k})$

    (d) $\mathbf{r} = \mathbf{i} + 4\mathbf{j} - 3\mathbf{k} + \lambda(-3\mathbf{i} - 2\mathbf{j} - \mathbf{k})$

    (e) $\mathbf{r} = \frac{1}{2}\mathbf{i} + 2\mathbf{j} + \frac{1}{3}\mathbf{k} + \lambda(2\mathbf{i} - 3\mathbf{j} - \frac{2}{3}\mathbf{k})$

8 $9\mathbf{i} + 3\mathbf{j}$

9 $(4, 8, -6)$

10 (a) Don't intersect

(b) Intersect at $(4, 5, 9)$

(c) Don't intersect

(d) Intersect at $(14, 3, -2)$

11 (a) $49.9°$ (b) $68.5°$ (c) $53.8°$

    (d) $47.1°$ (e) $28.7°$

12 Equation of AD is

$\mathbf{r} = 6\mathbf{i} + 8\mathbf{j} + \lambda(4\mathbf{i} - 3\mathbf{j})$

Equation of BC is $\mathbf{r} = 9\mathbf{i} + 12\mathbf{j} + \mu(\mathbf{i} + 3\mathbf{j})$

Intersect at $7\frac{1}{3}\mathbf{i} + 7\mathbf{j}$

13 $\mathbf{r} = \mathbf{i} - \mathbf{j} + 3\mathbf{k} + \lambda(3\mathbf{j} - \mathbf{k})$

$\mathbf{i} + \mathbf{j} + \frac{7}{3}\mathbf{k}$

14 $4\mathbf{i} + 7\mathbf{j} - 5\mathbf{k}$

15 $(1, 1, 2)$, $70.5°$

16 $\mathbf{r} = \frac{25}{11}\mathbf{i} + \frac{25}{11}\mathbf{j} + \frac{16}{11}\mathbf{k} + \lambda(-\mathbf{i} + 3\mathbf{j} + \mathbf{k})$

$\frac{26}{11}\mathbf{i} + \frac{22}{11}\mathbf{j} + \frac{15}{11}\mathbf{k}$

17 (a) $\frac{1}{\sqrt{14}}(\mathbf{i} - 3\mathbf{j} - 2\mathbf{k})$, $\frac{1}{\sqrt{14}}(3\mathbf{i} + \mathbf{j} - 2\mathbf{k})$,

$73.4°$

    (b) $\mathbf{r} = \mathbf{i} + \mathbf{j} + 3\mathbf{k} + \lambda(2\mathbf{i} - \mathbf{j} - 2\mathbf{k})$

    (d) $(\frac{19}{9}\mathbf{i} + \frac{4}{9}\mathbf{j} + \frac{17}{9}\mathbf{k})$

18 $P(5, -2, 3)$, $A(1, 0, 1)$

19 (a) $(5, 7, 6)$ (b) $26.3°$

20 (a) Equation of AB is

$\mathbf{r} = 3\mathbf{i} + \mathbf{j} + \mathbf{k} + \lambda(\mathbf{i} + 2\mathbf{j} + 3\mathbf{k})$

Equation of CD is

$\mathbf{r} = 2\mathbf{i} + 5\mathbf{j} + \mu(-\mathbf{i} + \mathbf{j} - \mathbf{k})$

    (c) $123°$

Review exercise 2

1 $\ln\frac{5}{3}$

2 (a) $27°$ (b) $u = -3$, $v = 5$

3 $\frac{1}{2}\ln 3$

4 (a) $9\mathbf{i} - 2\mathbf{k}$, $3\mathbf{j} - 2\mathbf{k}$ (b) $83.1°$

5 $\frac{\pi}{3} + \frac{\sqrt{3}}{2}$

7 $\ln\frac{3}{2}$

8 (b) $\frac{1}{3}, \frac{1}{2}$

9 (a) 5 (b) $3\mathbf{i} + 4\mathbf{j} + 2\mathbf{k}$

    (c) $\mathbf{r} = 5\mathbf{i} + \mathbf{j} + 5\mathbf{k} + t(2\mathbf{i} - 3\mathbf{j} + 3\mathbf{k})$

10 $\dfrac{1}{8(x+2)} + \dfrac{2-x}{8(x^2+4)}$

11 (a) $3\mathbf{i} + 4\mathbf{j} + 5\mathbf{k}$, $\mathbf{i} + \mathbf{j} + 4\mathbf{k}$

12 $\frac{\pi\sqrt{3}}{18}$

13 $\frac{1}{2}\ln 3$

14 (a) $3s + 4t = 10$ (b) $s = -\frac{15}{2}$, $t = -\frac{8}{5}$

15 (a) $0, \frac{1}{2}\pi$ (b) $12\pi c^2$

16 $\mathbf{r} = (-3\mathbf{i} + \mathbf{j} - 7\mathbf{k}) + t(4\mathbf{i} + \mathbf{j} + 6\mathbf{k})$

$\overrightarrow{OP} = \mathbf{i} + 2\mathbf{j} - \mathbf{k}$; $\sqrt{6}$

18 (a) $(x+3)^2 - 16$ (b) $\ln 2$

19 (a) $1, \frac{1}{5}$ (b) $-3\mathbf{i} + 3\mathbf{j} + 8\mathbf{k}$

    (c) $82°$

20 (a) $\frac{\pi}{6}$ (b) $2 - \sqrt{3} - \frac{\pi}{6}$

21 $\pm\frac{1}{2}\ln 3$

22 (c) 1

23 (b) $\sqrt{11}$ (c) $35°$ (d) 1.9

24 (b) $\frac{1}{2}[\sqrt{2} + \ln(1 + \sqrt{2})]$

    (c) $1 - \sqrt{2} + \ln(1 + \sqrt{2})$

25 (a) $\mathbf{r} = 5\mathbf{i} + 3\mathbf{j} + t(\mathbf{i} + \mathbf{j} - \mathbf{k})$

    (c) $3\mathbf{i} + \mathbf{j} + 2\mathbf{k}$ (e) $4\mathbf{i} + 3\mathbf{j} + 5\mathbf{k}$

26 (a) $\dfrac{e^x - e^{-x}}{e^x + e^{-x}}$ (b) $\dfrac{e^{2x} - 1}{e^{2x} + 1}$; odd function

27 (a) $\mathbf{r} = 7\mathbf{i} + \mathbf{j} + 7\mathbf{k} + t(\mathbf{i} + 4\mathbf{j} + \mathbf{k})$

    (b) $6\mathbf{i} - 3\mathbf{j} + 6\mathbf{k}$

28 (a)(iii) $\frac{41}{9}$ (iv) $-\frac{3280}{3281}$

    (b)(i) $\operatorname{arsinh}\dfrac{x+1}{3} + C$

    (c) $-\frac{1}{3}\operatorname{sech} 3x + C$

29 (a) $\dfrac{1}{1-x^2}$ (c) 0.131

31 $p = 1 + \sqrt{2}$

33 (b) 2 (c) $-5\mathbf{i} + 9\mathbf{j} - 4\mathbf{k}$

34 $\pm\ln 3$

35 4

36 (a) $\overrightarrow{AN} = \frac{3}{4}\mathbf{b} - \mathbf{a}$, $\overrightarrow{BM} = \frac{1}{2}\mathbf{a} - \mathbf{b}$

    (c) $\frac{1}{2}k\mathbf{a} + (1-k)\mathbf{b}$

    (d) $\frac{4}{5}, \frac{2}{5}$ (e) $4 : 1$

37 $-7\mathbf{i} - 2\mathbf{j} - 5\mathbf{k}$

39 $\ln\frac{5}{3}$

40 (a) $\operatorname{arsinh} 1$ (b) $\operatorname{arsinh} 1 - \sqrt{2} + 1$

41 $\pm\ln 3$

42 (a) $\mathbf{r} = (5\mathbf{i} - \mathbf{j} - \mathbf{k}) + t(\mathbf{i} + \mathbf{j} - 2\mathbf{k})$

    (d) $3\mathbf{i} - 3\mathbf{j} + 3\mathbf{k}$

43 (a) $\operatorname{arsinh}\dfrac{x-1}{3} + C$

    (b) $\frac{1}{3}\arctan\dfrac{x-1}{3} + C$

44 (a) $\operatorname{arsinh}\frac{1}{2}$ (b) $\frac{\pi}{6}$

45 (a) $\sqrt{3} - 1$

47 $\frac{10}{3}$

48 $\dfrac{1}{2\sqrt{2}}\ln\left(\dfrac{\sqrt{2}+1}{\sqrt{2}-1}\right)$

49 (a) $\tanh x$ (b) $2x\cosh(x^2)$

    (c) $\dfrac{2}{\sqrt{(1-4x^2)}}$

51 (c) $\frac{1}{2}\ln 2$ (b) $\ln\dfrac{8}{3\sqrt{3}}$

52 (a) $-\frac{1}{3}(4-x^2)^{\frac{3}{2}} + C$

    (b) $2\arcsin\frac{x}{2} + \frac{x}{2}(4-x^2)^{\frac{1}{2}} + C$

53 $C - \sqrt{(1-x^2)}$;

    $x\arcsin x + \sqrt{(1-x^2)} + C$

55 $x = y = \ln(3 \pm \sqrt{6})$

56 (a) $\mathbf{s} = \mathbf{r} + \mathbf{t}$ (b) $\mathbf{v} = \frac{1}{2}(\mathbf{s} + \mathbf{t})$

57 (a) $\frac{2}{\sqrt{3}}\arctan(e^x\sqrt{3}) + C$

59 (b) 0

60 $\frac{1}{3}$

Exercise 7A

1 (a) $8\mathrm{i}$ (b) $\mathrm{i}\sqrt{7}$ (c) $4 - 9\mathrm{i}$

    (d) $3 - 5\mathrm{i}$ (e) $3\mathrm{i}$

2 (a) $-\mathrm{i}$ (b) $-\mathrm{i}$ (c) $-\mathrm{i}$

    (d) -5 (e) $-5 + 5\mathrm{i}$

3 (a) $4 + 10\mathrm{i}$ (b) $3 + 4\mathrm{i}$

    (c) $404 - 1121\mathrm{i}$ (d) $15 - 22\mathrm{i}$

    (e) $-6 + 35\mathrm{i}$

4 (a) $2 - 4\mathrm{i}$ (b) $3 + 6\mathrm{i}$ (c) $-5 - 2\mathrm{i}$

    (d) $-7 + 3\mathrm{i}$ (e) $-4 - 2\mathrm{i}$ (f) 6

    (g) $-3\mathrm{i}$ (h) $7 + 3\mathrm{i}$

5 (a) $6 - 4\mathrm{i}$ (b) $-9 - 2\mathrm{i}$

    (c) $-5 - 13\mathrm{i}$ (d) $-1 + 10\mathrm{i}$

    (e) $4 + \mathrm{i}$ (f) $-1 + 3\mathrm{i}$

    (g) $-2 + 2\mathrm{i}$

6 (a) $7 + \mathrm{i}$ (b) $-34 + 34\mathrm{i}$

    (c) $-23 + 14\mathrm{i}$ (d) $-24 - 10\mathrm{i}$

    (e) $2 - 11\mathrm{i}$ (f) $8 + 6\mathrm{i}$

    (g) $17 - \mathrm{i}$

7 (a) $-\frac{1}{5}(12 + 11\mathrm{i})$ (b) $\frac{1}{10}(1 + 7\mathrm{i})$

    (c) $\frac{1}{25}(11 + 2\mathrm{i})$ (d) $\frac{1}{5}(1 - 2\mathrm{i})$

    (e) $\frac{1}{13}(-5 + 12\mathrm{i})$ (f) $-\frac{1}{5}(7 + 4\mathrm{i})$

    (g) $-\frac{6}{25}(3 + 4\mathrm{i})$ (h) $\frac{1}{25}(4 + 3\mathrm{i})$

8 (a) $\pm 5\mathrm{i}$ (b) $0, \pm 8\mathrm{i}$ (c) $2 \pm \mathrm{i}$

    (d) $-3 \pm \mathrm{i}$ (e) $2 \pm 5\mathrm{i}$

    (f) $\frac{1}{4}(-3 \pm \mathrm{i}\sqrt{47})$

    (g) $\frac{1}{3}(-1 \pm \mathrm{i}\sqrt{2})$ (h) $\frac{1}{3}(1 \pm \mathrm{i}\sqrt{5})$

9 (a) $\frac{2}{5}$ (b) $\frac{1}{130}(47 - \mathrm{i})$ (c) $\frac{4}{5}(7 - 4\mathrm{i})$

10 $-\frac{6}{5}(1 - 2\mathrm{i})$

12 $\lambda = \frac{1}{2};\ -\frac{1}{4}$

Exercise 7B

2 (a) $|z| = \sqrt{13},\ \arg z = -0.588^{\mathrm{c}}$

    (b) $|z| = \sqrt{10},\ \arg z = 0.322^{\mathrm{c}}$

    (c) $|z| = 6,\ \arg z = 1.57^{\mathrm{c}}$

    (d) $|z| = 5,\ \arg z = 3.14^{\mathrm{c}}$

    (e) $|z| = \sqrt{5},\ \arg z = 2.68^{\mathrm{c}}$

    (f) $|z| = \sqrt{10},\ \arg z = -1.25^{\mathrm{c}}$

    (g) $|z| = 2,\ \arg z = 1.05^{\mathrm{c}}$

    (h) $|z| = 13,\ \arg z = 1.97^{\mathrm{c}}$

    (i) $|z| = \frac{5}{2},\ \arg = 1.05^{\mathrm{c}}$

    (j) $|z| = \frac{\sqrt{6}}{3},\ \arg z = -0.421^{\mathrm{c}}$

    (k) $|z| = \sqrt{65},\ \arg z = -0.124^{\mathrm{c}}$

    (l) $|z| = \frac{1}{5}\sqrt{10},\ \arg z = 1.25^{\mathrm{c}}$

3 (a) $5,\ 13,\ \sqrt{2},\ 25$

    (b) $53.1^\circ,\ -67.4^\circ,\ -135.0^\circ,\ 106.3^\circ$

4 (a) $z = 1 + i$, $|z| = \sqrt{2}$, $\arg z = 0.79^c$

  (b) $z = 3(2 - i)$, $|z| = 3\sqrt{5}$,

    $\arg z = -0.46^c$

  (c) $z = -4$, $|z| = 4$, $\arg z = 3.14^c$

5 $z^2 = 3 - 4i$, $z^3 = 2 - 11i$

  $|z| = \sqrt{5}$, $|z^2| = 5$, $|z^3| = 5\sqrt{5}$

  $\arg z = -0.46^c$, $\arg z^2 = -0.93^c$

  $\arg z^3 = -1.39^c$

6 (a) $|z_1| = 1$, $\arg z_1 = \frac{\pi}{2}$

  (b) $|z_2| = 1$, $\arg z_2 = \frac{\pi}{4}$

  (c) $|z_3| = 1$, $\arg z_3 = \pi$

7 $5 + 12i$; $\frac{1}{169}(5 - 12i)$; 13; $\frac{1}{13}$; 1.18^c; -1.18^c

9 $-\frac{6}{5}(1 - 2i)$; $\dfrac{6\sqrt{5}}{5}$

10 (a)(i) $\sqrt{52}$ (ii) -3.08^c

  (b)(i) $\frac{1}{2}\sqrt{13}$ (ii) 1.11^c

  (c)(i) $(277 + 156\sqrt{3})^{\frac{1}{2}}$ (ii) -2.73^c

11 $-(1 + i)$

13 (a) $8(-1 + i\sqrt{3})$ (b) $\frac{1}{8}(1 - i\sqrt{3})$

  (c) $2(\sqrt{3} - i)$

14 (b) $127°$

15 (a) $\frac{1}{6}$ (b) 2.03^c

16 (a) $138.0°$ (b) $2 - i$ (c) 2.2

17 $z^2 = -\frac{1}{2}(1 + i\sqrt{3})$

18 $k = -3$

19 $|z| = 1$, $\arg z = -0.52^c$, $z^2 = \frac{1}{2}(1 - i\sqrt{3})$

20 (a) $56 - 33i$; $\frac{1}{25}(16 + 63i)$

21 $|z_1| = 2$; $\arg z_1 = -\frac{\pi}{6}$

  $|z_2| = 2$; $\arg z_2 = \frac{3\pi}{4}$

  $\dfrac{z_2}{z_1} = \frac{1}{4}[-\sqrt{6} - \sqrt{2} + i(\sqrt{6} - \sqrt{2})]$

22 $\arg z_1 = \frac{2\pi}{3}$, $\arg z_2 = \frac{\pi}{6}$;

  $\dfrac{z_1}{z_2} = i$; $\arg \dfrac{z_1}{z_2} = \frac{\pi}{2}$

23 $z_1 = 2(1 - i)$; $z_2 = -2$

  (b) $-\frac{\pi}{2}$

24 $|z_1| = \sqrt{2}$, $\arg z_1 = \frac{\pi}{4}$

  $|z_2| = 2$, $\arg z_2 = -\frac{\pi}{6}$

25 (b) $|z_1| = 2\sqrt{2}$, $|z_2| = \sqrt{10}$, $PQ = \sqrt{2}$

  (d) $-1 + i$

26 (a) $z = 4 - 3i$; $w = 3 + 4i$

  (c) $90°$

Exercise 7C

1 (a) $\pm(3 + 2i)$ (b) $\pm(4 - 3i)$ (c) $\pm(2 - i)$

  (d) $\pm\sqrt{10}(1 - i)$ (e) $\pm(2 - i\sqrt{3})$

2 (a) $(-4, 4)$, $(16, -1)$

  (b) $(7, 4)$ (c) $(1, -2)$

  (d) $(-\frac{650}{49}, -\frac{50}{49})$ (e) $(2, 4)$

3 (a) $A = \frac{7}{5}$, $B = -\frac{4}{5}$

  (b) $A = 2 - i$, $B = 2 + i$

4 $x = 1$, $y = -1$

5 (a) $p = 3$, $q = 1$ (b) $p = -\frac{2}{5}$, $q = \frac{6}{5}$

6 $x = -\frac{7}{25}$, $y = -\frac{24}{25}$ **7** $x = \frac{2}{13}$, $y = \frac{3}{13}$

8 $x = 1$, $y = -\frac{1}{2}$ **9** $a = 0$, $b = \pm 2$

10 $\dfrac{1}{z} = \frac{1}{169}(5 + 12i)$

  $z^{\frac{1}{2}} = \pm(3 - 2i)$

11 $x = 2$, $y = 0$

12 (a) $\frac{1}{50}(147 - 71i)$ (b) $m = -2$, $n = 3$

13 $x = 3$, $y = -1$

  (a) $\sqrt{10}$ (b) $-18.4°\ (-0.322^c)$

14 (a)(iii) -0.49^c (b) $w = \pm(1 + 2i)$

15 $A = 27$, $B = 8$

Exercise 8A

1 $2y = \sinh x + C$ **2** $3\cosh\frac{1}{3}y = x + C$

3 $\sec y = C \sin x$ **4** $e^{-2y} + 2\tan x = C$

5 $\ln\left|\dfrac{y - 1}{y + 1}\right| = 2\arctan x + C$

6 $\arctan\frac{1}{2}y = 2\operatorname{arsinh} x + C$

7 $2\ln|y| - e^{x^2} = C$ **8** $e^x + e^{-y} = C$

9 $Cy^2 = \dfrac{x - 1}{x + 1}$ **10** $\dfrac{1}{x} + \cot y = C$

11 $\dfrac{1}{y} + 4x + 6 = 0$ **12** $\ln|y| = e^x - 1$

13 $y = \tan x - x + \frac{\pi}{4} - 1$

14 $2e^{3x} = 2e + 3e^{-1} - 3e^{-2y}$

15 $y = 4x, x > 0$ **16** $2y^{\frac{1}{2}} = 5 - e^{-x}$

17 $2\arctan e^y = \ln|\tan\frac{x}{2}| + \frac{\pi}{2}$

18 $\ln|\sin y| = 3\ln|\sin x| + x - \ln 2 - \frac{\pi}{2}$

19 $y = -\frac{40}{3}\ln\left|\dfrac{5 - 3\sin x}{8}\right|$

20 $\dfrac{y+1}{y} = \frac{3}{4}(1 + \cos^2 x)$

21 $2y^2(1 - x^2) = 1 + y^2$

22 $\dfrac{x^2}{2} = \ln\left|\dfrac{2y}{y+1}\right|$ **23** $\tanh x = 2\sinh y$

24 $\dfrac{1}{y+2} + \frac{1}{2}e^{x^2} = 1$

Exercise 8B

1 $y = 4x + C$ **2** $y^2 = 8x + C$

3 $y = Cx$ **4** $y = \frac{1}{2}e^{2x} + C$

5 $y = \sin x + C$ **6** $y^2 = 2x - x^2 + C$

7 $2y^2 = x^2 + C$

8 $xy = C, x > 0, y > 0$

Exercise 8C

1 $3xy = x^3 + C$ **2** $4xy^2 = x^4 + C$

3 $y\sin x = \ln|\sec x| + C$

4 $ye^{2x} = \sin x - x\cos x + C$

5 $2\dfrac{x}{y} = \sin 2x + C$

6 $xy = x\sin x + \cos x + C$

7 $x^2 y = x^4 + x^3 + C$

8 $\dfrac{y}{x} = \frac{1}{2}(\ln|x|)^2 + C$ **9** $yx^{\frac{1}{2}} = C - \frac{1}{2}x^2$

10 $y\sin x = \frac{3}{2}\cos^2 x - \cos^4 x + C$

11 $y\sec^2 x = \sec x + C$

12 $\dfrac{y}{1+x} = x - \ln|1+x| + C$

13 $y = x^3\ln|x| - x^3 + 3x^2$

14 $y = \frac{1}{5}(2\sin x - \cos x + e^{-2x})$

15 $y\cot^2\dfrac{x}{2} = 2\ln\left|\sin\dfrac{x}{2}\right| + C$

16 $ye^{2x} = \dfrac{x^4}{4} + \ln|x| + C$;

$y = \frac{1}{4}(x^4 - 1)e^{-2x} + e^{-2x}\ln x$

17 $y = [e^x(x^2 - 2x + 2) + 1 - e]x^{-3}$

18 $y = \dfrac{5x}{2} - \dfrac{1}{2x}$

Exercise 8D

1 $y = Ae^x + Be^{2x}$ **2** $y = Ae^{-x} + Be^{-3x}$

3 $y = Ae^x + Be^{4x}$ **4** $y = Ae^{2x} + Be^{-9x}$

5 $y = Ae^{4x} + Be^{-2x}$ **6** $y = Ae^{2x} + Be^{-3x}$

7 $y = Ae^{2x} + Be^{-\frac{2}{3}x}$

8 $y = e^x(Ae^{x\sqrt{3}} + Be^{-x\sqrt{3}})$

9 $y = Ae^{\frac{2}{3}x} + Be^{-\frac{3}{2}x}$ **10** $y = Ae^{3x} + Be^{-\frac{7}{3}x}$

Exercise 8E

1 $y = (A + Bx)e^x$ **2** $y = (A + Bx)e^{-2x}$

3 $y = (A + Bx)e^{3x}$ **4** $y = (A + Bx)e^{-4x}$

5 $y = (A + Bx)e^{-\frac{1}{2}x}$ **6** $y = (A + Bx)e^{\frac{1}{3}x}$

7 $y = (A + Bx)e^{\frac{3x}{2}}$ **8** $y = (A + Bx)e^{-\frac{5}{3}x}$

9 $y = (A + Bx)e^{x\sqrt{2}}$

10 $y = (A + Bx)e^{-x\sqrt{\frac{5}{2}}}$

Exercise 8F

1 $y = A\cos x + B\sin x$

2 $y = A\cos 5x + B\sin 5x$

3 $y = A\cos\dfrac{3x}{2} + B\sin\dfrac{3x}{2}$

4 $y = A\cos\dfrac{7x}{4} + B\sin\dfrac{7x}{4}$

5 $y = e^x(A\cos 2x + B\sin 2x)$

6 $y = e^{-2x}(A\cos x + B\sin x)$

7 $y = e^{3x}(A\cos x + B\sin x)$

8 $y = e^{-4x}(A\cos 3x + B\sin 3x)$

9 $y = e^{\frac{1}{2}x}(A\cos x + B\sin x)$

10 $y = e^{\frac{2x}{5}}\left(A\cos\dfrac{3x}{5} + B\sin\dfrac{3x}{5}\right)$

Exercise 8G

1 $y = Ae^x + Be^{3x} + 4$

2 $y = Ae^{-x} + Be^{-2x} + 2x - 3$

3 $y = (A + Bx)e^x + e^{2x}$

4 $y = (A + Bx)e^{-2x} + \frac{1}{2}x - \frac{3}{4}$

5 $y = A\cos x + B\sin x - \frac{1}{3}\cos 2x$

6 $y = A\cos 3x + B\sin 3x + \frac{4}{37}e^{\frac{1}{2}x}$

7 $y = e^{-2x}(A\cos x + B\sin x) + 2x - 4$

8 $y = e^x(A\cos x + B\sin x) + \frac{1}{5}\cos x - \frac{2}{5}\sin x$

9 $y = Ae^x + Be^{3x} - x + \frac{2}{3}$

10 $y = A + Be^{-x} - xe^{-x}$

11 $y = A + Be^{3x} - \frac{5}{3}x$

12 $y = Ae^x + Be^{-\frac{1}{3}x} + 2 - x$

13 $y = e^{-2x}(A\cos x + B\sin x)$
$+ \frac{1}{65}\sin 2x - \frac{8}{65}\cos 2x$

14 $y = A\cos 4x + B\sin 4x + \frac{3}{2}$

15 $y = e^{-\frac{1}{2}x}(A\cos\frac{x}{2} + B\sin\frac{x}{2})$
$+ \frac{1}{10}\sin x - \frac{3}{10}\cos x$

16 $y = -\frac{13}{2}e^x + \frac{5}{2}e^{3x} + 4$

17 $y = -\frac{1}{2}(\cos x + \sin x - e^x)$

18 $y = (1 - \frac{1}{2}x)e^x - \frac{1}{2}\sin x$

19 $y = \frac{9}{4}e^x + \frac{1}{12}e^{5x} - \frac{1}{3}e^{2x}$

20 $y = 2e^{-x}\cos x + 2x - 2$

21 $y = \frac{1}{2}(e^{-2x} + 1)(x + 1)$

22 $y = e^{-x}(\cos 3x + \frac{5}{3}\sin 3x) + 2x - 1$

23 $y = \frac{1}{68}e^{-3x}(4\cos 4x - \sin 4x)$
$+ \frac{1}{17}(4\sin x - \cos x)$

24 $y = \sin 3x + \sin x$

25 $y = e^{6x} - 8e^{-x} + 6x + 7$

26 $y = A\cos x + B\sin x + \frac{1}{2}x\sin x$

27 $k = -\frac{2}{5}, \; y = \frac{1}{25}(e^{12x} - e^{2x}) - \frac{2}{5}xe^{2x}$

28 $y = e^{-x}(2\sin 2x - 4\cos 2x) + 5e^{-x}$

29 $y = Ae^{\frac{x}{4}} + Be^x - 4\cos x - \sin x$

30 $y = \frac{1}{2}(\sin 2x - 3\cos 2x) + 2e^{-x}$

Exercise 8H

1 $y^2 = 2x^2\ln|Cx|$ **2** $y = x\ln|Cx|$

3 $\arctan(y - x) = C - x$

4 $Cx^2y^2 = (y - x)^3$

5 $y = \ln|x + y + 1| + \frac{1}{2}x^2 + C$

6 $y = A\cos(\ln|x|) + B\sin(\ln|x|)$

7 $y = Ax^2 + Bx^3$

8 $y = Ax^3 + \frac{1}{2}x^2 + B$

9 $2\ln|3x - y - 3| = y - x + 1 + 2\ln 2$

10 $y = \dfrac{1}{x(C - 2x)^{\frac{1}{2}}}, \; y = \dfrac{1}{x(3 - 2x)^{\frac{1}{2}}}$

Exercise 9A

1 2.49   **2** 0.80   **3** 0.69

4 1.24   **5** 0.81

6 $x_0 = 0.933\,96\ldots$; 0.934   **7** 0.52

8 0.669   **9** 0.199 936   **10** 3.20

11 1.38   **12** 2.24   **13** −1.83

14 0.587   **15** 1.54

16 (a) 0.17   (b) 2.04   (c) 3.11   (d) 1.31
     (e) 4.33   (f) 0.51   (g) 3.59

17 3.73   **18** 0.5

19 (a) 2.207 99...   (b) 2.207 93...

20 0.905 08...

21 (a) 0.817 886...   (b) 0.809 86...

22 0.357

23 (b) −0.75   (c) −0.82

24 (b) 1.15   (c) $A = -1, B = \frac{1}{2}$

Review exercise 3

1 $3 + 2i, \; -3 - 2i$ **2** $1 - i$

3 $\ln|y| = x + C + \ln|x - 1|, \; y = \frac{3}{2}e^{\frac{1}{3}}$

4 0.92

5 (a) $\frac{7}{3}$ (b) $p = -3, \; q = -4$

6 $y = 4 + Ce^{-x^2}$

7 (a)(i) $3 - 7i$ (ii) $-16.6°$
   (b)(ii) $|2wi| = 2|w|$
     (ii) $\arg(2wi) - \arg w = 90°$

8 (b) 1.15, 1.11

9 $z_1 z_2 = -1 + 2i, \; \dfrac{z_1}{z_2} = \frac{11}{5} + \frac{2}{5}i, \; z_3 = \frac{6}{5} + \frac{12}{5}i$

10 $\frac{1}{2} \pm i\frac{\sqrt{3}}{2}, \; -1$

11 $y = \cos kx + \frac{1}{k}\sin kx$ **12** 3.12

13 $p = -1$, $q = 0$,
  $y = 2(2x + 1)e^{-2x} - \cos 2x$

14 $x_2 = \frac{3}{2}$, $x_3 = \frac{17}{12}$; error 2×10^{-6}

15 $y = e^{-\frac{1}{2}x}(A \cos \frac{x\sqrt{3}}{2} + B \sin \frac{x\sqrt{3}}{2})$

16 (b) $5\sqrt{2}$ (c)(i) $-1 - i$ (ii) $-\frac{3}{4}\pi$

17 $y = x \cos x$

18 (a)(ii) $\frac{3\pi}{4}$ (b) $\pm(5 - 3i)$

19 1.78   **20** 3.65   **21** 2.605

22 $a = -\frac{1}{2}$, $b = -\frac{1}{4}$;
  $y = Ae^{2x} + Be^{-\frac{2}{3}x} - \frac{1}{2}\cos 2x - \frac{1}{4}\sin 2x$

23 $y^{-2}e^{x^2} = 2x + C$ **24** 1.896

25 $y = \dfrac{2}{x}\sin\dfrac{x}{2} - \cos\dfrac{x}{2}$; $k = 0$

26 $a = -\frac{10}{39}$, $b = -\frac{5}{13}$;
  $y = A + Be^{-2x} - \frac{10}{39}\cos 3x - \frac{5}{13}\sin 3x$

28 $y = x(Ce^{2x} - 1)$ **29** 2.08

30 $k = \frac{1}{9}$; $y = e^{2x}(A\cos 3x + B\sin 3x) + \frac{1}{9}e^{2x}$

31 1.557

32 $p = 2$, $q = 0$;
  $y = 2\cos x + e^{-4x}(A\cos 3x + B\sin 3x)$;
  $y = 2\cos x + e^{-4x}(6\cos 3x + 9\sin 3x)$

33 $y\sec^2 x = \tan x - x + C$

34 $-\frac{1}{2}(1 + i) = z_1$, $-1 + i = z_2$

35 (b) 2   (c) $y = 2e^4\left(\dfrac{1}{x} - 1\right)e^{-2x} + \dfrac{2}{x}e^{2x}$

  (d) does not remain finite

36 1.139

37 $-\frac{5\sqrt{3}}{4} + \frac{3}{4}i$

38 $y\sin x = \frac{2}{3}\sin^3 x + \frac{1}{3}\sqrt{2}$

39 $y = Ae^{3x} + Be^{2x} + \frac{1}{2}(\cos x + \sin x)$

40 0.433

41 (a) 2   (b) $150°$ (c) $-60°$

42 $y = e^{-x}(A\cos 2x + B\sin 2x)$

43 $y = e^{-x}(A\cos 3x + B\sin 3x)$

  (a) $p = 2$, $k = 3$;
    $y = e^{-x}(3\cos 3x + 2\sin 3x) + 3e^{2x}$

  (b) (i) $y = e^{-x}\sin 3x$

  (ii) $e^{-\frac{n\pi}{3} - \frac{1}{3}\arctan 3}\sin(n\pi + \arctan 3)$

44 $y = \frac{1}{2}x^3 + Cx$

45 (a) $\sqrt{2}$ (b) 5   (c) $-2 + 3i$

  (d) $123.7°$

46 (b) 2.79   (c) correct to 2 d.p.

  (d) 0.146, 3 positive roots

47 $y = x\tan(\frac{\pi}{3} + \ln|x|)$

48 $y = Ax^2 + Bx^3 + \frac{1}{2}$

49 (b) $4, -2$ (c) $-\frac{\pi}{4}$

50 $y = \frac{1}{2}\cos x(e^{2x} + 3)$

51 (a) $\dfrac{3 - 4i}{25}$ (b) $\dfrac{-7 - 24i}{625}$; $-106.3°$

52 (b) 1   (d) 0.567

53 (c) 0.8604

54 $y = e^{-2x}(A\cos 3x + B\sin 3x) + \frac{1}{10}e^{-3x}$

55 $y = \dfrac{1}{(1 - 2x + Ce^{-2x})^{\frac{1}{2}}}$

56 $y = \sec x[\ln|\sec x + \tan x| + C]$

57 $y = (3x + 2)e^{2x} + x + 1$

58 1.444

59 (b) $|z| = \frac{1}{\sqrt{2}}$, $\arg z = -\frac{3}{4}\pi$

60 1.53 is correct to 2 d.p.

Examination style paper P3

1 26 800   **2** $-2 < x < 3$ or $x > 8$

3 (a) $\operatorname{arsinh}\left(\dfrac{x - 3}{2}\right) + C$ (b) $\ln\frac{4}{3}$

4 $25\cos(\theta + 0.284)$

  (a) 25, 6.00   (b) 0.88, 4.84

5 (b) 1.4   (c) 1.55

6 (a) 2.45   (b) $p = 3$, $q = -1$

  (c) $3 + i$

7 (a) $75°$

  (b) $\mathbf{r} = \mathbf{i} - 2\mathbf{j} + t(\mathbf{i} - 3\mathbf{j} - 3\mathbf{k})$

  (c) 2.1

8 (c) $1 + \frac{5}{2}x^2 + \frac{41}{24}x^4$

9 (b) $y = e^{-2x}(A\cos 3x + B\sin 3x) + \frac{7}{5}e^{4x}$

  (c) $y = -\frac{7}{5}e^{-2x}(\cos 3x + 2\sin 3x) + \frac{7}{5}e^{4x}$

List of symbols and notation

The following symbols and notation are used in the London modular mathematics examinations:

$\{\quad\}$	the set of
$n(A)$	the number of elements in the set A
$\{x:\quad\}$	the set of all x such that
$\in$	is an element of
$\notin$	is not an element of
$\varnothing$	the empty (null) set
$\mathscr{E}$	the universal set
$\cup$	union
$\cap$	intersection
$\subset$	is a subset of
A'	the complement of the set A
PQ	operation Q followed by operation P
$f : A \to B$	f is a function under which each element of set A has an image in set B
$f : x \mapsto y$	f is a function under which x is mapped to y
$f(x)$	the image of x under the function f
f^{-1}	the inverse relation of the function f
fg	the function f of the function g
○—○—○	open interval on the number line
●—●—●	closed interval on the number line
$\mathbb{N}$	the set of positive integers and zero, $\{0, 1, 2, 3, \ldots\}$
$\mathbb{Z}$	the set of integers, $\{0, \pm 1, \pm 2, \pm 3, \ldots\}$
$\mathbb{Z}^+$	the set of positive integers, $\{1, 2, 3, \ldots\}$
$\mathbb{Q}$	the set of rational numbers
$\mathbb{Q}^+$	the set of positive rational numbers, $\{x : x \in \mathbb{Q}, x > 0\}$
$\mathbb{R}$	the set of real numbers
$\mathbb{R}^+$	the set of positive real numbers, $\{x : x \in \mathbb{R}, x > 0\}$
$\mathbb{R}_0^+$	the set of positive real numbers and zero, $\{x : x \in \mathbb{R}, x \geqslant 0\}$
$\mathbb{C}$	the set of complex numbers
$\sqrt{\ }$	the positive square root
$[a, b]$	the interval $\{x : a \leqslant x \leqslant b\}$
$(a, b]$	the interval $\{x : a < x \leqslant b\}$
(a, b)	the interval $\{x : a < x < b\}$

$\lvert x \rvert$	the modulus of $x = \begin{cases} x \text{ for } x \geqslant 0 \\ -x \text{ for } x < 0 \end{cases}, x \in \mathbb{R}$
$\approx$	is approximately equal to
$\mathbf{A}^{-1}$	the inverse of the non-singular matrix $\mathbf{A}$
$\mathbf{A}^{\mathrm{T}}$	the transpose of the matrix $\mathbf{A}$
$\det \mathbf{A}$	the determinant of the square matrix $\mathbf{A}$
$\displaystyle\sum_{r=1}^{n} \mathrm{f}(r)$	$\mathrm{f}(1) + \mathrm{f}(2) + \ldots + \mathrm{f}(n)$
$\displaystyle\prod_{r=1}^{n} \mathrm{f}(r)$	$\mathrm{f}(1)\mathrm{f}(2)\ldots\mathrm{f}(n)$
$\displaystyle\binom{n}{r}$	the binomial coefficient $\dfrac{n!}{r!(n-r)!} \text{ for } n \in \mathbb{Z}^{+}$ $\dfrac{n(n-1)\ldots(n-r+1)}{r!} \text{ for } n \in \mathbb{Q}$
$\exp x$	e^{x}
$\ln x$	the natural logarithm of x, $\log_{\mathrm{e}} x$
$\lg x$	the common logarithm of x, $\log_{10} x$
$\arcsin$	the inverse function of $\sin$ with range $[-\pi/2, \pi/2]$
$\arccos$	the inverse function of $\cos$ with range $[0, \pi]$
$\arctan$	the inverse function of $\tan$ with range $(-\pi/2, \pi/2)$
arsinh	the inverse function of $\sinh$ with range $\mathbb{R}$
arcosh	the inverse function of $\cosh$ with range $\mathbb{R}_{0}^{+}$
artanh	the inverse function of $\tanh$ with range $\mathbb{R}$
$\mathrm{f}'(x), \mathrm{f}''(x), \mathrm{f}'''(x)$	the first, second and third derivatives of $\mathrm{f}(x)$ with respect to x
$\mathrm{f}^{(r)}(x)$	the rth derivative of $\mathrm{f}(x)$ with respect to x
$\dot{x}, \ddot{x}, \ldots$	the first, second, $\ldots$ derivatives of x with respect to t
z	a complex number, $z = x + \mathrm{i}y = r(\cos\theta + \mathrm{i}\sin\theta) = r\mathrm{e}^{\mathrm{i}\theta}$
$\mathrm{Re}\, z$	the real part of z, $\mathrm{Re}\, z = x = r\cos\theta$
$\mathrm{Im}\, z$	the imaginary part of z, $\mathrm{Im}\, z = y = r\sin\theta$
z^{*}	the conjugate of z, $z^{*} = x - \mathrm{i}y = r(\cos\theta - \mathrm{i}\sin\theta) = r\mathrm{e}^{-\mathrm{i}\theta}$
$\lvert z \rvert$	the modulus of z, $\lvert z \rvert = \sqrt{(x^2 + y^2)} = r$
$\arg z$	the principal value of the argument of z, $\arg z = \theta$, where $\left.\begin{array}{l} \sin\theta = y/r \\ \cos\theta = x/r \end{array}\right\} -\pi < \theta \leqslant \pi$
$\mathbf{a}$	the vector $\mathbf{a}$
$\overrightarrow{AB}$	the vector represented in magnitude and direction by the directed line segment AB
$\hat{\mathbf{a}}$	a unit vector in the direction of $\mathbf{a}$
$\mathbf{i}, \mathbf{j}, \mathbf{k}$	unit vectors in the directions of the cartesian coordinate axes
$\lvert \mathbf{a} \rvert$	the magnitude of $\mathbf{a}$
$\lvert \overrightarrow{AB} \rvert$	the magnitude of $\overrightarrow{AB}$
$\mathbf{a}.\mathbf{b}$	the scalar product of $\mathbf{a}$ and $\mathbf{b}$
$\mathbf{a} \times \mathbf{b}$	the vector product of $\mathbf{a}$ and $\mathbf{b}$

A'	the complement of the event A
$P(A)$	probability of the event A
$P(A\vert B)$	probability of the event A conditional on the event B
$E(X)$	the mean (expectation, expected value) of the random variable X
X, Y, R, etc.	random variables
x, y, r, etc.	values of the random variables X, Y, R, etc.
$x_1, x_2 \ldots$	observations
$f_1, f_2, \ldots$	frequencies with which the observations $x_1, x_2, \ldots$ occur
$p(x)$	probability function $P(X = x)$ of the discrete random variable X
$p_1, p_2, \ldots$	probabilities of the values $x_1, x_2, \ldots$ of the discrete random variable X
$f(x), g(x), \ldots$	the value of the probability density function of a continuous random variable X
$F(x), G(x), \ldots$	the value of the (cumulative) distribution function $P(X \leqslant x)$ of a continuous random variable X
$\mathrm{Var}(X)$	variance of the random variable X
$B(n, p)$	binomial distribution with parameters n and p
$N(\mu, \sigma^2)$	normal distribution with mean μ and variance σ^2
μ	population mean
σ^2	population variance
σ	population standard deviation
$\bar{x}$	sample mean
s^2	unbiased estimate of population variance from a sample,

$$s^2 = \frac{1}{n-1} \sum (x - \bar{x})^2$$

ϕ	probability density function of the standardised normal variable with distribution $N(0, 1)$
Φ	corresponding cumulative distribution function
α, β	regression coefficients
ρ	product-moment correlation coefficient for a population
r	product-moment correlation coefficient for a sample
$\sim p$	not p
$p \Rightarrow q$	p implies q (if p then q)
$p \Leftrightarrow q$	p implies and is implied by q (p is equivalent to q)

Index